LEAVING CERTIFICATE HIGHER AND ORDINARY LEVEL

GET CONSTRUCTIVE

A Modern Approach to Construction Studies

Eva Corcoran

Sean King

William Nolan

PUBLISHED BY
Educate.ie

Walsh Educational Books Ltd
Castleisland, Co. Kerry, Ireland
www.educate.ie

COVER ILLUSTRATION
Keith Mangan

COVER DESIGN
Kieran O'Donoghue

DESIGN
Kieran O'Donoghue and Don Harper

LAYOUT
Artwerk, Dublin

EDITOR
Peter Malone

PRINTED AND BOUND BY
Walsh Colour Print, Castleisland

ISBN 978-1-908507-96-9

CREDITS
The authors and publisher would like to thank the following for permission to
reproduce photographs:

Bigstock, Alamy Images, Construction Photography, William Nolan, Sean King,
Tom Fox. Photograph of the Céide Fields is reproduced courtesy of the National
Monuments Service, Dept of Arts, Heritage and the Gaeltacht; radon detectors
courtesy of the Radiological Protection Institute of Ireland; Ardnacrusha courtesy
of the ESB; Map of Carrick-on-Suir reproduced by permission of Ordnance Survey
Ireland Permit No. 8868, © Ordnance Survey Ireland/Government of Ireland.

CONTENTS

SECTION D
SERVICES AND SUSTAINABILITY

CAD
TECHNICAL DRAWINGS AND 3D MODELS

ACKNOWLEDGEMENTS

The authors would like to acknowledge the great many people who have contributed to this book. We thank all the subject reviewers who lent their expertise to improving the book's content, and we would like to express our gratitude to the team at Educate.ie, particularly Kieran O'Donoghue for his creative input, and Paula Byrne and Margaret Burns for their advice and assistance in keeping our progress on track.

We would like to express our appreciation for the editorial input of Jane Rogers, Síofra Ní Thuarisg and Fiona McPolin, and pay particular thanks to picture researcher Tom Fox, designer Don Harper (Artwerk) and project leader Peter Malone, whose work made this book possible.

To our work colleagues who have offered us their professional expertise and constructive commentary, we would like to extend our grateful thanks. We would also like to thank the vast number of educators who have inspired us to teach today.

'Who dares to teach must never cease to learn.' (John Cotton Dana)

Finally, we would like to thank our families and friends who have stuck with us throughout this project and endured the late nights and early mornings we spent on it. Their support and encouragement was much appreciated.

Míle Buíochas.

William Nolan
Sean King
Eva Corcoran

INTRODUCTION

This book is aimed at second-level students studying for Leaving Certificate Construction Studies at both Higher and Ordinary Level. For ease of use it is broken into four units: Planning and Preparation, Substructure, Superstructure, and Services and Sustainability. This structured approach to the content allows the theory to follow similar lines to an actual build.

- This textbook is intended to provide a structured learning guide to modern construction theory and practice in the Irish context.

- It aims to provide exemplars and local examples of styles and practice.

- The content is divided into units and subdivided into chapters that provide a step-by-step approach to building theory.

- Keywords are listed at the beginning of each chapter and calculations are broken down into their simplest elements in order to address literacy and numeracy concerns.

- The content in this textbook is aimed at both Higher and Ordinary Level. The basic concepts covered in the book should be considered for both levels.

- The wide range of full-colour images and illustrations will help the student visualise the materials and techniques that go into constructing a building.

- Extensive technical drawings accompany the text and are then compiled in a separate section as a valuable aid for students to follow in their own construction drawings.

- Realistic 3D models show the placement of the various building elements and features, making it easier for the student to visualise the materials as they are described in the text.

- Several elements of buildings are sketched as students might draw them, showing students the kind of work they should aim to reproduce in an exam context. These sketches are indicated with an icon of a pencil.

- Practice questions and sample exam questions are included at the end of each chapter.

- The text will give the student an awareness of the impact that building and building technologies have on the environment, landscape and human comfort.

- It provides a sound background for further study in this area, and also gives future consumers of the construction industry a basic knowledge of building processes.

GUIDE TO ILLUSTRATIONS

This textbook contains technical drawings, 3D models and illustrations of all aspects of building.

There are detailed technical drawings throughout the text of the most important building features found in Irish homes, with up-to-date building regulations. These 2D drawings were created using AutoCAD. Students should be able to recognise the style of these drawings from other technical subjects they have studied and reproduce them using the skills they have learned.

In keeping with draughting standards, CAD drawings do not include a unit of measurement, but unless otherwise stated all details are in millimetres.

To complement the technical drawings, realistic 3D models illustrate particular building features. These models are an example of Computer Aided Design (CAD) using SolidWorks software, which can be found in all technology classrooms. It is hoped that these 3D models will show students the potential of CAD and its close relationship with the design and construction industry.

The technical drawings and 3D models are also compiled in a full section, which includes some variations not shown in the main text.

The design key shows how materials are illustrated.

DESIGN KEY	Technical key	Artistic key
Brick		
Concrete block		
Thermal block		
Wood		
Wood fibreboard		
Insulation (rigid)		
Insulation (non-rigid)		
Breather membrane		
DPC		
DPM/Vapour barrier		
Wall tie		
Sand blinding		
Concrete		
Hardcore		
Reinforced steel		
Earthworks		

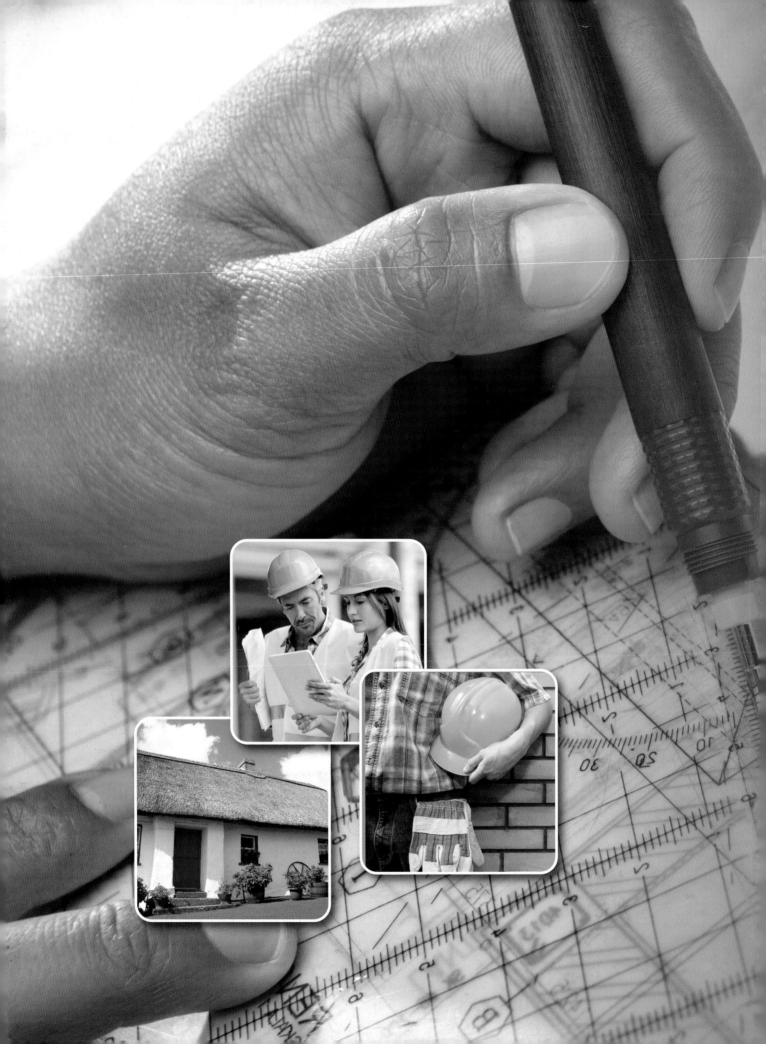

PLANNING AND PREPARATION

CHAPTER 1
BUILT HERITAGE AWARENESS AND CONSERVATION

LEARNING OUTCOMES:

After studying this chapter students will:

- Have an understanding of the natural and built environment and the importance of shelter to humans.
- Be able to identify and distinguish various forms of architectural heritage in Ireland.
- Grasp key design principles and proportions and be able to demonstrate them graphically.
- Gain an understanding of how architectural styles have developed over time.
- Have an insight into the conservation of heritage buildings.

KEYWORDS:

- SETTLEMENT • SHELTER • ENVIRONMENT • HERITAGE • MEDIEVAL• ROMANESQUE
- GOTHIC • VERNACULAR • GEORGIAN • CONSERVATION • RESTORATION

INTRODUCTION

People have built settlements on the island of Ireland for thousands of years. One of the earliest settlements, at Mount Sandel in Coleraine, Co. Derry, dates back to 7000 BC. Archaeologists found evidence of seven structures there. Six were circular huts of six metres across, with a hearth in the centre of the hut for fire. The huts were made of bent saplings (wattle), which were inserted into the ground in a circle and then bound using clay and mud (daub). The roof structure was probably covered with deer hide, straw or lighter materials.

Prehistoric settlements like this were the beginning of Ireland's great building tradition. Fig. 1.1 shows the construction of a later style of hut made from timber poles, which were then covered with a framework of reeds or branches and plastered with mud or clay.

SETTLEMENT

In order to explore how our ancestors lived and what they built, we must look at the factors that influence settlement. Settlement describes the formation of communities, when people settle in an area. A number of factors affect the location of settlements, including:

- Shelter
- Supplies of fresh water
- Availability of food
- Availability of raw materials for building and industry
- Trading routes.

Shelter is a basic human necessity. From earliest times, humans have sought out and constructed shelters for the purpose of comfort and defence.

Fig. 1.1 Early Bronze Age hut, made from timber poles covered with wattle and daub.

The natural resources of an area play a large part in how settlements grow. The resources of the River Liffey and River Suir, for example, played a major role in Dublin's and Waterford's earliest development.

Once a settlement is established, trade and industry follow. Trading settlements thrive in central locations or in places where two or more routes meet. These basic factors can influence settlement for generations to come. In fact, many of our villages, towns and cities exist to the present day on the site of their original settlement.

ENVIRONMENT

Before we look at the development of settlement in Ireland, we must understand the difference between the natural and the built environment. An environment is the surroundings we find ourselves in. The surroundings can be natural, created by people, or a combination of both. Natural elements and built elements can be seen in Fig. 1.2. It is important that they exist in harmony with each other.

Fig. 1.2 Elements of the natural environment and the built environment.

BUILT HERITAGE

Built heritage or architectural heritage refers to the buildings and structures in our ancestors' settlements. It is important to look at the materials and methods used in these constructions in order to appreciate the building standards and methods used in modern building.

The National Inventory of Architectural Heritage (NIAH) uses the following categories to catalogue Ireland's architectural heritage:

- Fortified buildings: castles, defence towers, ringforts, military buildings
- Religious structures: cathedrals, churches, shrines, monasteries
- Formal architecture: state institutions, estate homes, public buildings
- Informal architecture: vernacular buildings, rural cottages.

Architecture has different styles and periods, marking its development over time. There are also regional differences in style, depending on where in the country the building is located. Our heritage buildings today are in both private and public ownership.

PREHISTORIC SETTLEMENT

One of the earliest settlement patterns made on the Irish landscape can be seen in the Céide Fields, Ballycastle, Co. Mayo (Fig. 1.3). These are the oldest known field systems in the world, and this is where people on this island first built walls and developed fields.

The pattern of early settlements continued through the Stone, Bronze and Iron Ages in Ireland. Over time, there were small technological advances in construction, as people discovered new materials and building methods. While the physical remains of the earliest buildings have not survived, recreated and excavated settlement sites can be seen at Ballyglass, Co. Mayo, and Craggaunowen, Co. Clare. Fig. 1.4 shows the recreation of an Iron Age hut at Craggaunowen.

Fig. 1.3 The outline of the earliest fields in Ireland can be seen in the Céide Fields, Co. Mayo.

Fig. 1.4 Iron Age hut, Craggaunowen, Co. Clare.

Prehistoric buildings that are still in existence were mostly religious or defensive in nature. They are often larger in scale, and were built of stone. Ancient tombs – such as Creevykeel court tomb in Co. Sligo and the passage tombs at Brú na Bóinne, in Co. Meath – are examples of such heritage sites. Brú na Bóinne is the site of one of the most well-known passage tombs, Newgrange (Fig. 1.5). This was a major religious and scientific centre, renowned even today for the accuracy of the astronomical observations carried out there.

Fig. 1.5 Newgrange passage tomb, Co. Meath, which dates back to 3200 BC, is a world heritage site.

Newgrange is a good example of large-scale corbelling, a method of construction that uses a technique in which stones are stacked in overlapping layers, which rise closer and closer to the centre, creating what looks from the exterior like a mound of stones. The weight of the stone gives strength to the roof structure. The monastic settlement on Skellig Island, Co. Kerry, also uses this type of construction, as shown in Fig. 1.6.

When people began to use metal tools, they shaped and inscribed the stones in these

Fig. 1.6 Corbelled roof at Skellig settlement, Co. Kerry.

settlements. Later settlements were often sited close to copper, tin and iron mines, where metal tools could be smelted. An example is Mount Gabriel in Co. Cork, which was rich in copper.

PRE-CHRISTIAN

A typical residence at this period was a single building, or a small group of buildings, surrounded by a bank of earth for protection. These are commonly called raths or ringforts, and are found all around the country. In addition to mud embankments, some forts had a concentric wall of stone (or stone and clay) as a defence against wild animals or, indeed, human enemies. Many forts are great examples of dry stone walling. Examples of this type of settlement can be seen in Dún Aengus on Inis Mór, Co. Galway, and Staigue Fort, Co. Kerry (Fig. 1.7).

Fig. 1.7 Staigue Fort, Co. Kerry. The walls are up to 5.5m high and 4m thick, surrounding a circular area 27.4m in diameter.

Fig. 1.8 Round tower at Clonmacnoise, Co. Offaly.

EARLY CHRISTIAN

At this time in history, monastic settlements began to spread, as communities and centres of education. One of the most notable buildings of the later years of this era, found in many monastic settlements, is the Irish round tower.

The round tower was used as a watchtower, to look out for invaders; as a refuge in times of attack (for safety, the door was usually located at a height above the ground); and for storage. Modern theories see the round tower as a belfry. The Irish name, *cloigtheach*, literally means 'bell house'. Remains of these structures can be found at Clonmacnoise, Co. Offaly, Glendalough, Co. Wicklow, and Monasterboice, Co. Louth.

The construction of these towers was a major feat of engineering and required skilled builders. The tower typically had a 5m diameter base and reached a height of 30m. Because of its height, the structure needed to have a firm base, which was solid up to the level of the main door, which was usually high above ground level. This ensured that the tower had a stable base to accommodate the height of the structure.

Fig. 1.9 King John's Castle, Limerick, a Norman structure built on an earlier Viking settlement.

VIKING SETTLEMENT

In the later years of the Early Christian period, Viking settlers invaded Ireland and began to build towns around the country. Viking settlement strongly influenced the founding of Ireland's major towns and cities, including Dublin, Wexford, Waterford, Cork and Limerick. While hardly any building evidence still exists from that time, these towns' street arrangements and city plans have their origins in Viking layouts.

MEDIEVAL SETTLEMENT

Great defensive buildings such as castles and tower houses were built during the medieval period. Built of stone, they had thick walls with small windows and few openings so as not to weaken the structure.

Tower houses were defended residences or castles that were built by the better-off members of society, both Gaelic and Anglo-Norman, in many parts of Ireland in late medieval times – the 15th and 16th centuries. They consist of tall, usually

Fig. 1.10 Ross Castle, Killarney, Co. Kerry, a tower house with surrounding walls.

Fig. 1.11 Bunratty Castle, Co. Clare.

rectangular towers of between three and sometimes five storeys, with either a spiral stairs or lengths of straight stairs within the walls giving access to the upper floors.

The larger and more elaborate tower houses were built mainly on the richer land in the east of the country. Due to their height, the walls on the lower floors were splayed outwards at the base to support the upper floors. The ground floor walls are wider than those at the top; this base level was called the batter. There were battlements along the ridge of the roof, and small slit windows in the walls. From these windows the inhabitants could shoot arrows and muskets and throw rubble and other items for defence.

Three tower houses that have been restored in recent times are Ross Castle, on the lakes of Killarney, Co. Kerry; Blarney Castle in Blarney, Co. Cork; and Bunratty Castle, Co. Clare. The remains of some 3000 tower houses can still be seen around the country.

Apart from defensive structures, several other styles of architecture came to the fore in the medieval period, including Romanesque and, evolving from Romanesque, the Gothic style.

ROMANESQUE

The first examples of Romanesque architecture in Ireland date from the 12th century. Influenced by the highly decorated churches found elsewhere in Europe, this style of architecture shows Ireland's increasing contact with the outside world. The finest example is Cormac's Chapel on the Rock of Cashel in Co. Tipperary.

This style is most commonly characterised by:
- Decorative semi-circular arches over windows and doors
- Vaulting
- Heavy columns
- Large towers.

Fig. 1.12 Romanesque arch. The arrows show the distribution of the load on the arch.

Bulky walls – to support the buildings' heavy stone ceilings – are also characteristic of this style. However, in Ireland there are also examples of Romanesque buildings with wooden roof structures. Where stone was used, the arched chambers allowed for the weight of the roof load to be transmitted to the walls and foundations. Builders found that if the columns holding up these arches were too high, the columns would buckle outwards due to the stress on the arch above them. The stresses on the arch can be seen in Fig. 1.12.

'Vault' is the term for an arched roof structure, most commonly seen in churches. Vaulting was a common building method in both Romanesque and Gothic architecture. Where two vaulted chambers meet is called a groin. Fig. 1.13 shows an example of a simple Romanesque groin vault.

One of the most influential buildings of this period was Cormac's Chapel in Cashel, Co. Tipperary (Fig. 1.14). Its construction is one of the earliest examples of planned building in Ireland. All details, including internal components, were designed using drawings.

The Romanesque style is largely found in religious buildings. The door of a Romanesque church or cathedral was a focal point, with highly decorative entrance arches, as shown in Fig. 1.15. This decoration was to emphasise the transition as you entered the building from the ordinary world outside to the religious world within.

The Romanesque style combined proportions and construction technology from early Roman architecture, but used geometric designs from northern Europe. The proportion of these elements can be traced back to the golden ratio, also known as 'the divine proportion'.

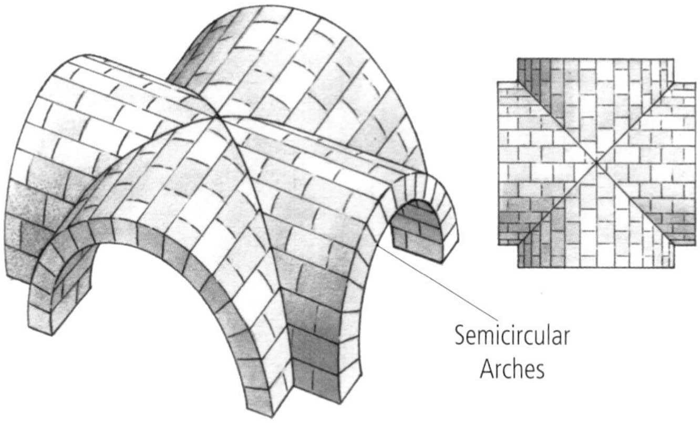

Semicircular Arches

Fig. 1.13 Romanesque groin vault.

Fig. 1.14 Cormac's Chapel at the Rock of Cashel, Co. Tipperary.

Fig. 1.15 Front door arch, St Fin Barre's Cathedral, Cork.

The Golden Ratio

The golden ratio (Fig. 1.16) expresses the idea that things in nature, and in design, are linked by the proportions between them. The ideal dimensions are 1:1.6. Designers and builders around the world strive for this golden ratio. The golden ratio places certain elements of the building in proportion to each other: starting with the smallest feature, the next one is 1.6 times as big. For example, if we take a structure's height as a unit of 1, the building will be 1.6 times as wide. This ratio has been used for centuries to help create aesthetic design in art and architecture.

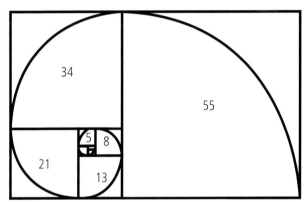

Fig. 1.16 The golden spiral: as each arch is created, the box that surrounds it becomes 1.6 times as big.

The front face of the Parthenon (Fig. 1.17) in Athens, Greece, is a classic example of proportion and the golden ratio. Taking account of a person's view of the structure from the ground, certain elements have been shaped to 'correct' what the eye sees. For example, the columns at the front of the building have a slight taper so that to someone looking from ground level they appear to rise perpendicular to the ground. The outer columns angle inwards towards the structure, and are thicker than the rest, to maintain the aesthetic lines of the building.

Fig. 1.17 The Parthenon, Athens, Greece (front elevation).

GOTHIC

Evolving from the Romanesque style, Gothic architecture is noted for simpler detail, more open space, and pointed rather than rounded arches. The use of finer detail was made possible by improvements in stonemasons' carving techniques, more sophisticated tools, and the development of three major construction technologies:

- Pointed arches
- Flying buttresses
- Ribbed vaults.

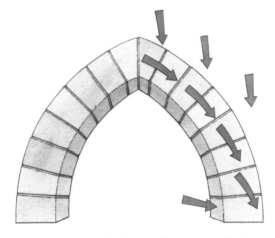

Fig. 1.18 Gothic arch showing the pressure loads placed on the arch.

Pointed Arches

The change from rounded arches to pointed arches gave church buildings more stability, as the load that travels down the arch to the walls and the ground is a more vertical load due to the shape of the arch. Pointed arches were also higher than rounded arches, which allowed for the construction of taller buildings. One example of high pointed arches is St Colman's Cathedral in Cobh, Co. Cork.

The pointed arch meant that the columns supporting the arch could be higher because the load travels along the arch more easily, as can be seen in Fig. 1.18. The weakness of this type of arch, however, was the base stone. Due to the forces placed on it, the stone tended to push outwards. To overcome this pressure, another advance in building technology was required.

Flying Buttresses

Flying buttresses provided an additional, external means of support. The buttresses were external columns which distributed the loading of the arch to the outside of the building (Fig. 1.19). They often had a decorative appearance and added to the ornate design of the building's exterior. They also allowed for smaller internal column supports inside the building, which made the internal space more open. As a result, the main body of the church, the nave, had the largest internal space.

In Fig. 1.20 the pressure loads coming from the apex of the building are distributed down the columns and out onto the flying buttresses.

Ribbed Vault

Developed from the Romanesque vault, the ribbed vault uses supports – or ribs – to construct the vault. This allows all the strain of the roof to be placed on the rib members. The rest of the roof structure rests on these members. The parts of the roof between the ribs could now be made of lighter material, because they only served as a covering for the internal space (Fig. 1.21).

The best examples of Gothic style can be seen in some of Ireland's finest cathedrals, including Christ Church and St Patrick's cathedrals in Dublin.

Fig. 1.19 Flying buttress: the pillar on the outside is the buttress; the arch between it and the building is the flying buttress.

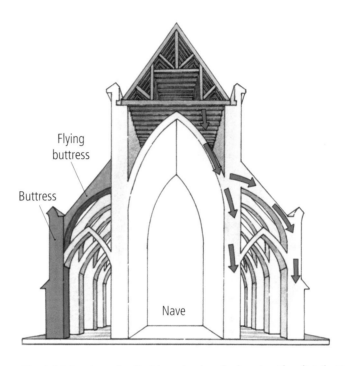

Fig. 1.20 Section of a Gothic style church showing the distribution of pressure loads.

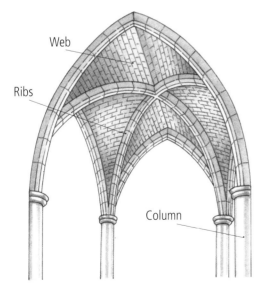

Fig. 1.21 Gothic rib vault. The stone arches crossing the centre are the ribs; the infill between them is known as the web.

Fig. 1.22 Christ Church Cathedral, Dublin.

VERNACULAR ARCHITECTURE

While some architectural styles follow rigid rules of construction, vernacular architecture – i.e. local or native architecture – is a more informal style of building.

Vernacular styles vary from country to country, as well as within countries, to meet the needs of local people. Two vernacular styles that have become famous worldwide are the igloo of the Inuit people of the central Arctic and Greenland, and the tipi of the Native Americans of the Great Plains. These simple structures were made from local materials (ice and animal skins) available to the builder.

As a method of construction, native style is based on:

- Local needs
- The raw materials found in the area
- Local building traditions.

Vernacular buildings are usually simple, and use a limited range of materials. The scale of the dwellings is modest, enough to house their inhabitants.

Local resources and methods were used to build them, and they reflect the culture and history of their area. Vernacular housing was not standardised. Its style was limited by the building materials available, the local terrain and climate, and the skill of the builder.

Even so, local builders achieved great things. The thatched cottage, for example, has come to symbolise Ireland across the world. These were built from clay, mud and stone – some were even made of turf. The thatch was made from local materials: reeds, sedges and beet in wetland areas; or the straw from cereal crops such as rye, barley and wheat in richer farming land.

The use of native materials meant that the house mirrored the local landscape. Building methods were also environmentally sustainable, as the materials did

Fig. 1.23 Native Americans were nomadic people, so their settlements had to be mobile. These simple tipis are made of timber frames with animal skins stretched over them to provide a solid structure. The igloo of the Inuit was built to provide shelter from strong, freezing winds, using ice to provide a solid structure.

not need to be transported over long distances, and were usually either waste material from other activities or found in abundance in the region. It is worth noting this in a modern context, when it is still important to harmonise with the landscape.

WEST COAST DWELLINGS

Traditional dwellings in the west of Ireland were modest and simple. Usually they had one main room which was used by the family day and night. They also sheltered their animals inside the house when the weather was particularly bad. These houses were usually built on a slope, due to the mountainous terrain, and the lower half of the building housed the animals. Wealthier families built a separate byre, usually attached to the house, which could house the animals.

The buildings were simply constructed using stone (with lime mortar), mud or peat (in some areas) and usually had a white limewash exterior. The simple layout of the building was sufficient for the needs of the family. The internal furnishing of the home was simple, usually just the bare necessities. Storage space for pots and other implements was sometimes provided by spaces carved in the walls. Fig. 1.24 shows the simple layout of a byre dwelling.

Most of these buildings had a loft, which acted as an upstairs room. The roof, particularly in houses on the coast, might, if people could afford it, be made of slate, which held up better in rough weather coming in from the sea, but it was more often made of thatch. As an added defence, the gable end of the building was built facing the prevailing wind (Fig. 1.25). These west coast-style dwellings can be seen mostly in Munster and Connacht, with some found in parts of Ulster.

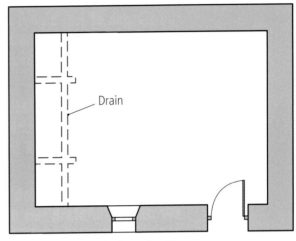

Fig. 1.24 Layout of a byre dwelling.

Fig. 1.25 The gable was built on the exposed side of the building for protection against the wind.

Fig. 1.26 West coast dwelling.

Fig. 1.27 East coast dwelling.

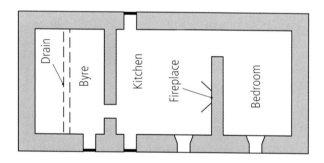

Fig. 1.28 The east coast cottage was more developed than the western cottage, with more rooms and furniture.

EAST COAST DWELLINGS

The east coast of Ireland has a less harsh climate and better land than the west, and families there were generally wealthier. As a result, dwellings in this region were commonly more elaborate, and had more rooms. Some had their sleeping quarters in a full loft over the entire ground floor, and wealthier families had their houses lime rendered both inside and out. The roofs were usually half hipped or hipped. These dwellings were most commonly found in Leinster and parts of Ulster. An example can be seen in Fig. 1.27.

The buildings themselves were usually constructed of stone and washed with lime render similar to that used for western cottages. Unlike houses in the west, they often had separate living and sleeping areas, with the living area usually located around a central hearth at the middle of the building; and they contained more furniture. A simple layout of the interior can be seen in Fig. 1.28.

Lime Render

Lime has been used as a binding base for mortar and plaster for over 10,000 years. Lime render is a natural building material which lets walls breathe. Lime render allows moisture to be absorbed from the exterior of the building, but through natural evaporation within the wall the moisture dissipates. This process helps to stabilise the internal humidity of the building. It provides a comfortable environment by reducing surface condensation and natural mould growth.

Lime render is made up of a mix of lime, sand and water. The consistency of the mix is slightly stiffer than modern cement or gypsum render. As a rule of thumb, the mix is made with 1 part lime to 2.5–3 parts sand. Coarse sand can be used: if the sand is too fine it can crack after the mix has set on the wall. Lime render is used mainly for vernacular cottages of both east and west of Ireland design.

DEVELOPMENT OF COTTAGE STYLE

Over time the style of the country cottage evolved. As grants were made available, extensions and even second storeys were added. These improved houses were dubbed 'thatch mansions'. Sometimes the thatch was replaced with slate on the main dwelling and with corrugated iron on the outhouses surrounding it.

CLASSICAL STYLE

Around the turn of the 18th century, classical and Palladian architecture found its way to Ireland. Rich landlords remodelled and extended their homes or built new dwellings to add to their estates. These larger homes were usually of simple design and two storeys high. In contrast to the standard cottage, visitors entered into a hallway rather than the kitchen, and all rooms were accessible from this hallway.

Fig. 1.29 Irish farmhouse, the vernacular form of a classical architectural style.

These buildings had a wooden panelled door with fanlight overhead, and sliding sash windows, three bays across. The walls were rendered and sometimes painted. Roofs were slated and sometimes hipped.

For this classical style, proportion was key. All elements, including windows, doors and heights, were constructed using set ratios and values for aesthetic purposes. The style spread throughout the country, and was the basis of the typical Irish farmhouse seen in Fig. 1.29.

Palladian architecture was elegant and understated. It was based on the architecture of ancient Rome and its philosophy of design was drawn from the work of Andrea Palladio, a 16th-century Italian architect. This type of architecture used symmetry and perspective and followed the principles of design used in ancient Roman temple architecture. Great Irish examples of this type of architecture are Bessborough House, Piltown, Co. Killkenny, and Leinster House in Dublin, the location of Dáil Éireann.

GEORGIAN ARCHITECTURE

While the cottage styles described above are examples of the rural vernacular style, many of Ireland's urban heritage buildings were built in the Georgian or Victorian periods. Georgian architecture was influenced by the English styles developed during the reigns of four kings, all called George (hence the name), who were in power from 1714 to 1830. Georgian buildings can be seen in many

Fig. 1.30 Typical Georgian street façade.

places in Ireland, for example Pery Square, Limerick, and Merrion Square, Dublin. The buildings, which made elegant family homes, were commonly built around squares or in terraces. Terraced houses were four storeys high over a basement, with the most important reception rooms on the first floor, and in the midlands and east of the country were usually clad in a brick façade.

Another typical feature of this style is the sash window with multiple panels of glass, which added proportion and a sense of height to the façade. The windows on the upper storeys were smaller in height to maintain the building's proportions when viewed from the street. An example of a typical sash window can be seen in Fig. 1.31.

The door was a focal point and was usually ornamented. A half-circular fanlight over the front door was a very common feature (Fig. 1.32), and there were often pillars or windows at either side of the door. Georgian terrace homes usually had steps leading up to the front door with decorative iron railings around the front outside wall.

The front elevation of the building was very simple in appearance, so features such as windows and doors are the major points of interest on the exterior of this style of building.

Fig. 1.31 Sash window.

Fig. 1.32 Georgian fanlight over the main door.

Different materials were used to build Georgian houses in different parts of the country. For example, in Georgian times brick was often used as ballast in ships sailing from England to Dublin, and the surplus brick was used to build the city's great Georgian terraces. Buildings in other places might not be built with brick, but they still have the overall look of the style.

CONSERVATION

It is important that Ireland's heritage buildings, which are a national treasure, live on and are preserved for our descendants. Heritage conservation endeavours to protect and safeguard man-made structures of historic or architectural significance.

Conservation aims to prevent buildings from deteriorating and to return them to their original state. Conserving buildings is delicate work, so there are certain principles that need to be followed:

- **Research:** Research must be carried out on the building prior to any work being undertaken.

- **Restore:** It is better to repair than to replace. Where possible, features should be repaired to look as they did when the building was first built.

- **Respect:** The role of the building in its environment is important. With proper research the building can be restored to complement its surroundings.

By following these simple principles, buildings can be conserved to a high standard. The key to success is sympathy for traditional methods and the materials used.

There are two approaches to conserving buildings: restoration and reconstruction.

- **Restoration** is the refurbishment of the building, with the aim of returning it to its original state. For example, a mill might be restored using traditional methods and materials.

- **Reconstruction** means rebuilding the building using complementary or sympathetic materials, even though these may be modern. An example is shown in Fig. 1.33. In reconstruction, it is clear that the building has changed; the aim is not to mask the alterations, and it can be clearly seen that there is an old and a new part to this building. In many cases, the function of the building may be changed.

Fig. 1.33 Modern and heritage architecture merged in one building.

In Ireland, buildings of architectural interest can be recorded in the National Inventory of Architectural

Heritage (NIAH), which keeps records of heritage buildings built after 1700 and aims to protect and conserve them. The NIAH is a state initiative under the administration of the Department of Arts, Heritage and the Gaeltacht. It makes recommendations to local planning authorities about buildings to be included in their Record of Protected Structures (RPS).

GOVERNMENT ORGANISATIONS

A number of local and national government agencies are responsible for protecting Ireland's built heritage.

Office of Public Works (OPW)

The Office of Public Works (OPW) looks after all state buildings. The OPW's duties cover the management and maintenance of all state properties, including the purchase, construction or renting of office accommodation for government departments, offices and agencies. The OPW also manages and operates state-owned heritage properties, and looks after the restoration of any buildings under its care.

Local Authorities

City/town and county councils are responsible for planning applications, roads and infrastructure. As well as being in charge of building this infrastructure, they are in charge of budgeting for it. They are also responsible for ensuring that there is no negative impact on our built heritage in the area they govern.

The Heritage Council

The Heritage Council is primarily an educational and advisory body. It builds on the work of the state heritage bodies that have primary responsibility for the care of property in state ownership and the designation of protected areas. The Heritage Council does this by putting forward policies to protect the national heritage in its widest sense, including monuments, buildings, archaeological sites, landscapes, seascapes, heritage gardens, waterways and parks. It also establishes infrastructure and networks to enable communities to take responsibility for and participate in the development and conservation of their heritage assets.

National Inventory of Architectural Heritage (NIAH)

The NIAH is a state body whose role is to identify, record and evaluate buildings of architectural merit built from 1700 to the present day. It carries out local surveys, which are the basis for recommending that buildings be listed in local authorities' Record of Protected Structures (RPS).

The RPS is a list of structures or buildings that are deemed to be good examples of architecture of a certain period or to have architectural merit according to certain criteria.

Civic Trusts

These are independent charitable bodies that recognise and protect architecture that has particular value. They strive to identify, conserve and repair buildings of merit. They are independent of the government, although they often work with government bodies to achieve their aims.

An Taisce

This independent body monitors the application of European environmental legislation at local level. It also promotes sustainable living and environmental awareness through the Green Schools, Green Homes, and Green Communities programmes run by its Environmental Education Unit. An Taisce also acts as consultants for policy formulation in the area of waste management and the protection of the natural environment.

ACTIVITY:

Choose a local heritage building and comment on its location and features, and the materials and methods that were used to construct the building. Sketch the overall appearance of the building and pick one interesting feature to sketch in detail.

PRACTICE QUESTIONS

1. Why is shelter necessary? Consider this with reference to three basic needs.

2. What is the importance of heritage buildings?

3. 'Irish built heritage is a national treasure.' Write a short paragraph giving your view on this statement.

4. Describe the development from Romanesque to Gothic architecture.

5. Explain the benefits of the flying buttress in the construction of buildings.

6. Highlight the differences between the western and eastern styles of Irish vernacular architecture, and comment on how these differences came about. (Sketches may be used.)

7. 'Georgian architecture in Ireland was simple in design.' Comment on this statement, referring to the features of Georgian homes.

8. Discuss the benefits of conserving our built heritage and comment on conservation principles.

9. Describe the difference between restoration and reconstruction and discuss which would be more appropriate for conserving a Georgian building.

PRACTICE QUESTIONS

10. Define the terms below with regard to heritage building and conservation. Use thumbnail sketches where necessary.
    (a) Vernacular construction
    (b) Sympathetic materials
    (c) Sash window
    (d) Groin vault.

11. Comment on the role of the following groups in relation to heritage and conservation:
    (a) Office of Public Works
    (b) Local authorities
    (c) Heritage Council
    (d) Civic trusts
    (e) An Taisce.

CHAPTER 2
PLANNING DEVELOPMENT

INTRODUCTION

Despite many advances, Ireland's planning record is poor. In this country there is a great deal of urban sprawl, caused by building large estates on the edge of urban areas, and this has a detrimental effect on cities, small towns and villages. Many large housing estates in modern Ireland do not have enough public spaces or adequate amenities. The practice of siting one-off houses along main roads has led to ribbon development, which stretches the boundaries of towns and villages and increases the demands on services in the area. All of this is due to poor planning and poor control of development.

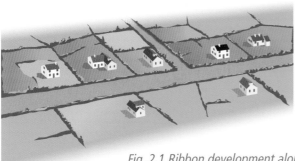

Fig. 2.1 Ribbon development along major roads elongates settlement areas and places strain on the services of the area.

Fig. 2.2 Urban sprawl is the expansion of low-density settlement in an urban area. Local services may not be viable in such low-density settlements.

*Fig. 2.3
Dublin:
Ireland's
largest urban
landscape.*

In the context of the building industry, development means the construction of new buildings or services, such as houses, roads, schools and hospitals. Development takes place throughout the whole country, so it is important to have standards and regulations to control it. These regulations prevent random development and ensure that adequate services are provided in areas as they grow.

Development is controlled by planning. Planning is the responsibility of national and local authorities, including the Department of the Environment, Community and Local Government, county councils and town councils; so planning decisions are made at both national and local level.

In recent times there has been a move to correct the planning and development mistakes of the past and to take more issues into account before allowing a development to take place. These considerations include providing for:

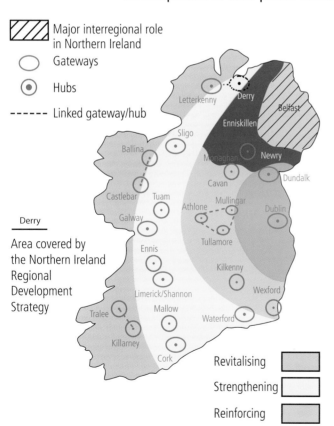

Fig. 2.4 The National Spatial Strategy's development plan, showing hubs and gateways.

- Services: roads, sewers, public lighting
- Amenities: parks, swimming pools, play areas
- Community needs: community centres, the location of developments in an area
- Sustainability: meeting the needs of the present without compromising the needs of future generations.

NATIONAL SPATIAL STRATEGY (NSS)

The National Spatial Strategy (NSS) is the national planning framework. It sets out a development plan for the entire country over a 20-year period. The principles and goals of the NSS are to achieve:

- Balanced regional development
- More effective planning
- A better balance of social, economic and physical development

- The improvement of cities, towns and rural areas
- An equal spread of opportunities, quality of life and places to live.

The NSS outlines nine 'gateways' and nine 'hubs' nationwide. The gateways act at a national level as passages for economic activity for businesses, residential services and amenities, while the hubs act for wider rural areas to support, and be supported in turn, by the gateways. Fig. 2.4 shows the gateways and hubs around the country. The NSS itself can, of course, be changed to meet new needs.

NATIONAL DEVELOPMENT PLAN (NDP)

The National Development Plan (NDP) promotes balanced development across the country, following the principles and goals of the NSS. Infrastructure and services of all kinds are covered in the NDP.

AREA DEVELOPMENT PLANS

An Area Development Plan is a document compiled by a local authority that sets out the terms of development in the local authority area. The principles and goals of the NSS are applied to the Area Development Plan.

Area Development Plans are drawn up every six years. They are used as a means of controlling the development of an area over time. Area Development Plans are available from local authority websites and planning offices.

The Area Development Plan zones land for specific kinds of development: residential, industrial, agricultural, commercial, etc. This means that some kinds of building cannot be developed in an area where they are not authorised by the plan. All planning applications made to the local authority are assessed under the criteria set out in the plan.

When purchasing land for a building project, it is important to consider various aspects of the Area Development Plan, such as:

- Protected buildings near the development
- Road and access layout
- Access to services (electricity, water and waste water connections)
- Controls on development in the area
- Environmental restrictions.

As well as the Area Development Plan, some authorities also provide a guide to planning in the local area. These planning guides provide examples of what is and what is not considered good design in that area. They help builders and consumers design houses that suit local styles and materials.

It is important that the developer reviews the guidelines for the local area where they want to build. Building materials and methods, as well as environmental considerations and conditions in relation to preserving scenic areas, are different in different parts of the country. The local planning authority can give advice on the type of development acceptable in a particular area.

LOCAL AREA PLAN

A local area plan covers a smaller area than the Area Development Plan. It applies to a village, town or district rather than the entire county or local authority area. Local area plans identify the need for new development, and set out rules and regulations specific to the locality.

LAND ZONING

Land zoning means assigning land for a particular use. Originally used to separate industrial from residential areas, it is now used to further divide land for different uses. However, as a result of the increase in residential land zoning, many developers have built large housing estates, while work on schools, hospitals, libraries and other amenities has not been as intensive. This has led to housing estates being built with no local services and no link to the local town or city.

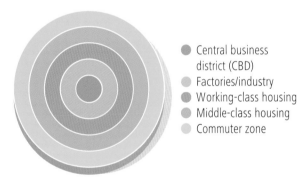

- Central business district (CBD)
- Factories/industry
- Working-class housing
- Middle-class housing
- Commuter zone

Fig. 2.5 The Burgess concentric urban development model, with different areas radiating from the centre.

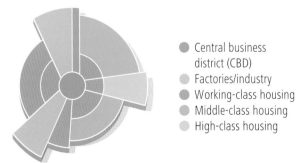

- Central business district (CBD)
- Factories/industry
- Working-class housing
- Middle-class housing
- High-class housing

Fig. 2.6 Hoyt sector model of urban development. The core is still the central business district, while the other areas merge with each other.

Best practice in planning and zoning land now looks at settlement patterns that are oriented towards creating active town centres. An active town centre is one that is easily accessible, contains all the amenities and services that people need, and minimises the use of cars. This is achieved by keeping the settlement compact and accessible, and by providing public transport, pedestrian areas and shared public spaces.

The general model for this kind of planning is shown in Fig. 2.5, where the central business district is at the centre and the town or city develops evenly outwards from it in all directions.

There are alternatives to this model. One example is shown in Fig. 2.6: the central business district is still in the centre, but other land uses form wedge-shaped sectors radiating out from it.

Adamstown in Dublin is an example of an urban settlement that follows best practice ideals in planning and zoning land. Built in 2006, Adamstown is a purpose-built commuter town, where schools, shopping centres, transport systems and other services were included as part of the overall development. The key to this kind of development is to provide the amenities and services that people need in a self-contained area.

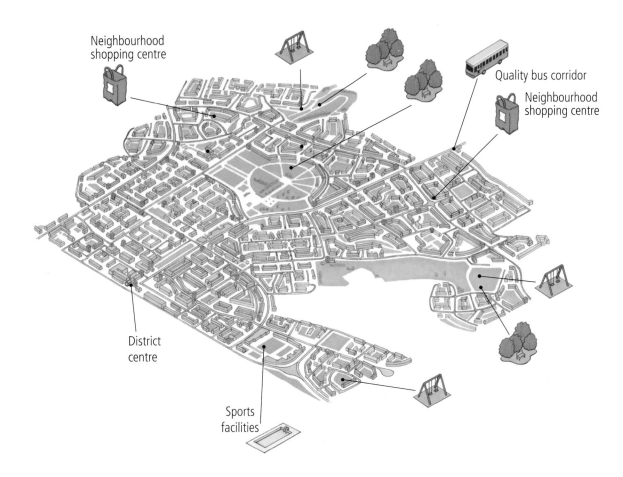

Neighbourhood shopping centre

Quality bus corridor

Neighbourhood shopping centre

District centre

Sports facilities

Fig. 2.7 Adamstown is a purpose-built settlement which provides varied accommodation and services which meet the needs of each area of the town.

RURAL AND URBAN

An urban area has a high population density, while the population density of a rural area is low. Cities and towns are considered urban; villages and country areas are rural.

In the Irish context it is important that these two cultures, rural and urban, are maintained, because people have formed direct links with the culture of their own locality. There are different development requirements associated with urban and rural areas.

Much like the planning strategies employed for Ireland as a whole, development in rural and urban areas must be considered as part of a larger picture, from the community down to the individual home.

● Neighbourhood/locality
● Site
● Home (building)

Fig. 2.8 Look at all scales of the development, from the locality to the home.

By looking at these three elements – neighbourhood, site and individual building – the best and most efficient housing plan for the area and for the developer can be worked out. Because there are so many differences between what is acceptable in an urban and a rural locality, we shall look at these two areas separately.

URBAN DEVELOPMENT

Urban development involves shaping towns and cities to make them desirable places to work and live in. Development can happen on a small or large scale, from a single building to a complete neighbourhood. Good urban planning promotes community spirit and puts the community (the place and its people), not just the buildings, at the centre of development.

For this to happen it is important that communities are provided with essential services and infrastructure, such as roads, schools, shops, public spaces, parking areas and so on. In an urban area, the density of development is quite high, so service centres are centrally located in the community. For urban areas to grow in a sustainable manner, three essential elements must be considered:

- **Community development:** The aim of sustainable development is not just the accommodation of people, but the building of communities. Local service centres should be developed within these communities.

- **Economic development:** A major element of the urban landscape is the economic opportunities it provides. Development must plan for shops and stores, factories, offices and other economic centres.

- **Viable natural environment:** Development should not have a negative impact on the natural environment where it is set.

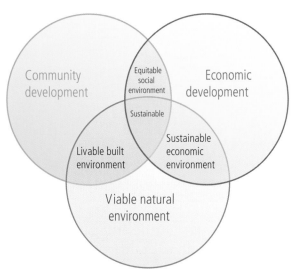

Fig. 2.9 The community, the economy and the environment all overlap when planning for development.

While urban planning employs many new strategies of design, developers and planners are constantly learning from poorly implemented practices and seeing how they can be improved. This is in the hope of providing people with more enjoyable places to live. New approaches to designing urban spaces rely on two sources for ideas:

- Modern urban design principles
- Local community participation.

MODERN URBAN DESIGN PRINCIPLES

Urban design encompasses a huge variety of elements. Urban planners strive to create sustainable communities, areas with accessible amenities and good local transport, and neighbourhoods where services like shops, schools and offices are within easy walking distance. Ease of access along streets, and public spaces to enjoy, add to the quality of life for the people living in the area.

Fig. 2.10 shows a model of urban development. Here, residential neighbourhoods are clustered around local service centres, which provide everyday needs such as shops, childcare, buses, etc. The neighbourhoods are connected, and within 10 or 15 minutes' walk of one another. Local public transport stops may be provided at these neighbourhood centres. This reduces people's dependency on cars.

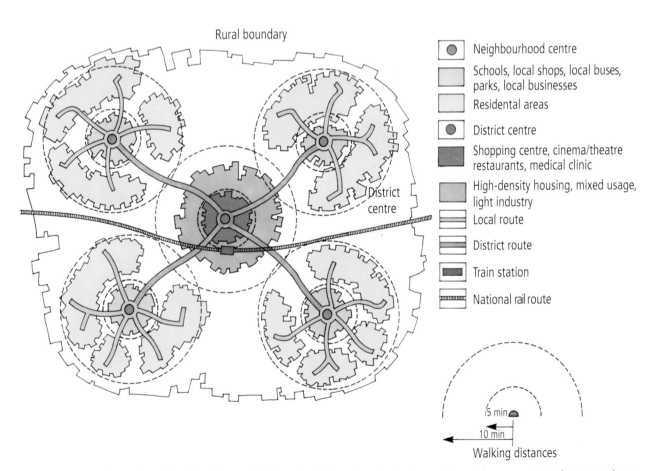

Fig. 2.10 Modern urban planning draws neighbourhoods together in clusters and provides easy access between them.

The residential neighbourhoods also connect to a regional centre, where large-scale services such as shopping centres, medical clinics, restaurants and cinemas or theatres are located. This central region also has high-density accommodation. National public transport is available at this central point. Light industry may be located on the outskirts of the area.

Urban design principles aim to provide a sustainable environment in which people can trade, live and work. Good planning also nurtures the character of an area by reflecting on its past and creating a bridge between those traditions and the area's future. Planners must consider street layout, the position of industrial and retail areas, service areas, public spaces, local heritage, amenities and public transport, as well as the physical barriers to development, such as the topography of the landscape.

There are many aspects to consider, and some of the major factors are looked at here.

STREET LAYOUT

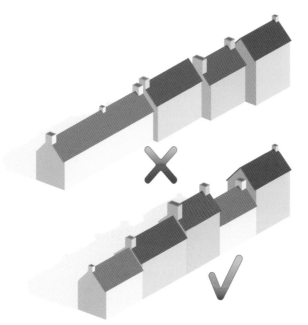

The layout of streets and building lines makes up some of the local character of the urban scene. This is referred to as the urban structure. It is created by respecting street patterns (Fig. 2.11) or street widths to keep them consistent with their historic surroundings. By linking with existing elements, the street design is anchored to the region.

New developments should not simply copy or imitate historic developments. A better approach is to appreciate the basics that made historic development sustainable and encourage these in new constructions.

Fig. 2.11 Street patterns are respected by keeping the buildings at a similar size along the street.

STREET FAÇADE

New development should match the character and potential of the existing built environment. It should carry through the traditions and styles of the local neighbourhood. An example is the street shown in Fig. 2.12.

This continuity of the street's façade helps to create 'active frontage'. Active frontage is the characteristics of streets and open spaces that help to animate the area, making it feel safer and more welcoming. These characteristics include the position and detailing of windows; style of plasterwork; colour of buildings; and signage. Façades are made more interesting for the people passing by, and add vitality to the area. In contrast, blank, uninteresting buildings reduce the interest of the passer-by and are said to be 'dead frontage'.

Fig. 2.12 Continuation of street façade with parking at the rear accessed through the arch.

CURTILAGE

Urban areas have a high density of houses, but people must also be given some privacy. Curtilage is a term used to define the land immediately surrounding a building, and it includes any associated buildings or structures, i.e. garages, sheds, etc. It can also be evident from the position of trees, fences and hedges, as seen in Fig. 2.13. Curtilage must be considered in urban planning to allow homeowners a reasonable degree of privacy.

Because dwellings are positioned close together in towns and cities, overlooking other properties is a major concern when designing for urban areas. To maintain privacy, the minimum recommended distance between houses back to back is 22m. Visual obstruction should also be provided above the eye line at the margin of the site (Fig. 2.14).

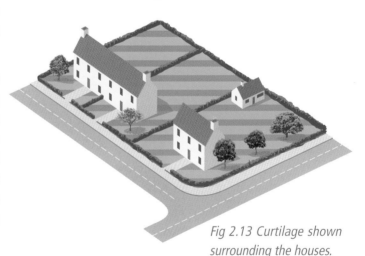

Fig 2.13 Curtilage shown surrounding the houses.

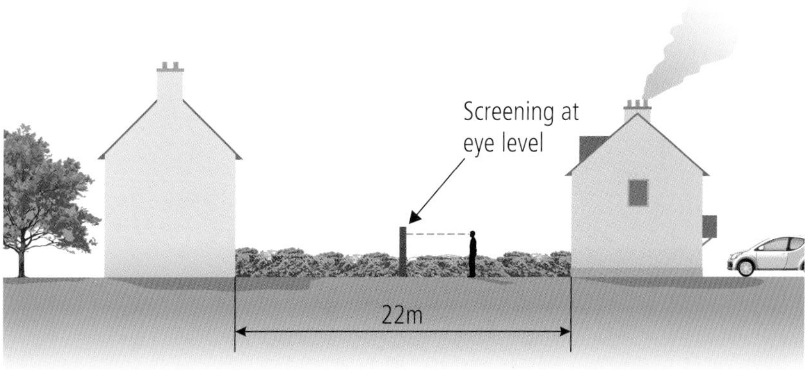

Screening at eye level

22m

Fig. 2.14 Privacy is maintained by keeping a minimum distance between houses and obstructing the view between them.

PARKING

In-curtilage parking

Parking can be provided in many ways in modern urban residential areas. Depending on the density of the accommodation, it may be useful to have communal parking for high-density areas or in-curtilage parking for low-density areas. A compromise is to combine both methods, with mixed on-street and off-street parking. The different possibilities are illustrated in Fig. 2.15.

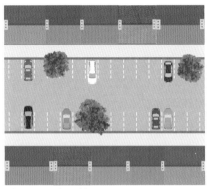

Communal parking

A mixture of communal and in-curtilage parking

Fig. 2.15 Parking can be laid out in different ways.

HOME ZONE

Much of the modern thinking on designing sustainable residential development in urban areas is drawn together in a planning concept used in the United Kingdom called Home Zone areas. Many of the development principles it employs are now being used by planners in this country. Home Zone sets out to create mixed clusters of residences within developments so as to build a sense of community. As shown in Fig. 2.16, Home Zone-style planning promotes:

- Mixed residential accommodation to suit different people, whether as families, single people, the elderly, etc. (mixed residences are shown in grey and red)
- An emphasis on open public spaces, most of which are overlooked from the front of the dwellings
- The use of reduced speed zones (in yellow in the image), which creates a more relaxed atmosphere on the streets.

Parking places for residents are situated on the street or in clusters for security, as shown in Fig. 2.17.

Traffic calming measures are encouraged in order to maintain a relaxed environment. Measures include extended paths, speed ramps, pedestrian crossings and tight corner turns to reduce speed.

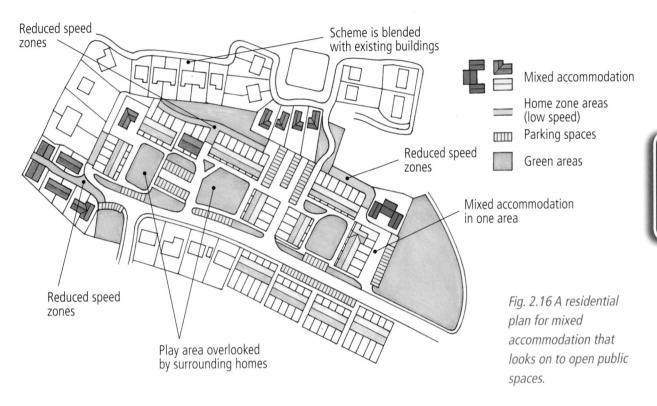

Reduced speed zones

Scheme is blended with existing buildings

Mixed accommodation

Home zone areas (low speed)

Parking spaces

Green areas

Reduced speed zones

Mixed accommodation in one area

Reduced speed zones

Play area overlooked by surrounding homes

Fig. 2.16 A residential plan for mixed accommodation that looks on to open public spaces.

CHAPTER 2

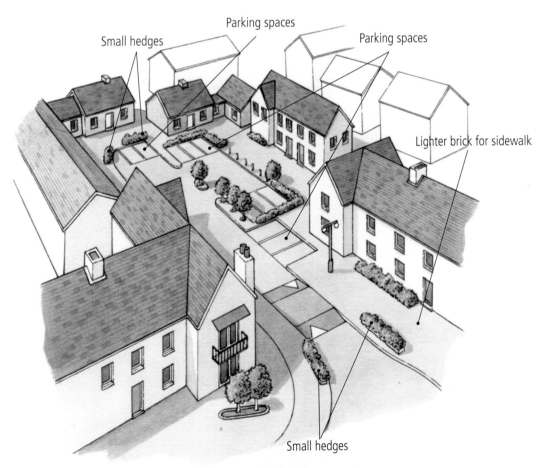

Parking spaces

Small hedges

Parking spaces

Lighter brick for sidewalk

Small hedges

Fig. 2.17 Small neighbourhood clusters of mixed accommodation.

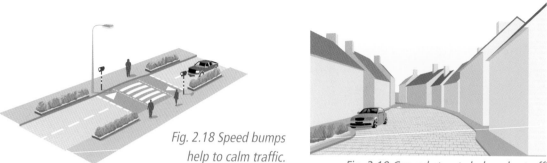

Fig. 2.18 Speed bumps help to calm traffic.

Fig. 2.19 Curved streets help calm traffic and add aesthetic appeal.

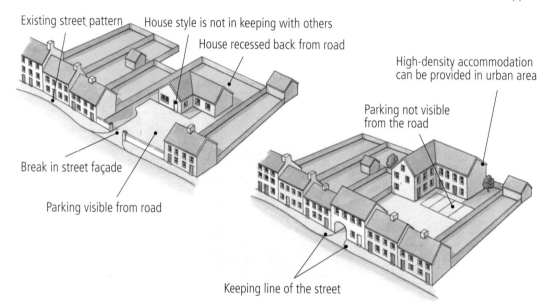

Existing street pattern

House style is not in keeping with others

House recessed back from road

High-density accommodation can be provided in urban area

Parking not visible from the road

Break in street façade

Parking visible from road

Keeping line of the street

Fig. 2.20 A suburban approach to a residence in an urban setting, contrasted with a more appropriate approach for an urban setting.

Simple traffic calming can be encouraged by street layout and design, using simple curved and narrow streets (Fig. 2.19). Simple curved streets encourage motorists to slow down – and provide points of interest for both pedestrians and drivers.

The existing urban landscape must be considered in any plans for urban development. This is particularly important for a one-off residential development. The new building must reflect the context of the area and the street. This is evident in Fig. 2.20, which shows two different approaches.

LOCAL COMMUNITY PARTICIPATION

Urban planners set out development policies and plans. However, they also consult with members of the community as these are the individuals who interact with the area on a daily basis.

Involving local people's aspirations for the area in the development plan, or any regeneration plans, adds to the positive effect which good urban design and planning can have on an area. Local people can often foresee the difficulties which may arise in the day-to-day running of a new development as they are accustomed to how the locality operates.

URBAN SPRAWL

Urban sprawl – the uncontrolled development of communities – is one of the biggest challenges to urban development. It hampers sustainable growth because it does not accommodate adequate services and infrastructure for the area. The lack of local service centres creates a greater dependency on cars, as people travel to shops and other services located some distance away. Coupled with this, there is usually a lot of private space in these areas, with very little public space available for community and other activities. The density of dwellings is often too low for public transport to be viable, which also adds to people's reliance on cars.

Out of town shopping centres and retail parks have also become a common sight on the outskirts of many towns and cities. These centres serve to reduce footfall in the centre of the town or city, and encourage car use. This is completely at odds with the stated aims of urban planning, and is a problem throughout the country.

Better planning, which reduces urban sprawl, can help to create a better-quality urban environment for the public.

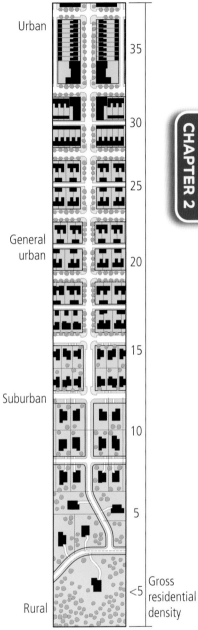

Fig. 2.21 Urban and rural density, showing the number of residences per hectare. Density refers to the amount of housing units found in an area. The urban centre has a high density of housing units, as well as tall buildings, multi-storey apartments, etc. The density of buildings decreases as we move out through the suburbs and into rural areas, as shown here.

RURAL DEVELOPMENT

Rural development refers to the expansion of settlement in the countryside. Rural development should be both sustainable and sympathetic to the traditions and materials of the area. In contrast to the urban setting, rural development is low density and it should have an equally low impact on the landscape.

Different patterns of settlement can be seen in rural areas. While it may appear unplanned or scattered, rural settlement can in fact be grouped according to certain traits.

Villages, with a small number of houses clustered around the local service, be it a shop or a church, are typical of the Irish countryside. This type of settlement is called a nodal settlement (Fig. 2.22). Nodal settlements form small rural clusters of communities with shared services.

When considering further development to a nodal settlement, planning policies encourage the expansion of the natural cluster. Building between clusters is avoided in order to maintain the natural settlement pattern. Bridging two or more settlements in a rural location causes elongation of the settlement, and thus is a drain on services. This can be seen in Fig. 2.23.

Another type of settlement is linear or ribbon development (Fig. 2.24). This kind of settlement uses the road as an access point to obtain services and so is usually located on an important local route.

Nowadays this type of development is not encouraged in groups of five or more dwellings on one side of the road over a 250m stretch. This is because of a number of factors:

- It results in houses being strung out along the road
- It imposes an urban influence on the rural landscape
- It creates numerous accesses on to rural roads, which are a hazard

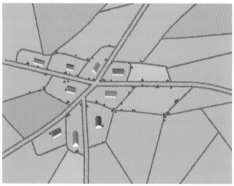

Fig. 2.22 A nodal settlement is a cluster of homes that usually occurs at the intersection of major routes.

Fig. 2.23 The site between two settlements (shown in red) is not an ideal location for a new build as it will bridge the two settlements.

Fig. 2.24 Linear development or ribbon development is common, but not encouraged today as it places a burden on services.

Fig. 2.25 Dispersed settlement is a random scattering of buildings across the landscape, usually including buildings from farm holdings.

- It landlocks farms
- It intrudes on views
- It leads to loss of natural hedgerows, banks and ditches.

The final style of rural development is the dispersed pattern of settlement, seen in Fig. 2.25. This is a random mix of buildings that appear scattered across the countryside. This pattern is often the result of the land being divided into separate farms or farm areas. The buildings are often a mixture of residential and agricultural (e.g. sheds for farm use).

When choosing to build in a rural setting, the scale of the development will most likely be small. This is due to the lower settlement density in the rural landscape. The scale of the development is an important factor when applying for planning permission.

THE RURAL LANDSCAPE

Respect for the topography of the land – the natural layout of the area – is vital in rural development. Over-excavated sites and over-manicured areas do not respect the natural environment and should be avoided. As will be discussed in more detail in the next chapter, natural shade and shelter need to be used to best advantage when building.

There are a number of planning guidelines associated with building in a rural area. These are provided to help the developer to sensitively integrate their new building into the landscape. The planning guidelines include:

- Reading the landscape
- Maintaining the existing features of the site
- The design and form of the development
- Ecological design and orientation
- Road boundaries and access to the site.

Reading the Landscape

The landscape should always be considered when choosing to locate a new development in the countryside. A new build should not intrude on the landscape, but neither should it be hidden. The development should be linked to the landscape. Huge amounts of excavation or movement of material should be avoided. The contour of a site needs to be considered, and the existing contour should be retained as far as is practical. Fig. 2.26 shows how this can be achieved.

The settlement patterns of the area surrounding the site should also be taken into consideration, as well as the style and scale of the buildings in the locality.

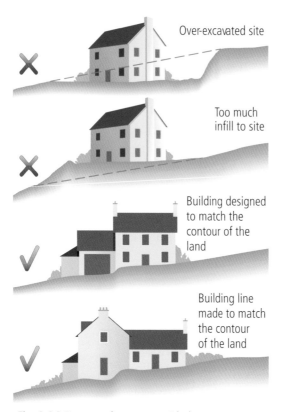

Over-excavated site

Too much infill to site

Building designed to match the contour of the land

Building line made to match the contour of the land

Fig. 2.26 Respect the countryside by constructing the building to suit the natural landscape.

The features of the site, such as existing walls, planting patterns and shelter, must also be considered. Fig. 2.27 shows how the natural landscape can be used to provide shelter for a new build.

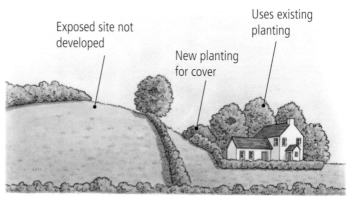

Exposed site not developed

New planting for cover

Uses existing planting

Fig. 2.27 Using natural shelter to protect against the weather. This also preserves the rural sightline.

Maintaining the Existing Features of the Site

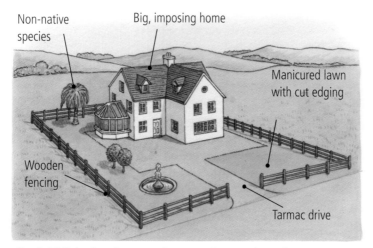

Non-native species

Big, imposing home

Manicured lawn with cut edging

Wooden fencing

Tarmac drive

Fig. 2.28 Suburban home and surrounds transplanted into a rural setting.

The new building should not look as though it has simply been transplanted from the urban scene or another area of the country into a new setting. This can be seen in Fig. 2.28.

Where possible, the existing features of the site should be retained. Over-manicured lawns and hedges, fenced boundaries and other urban elements are frowned upon in the rural setting. To integrate the building into the landscape, at least two existing natural boundaries should be used. Existing hedgerows, stone walling, etc. should be retained as a link to the landscape. The building must not break the skyline (or waterline where applicable), as this breaks into the local scenery. Indigenous trees and shrubbery planted around the site can help the development to blend in, as well as providing a shelter-belt against the wind.

In places where agriculture is or was commonplace, there may be older unused buildings that could be converted for modern living while retaining the outside envelope of the vernacular building. This allows for a blending of old and new without having to go to the lengths of building new structures.

Design and Form of the Development

The development itself needs to be carefully considered as it will be a part of the landscape for many years. It is best to use simple, restrained forms as they integrate more easily into their surroundings. The lines of the build should not compete with the natural topography but should complement it.

Local building materials should be used where possible, i.e. local stone and shrubbery, as this ties the building to the landscape. It should be noted, too, that a restricted range of materials should be used in order to prevent 'fussiness' in the finished building.

Where a developer chooses to build in a contemporary style, the inspiration should come from indigenous house forms in the local area. Although the build will be contemporary, this will help to prevent it standing out.

The construction of the house must be solid and simple in order to integrate it into the landscape.

Ecological Design and Orientation

A developer must take into account the wind direction, path of the sun, passive solar design, shelter and planting in relation to the build. These attributes will be discussed in detail in the next chapter.

Road Boundaries and Access to the Site

To integrate into the local landscape, the entrance to the site must be discreet and simple. Gates with alarms, high walls and decorative architecture must be avoided as they distract from the natural environment.

Driveways need to be carefully considered. Tarmacadam can be unsightly in areas of natural beauty. Shale or gravel should be considered as alternatives, as they bring a more natural look to the site.

The boundary of the site facing the roadside must complement the existing boundary to prevent any break of the eye line when viewing the house from the road.

FAÇADE

Whether building in the countryside or in town, the front façade of the building is obviously important. Best design practice today suggests that buildings should aim to have simple shapes and good proportions, and to avoid over-elaborate features. These differences in style are illustrated in Figs 2.29 and 2.30.

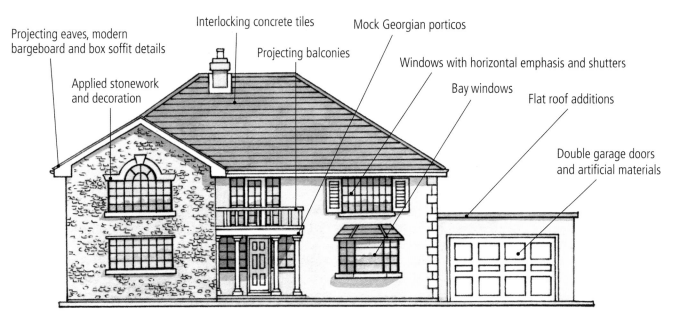

Projecting eaves, modern bargeboard and box soffit details

Applied stonework and decoration

Interlocking concrete tiles

Projecting balconies

Mock Georgian porticos

Windows with horizontal emphasis and shutters

Bay windows

Flat roof additions

Double garage doors and artificial materials

Fig. 2.29 Over-elaborate façade.

TRY TO AVOID

- Too much stonework and decoration
- Shallow-pitched, hipped roof
- Shallow-pitched, over-sailing roof
- Over-scaled dormers
- Chimney on pitch of roof
- Large, elaborate front door
- Projecting 'fussy' bay windows
- Multi-paned windows flush with façade
- Inconsistent detailing around window openings
- Randomly placed windows with horizontal emphasis and mixed detailing
- Dominant garage with addition of artificial materials
- Randomly applied quoins.

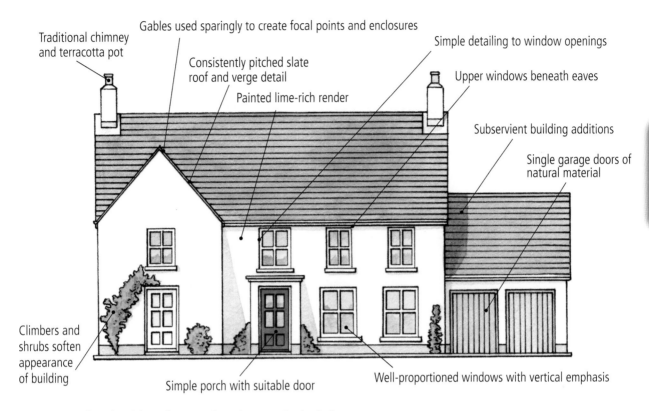

Traditional chimney and terracotta pot

Gables used sparingly to create focal points and enclosures

Consistently pitched slate roof and verge detail

Painted lime-rich render

Simple detailing to window openings

Upper windows beneath eaves

Subservient building additions

Single garage doors of natural material

Climbers and shrubs soften appearance of building

Simple porch with suitable door

Well-proportioned windows with vertical emphasis

Fig. 2.30 A façade with well-proportioned, sympathetic design.

CHAPTER 2

AIM TO ACHIEVE

- Uninterrupted pitched roof
- Eaves with simple end detail
- Chimneys flush with gables
- Vertical window emphasis with plaster surround and cill
- Simple porch and door detailing
- Well-proportioned arrangement of recessed openings
- Subservient additions (garage/workshop) with similar detailing.

ACTIVITY:

Using the information in either the Urban Development or Rural Development section above, analyse a local development in your area, highlighting factors that the developer had to consider when planning this building project.

Pick out key elements of this development that either take from or add to the character of the area.

PLANNING PERMISSION

The planning process, which is set down by the Planning and Development Acts, is an important part of controlling development. It allows the government to anticipate and control growth in an area, and is the starting point for providing services there. As stated earlier, the Area Development Plan sets out guidelines for building in a locality. All planning applications are judged according to this plan. This ensures consistency across the region and allows building to be controlled. This in turn helps planners provide the correct level of services to the area.

Planning permission needs to be obtained for any significant building project. Planning permission is granted by the local authority.

There are many reasons why planning permission is needed:
- It is a legal requirement
- It informs the public about the development
- It prevents the development of unsafe buildings
- The local council must be aware of any development in its area
- It ensures that buildings are in line with the local council's Area Development Plan
- It regulates all new building work in the area
- It controls the height, shape, design and location of buildings.

The purpose of planning permission is to:
- Provide better design in communities
- Maintain the tradition of the area
- Promote Irish building methods and styles.

A house that is granted planning permission in one area may be refused in another due to local considerations.

TYPES OF PLANNING PERMISSION

There are four types of planning permission in Ireland.

1. **Full permission.** This is the most common type of planning permission. If granted full planning permission, a person or company may build a new development or reconstruct an existing building according to the plans and specifications they submitted. It is a clear permission to start the build, subject to conditions laid down by the local authority.

2. **Outline permission.** This is used to establish whether the local authority is likely to agree to development on the site. The plans are not considered in exact technical detail, and detailed drawings do not need to be submitted. While outline permission does not allow a build to proceed, there are a number of reasons to apply for this type of planning

permission. It increases the value of a site, and it helps the developer to discover:

- The intentions of the local authority
- Whether there will be any issues in relation to heritage, road access, visual impact, percolation area and proximity to other buildings.

3. **Permission consequent to outline permission.** This follows outline permission, and an application must be made within three years of outline permission being granted. This planning permission clarifies the exact plans and specifications of the development that is to be constructed.

4. **Retention planning permission.** This is applied for when an unauthorised development has taken place, or where conditions laid down by the local authority have not been adhered to. There are two main disadvantages to having to apply for retention planning permission:

- If retention is not granted, the build must be deconstructed.
- Applying for retention permission costs three times more than an application for full planning permission.

Planning permission is not always necessary. An extension to an existing property may be constructed without planning permission if the extension is to the rear of the property, does not exceed 40m², does not affect the façade, and if the property has not previously been extended. Where the proposed extension is larger than this or is not to the rear of the property, planning permission must be sought.

It is sometimes necessary to apply for planning permission in order to change the use of part of an existing building, such as converting a garage into a living room. In the original build, the garage would not have had to meet the criteria that apply to living spaces in relation to thermal and lighting requirements. To change the use of the room, the building must adhere to the technical details of the proposed change, e.g. upgraded insulation, increased number of windows, etc.

Refusal of Permission

All proposed developments must go through the same process and are judged on criteria set out by the local authority. Planning permission can be refused for different reasons, including the following:

- The application does not comply with the Area Development Plan.
- The planning authority was not consulted about the build.
- The proposed build does not blend with the existing built and/or natural environment.
- Once-off developments are not permitted at the proposed site.
- Proper sewage treatment is not available.
- Site is deemed unsuitable for private sewage treatment facility.
- Access road is deemed unsuitable for extra traffic.

- Entrance to site is deemed unsafe for traffic and/or residents.
- Developer is not from local area (a condition of some local authorities).

Before refusing planning permission, the local authority will usually contact the developer and alert him or her to its objections. Where these concerns can be addressed, the developer is given the opportunity to do so.

PLANNING STAKEHOLDERS

As with any process, there are many groups and persons involved. The main parties to the planning process are:

- **Developer.** The person or company seeking planning (this can be for a single house or a large development).
- **Local planning authority.** The planning office of the area where the development is to take place.
- **General public.** Individuals, groups or associations with an interest in the development.
- **An Bord Pleanála** (the Planning Appeals Board). Any person or developer wishing to object to a proposed development does this through their local authority. All appeals to decisions made by the local authority are directed to An Bord Pleanála, whose decision is final, except on points of law.
- **The Environmental Protection Agency (EPA).** Involved when an Integrated Pollution Prevention Control (IPPC) licence is required for the development. The role of the EPA is to assess, license, enforce and monitor environmental issues.
- **An Taisce.** Aims to conserve the country's built and natural heritage.

THE PLANNING PROCESS

The planning process provides developers and home builders with a method of applying for permission to build while allowing consultation with the public and the local authority. The local authority is the local rural or urban council. Each authority has a planning department, which deals with applications.

Planning permission (full permission or outline permission) is valid for a period of five years from when it is granted. In certain circumstances the planning authority may extend the life of the permission. This happens when substantial works have been carried out and a reasonable timeframe is agreed for completion.

If planning permission expires, it is possible to reapply for permission, but, as with a new application, this may or may not be granted. The planning policies or parameters may have changed in the meantime, or the plans may now be deemed to have a negative effect on the landscape if other development has taken place near the proposed site.

There are many different documents required at each stage of the process. The length of time taken to gain planning permission can be affected by the number of objections to the proposal and whether the applicant has supplied all the necessary documents, properly completed. If the planning permission is appealed, the timeframe can often extend dramatically. The planning process is laid out in simple terms in Table 2.1.

Planning Procedure

- Engage an architect
- Give clear brief of development
- Produce sketches and drawings
- Put notice in newspaper and on site
- Submit plans within 14 days of notices.

TABLE 2.1 PLANNING PROCESS

Timescale	Action
Beginning	Application for planning permission in local paper and site notice
Within 2 weeks	Applicant submits permission application and fee, as well as all necessary documents and drawings
2–5 weeks	Application is considered by local authority, including all submissions and objections
5–8 weeks	Local authority issues notice of their decision or asks for more information
4 weeks after notice of decision	If the authority had issued notice granting permission and no appeal is made, the authority will grant permission

If the planning permission is denied after these stages, variations of the plans may be submitted to the planning department, though the application fee must be paid again. Decisions of the planning authority can also be challenged. This means that the planning documents are passed to the higher authority of An Bord Pleanála.

PLANNING DOCUMENTATION

Documentation allows the local authority to fully understand the proposed development as well as its impact on the local area. The documents needed to apply for planning permission are:

- A completed application form
- A copy of the page in which the newspaper notice appeared
- A copy of the site notice
- 6 copies of site location map, scale 1:1000
- 6 copies of site layout plan, scale 1:500
- 6 copies of properly dimensioned plans, elevations and sections to include all specifications
- Details of septic tank treatment system, if applicable
- Relevant fee.

Site Notice

A site notice is erected at an accessible part of the site where the developer wishes to carry out works and it should be clearly visible to passers-by. The site notice serves as a public notice of intention to seek planning.

CHAPTER 2

The site notice must remain in place for the duration of the application and must be maintained by the developer.

Newspaper Notice

This is another public notice of intent to seek planning, this time through a newspaper, where more people can become aware of the intentions of the developer. The notice must reach the local authority within two weeks of the original date of the newspaper to be considered valid.

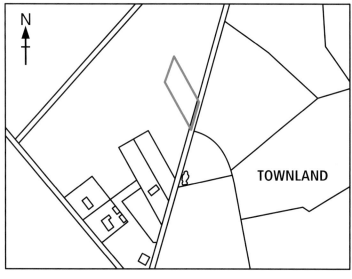

Scale 1:2500

Fig. 2.31 Site location map.

Site Location Map

A site location map identifies the location of the site in relation to the local area. An example is shown in Fig. 2.31. The scale should be no more than 1:1000 in built-up areas or 1:2500 in other areas.

This map must be marked and coloured to show boundaries. The site location map should be an Ordnance Survey map.

Site Layout Map

A site layout map is different from a site location map. This map highlights what the developer proposes the site will look like when construction is completed, including the location of any buildings on the site and any major landscaping that may take place there. The position of the site notice must be indicated on this map. The scale of this map must be 1:500. An example can be seen in Fig. 2.32.

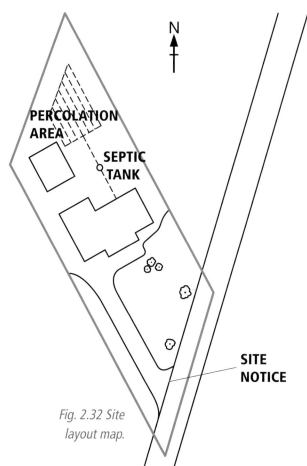

Fig. 2.32 Site layout map.

Plans

Plans contain detailed structural drawings of floor plans, elevations and sections, along with other details necessary to describe the works to which the application relate, including specifications of materials. The scale of these plans must be no less than 1:200.

Fees and Charges

The cost of applying for planning permission varies with the type of permission sought and the size of the proposed development. There are also local area charges and service charges. Site location and site layout maps are available from Ordnance Survey Ireland.

 PRACTICE QUESTIONS

1. Explain the need for planning controls in Ireland today.

2. Give a brief explanation and explain the function of:
   (a) The National Development Plan
   (b) An Area Development Plan.

3. Discuss why every county will have a unique Area Development Plan.

4. Using sketches, describe the planned elements of urban development that can lead to a safer environment and help foster a local community.

5. Compare and contrast the various considerations taken into account in rural and urban development.

6. Describe, using sketches, the most common settlement patterns found in the rural landscape.

7. Contrast the different types of planning permissions that can be granted for building.

8. Explain what is meant by retention planning permission.

9. What documents must you enclose when applying for full planning permission?

10. Describe the functions of the following parties with regard to planning:
    (a) Developer
    (b) Local authority
    (c) Planning objector
    (d) An Bord Pleanála.

SAMPLE EXAMINATION QUESTIONS

2012 Ordinary Level Question 7

A homeowner wishes to obtain planning permission to convert an existing garage to a living room, as shown in the accompanying sketch.

(a) Discuss **two** reasons why it is necessary to apply for planning permission to convert the garage to a living room.

(b) Outline the information that must be contained in **each** of the following documents when making a planning application to the planning authority:
  - site location map
  - copy of site notice.

(c) Discuss **one** reason why a planning authority might refuse planning permission for the proposed conversion.

2011 Higher Level Question 10

'A good neighbourhood is one where people can easily satisfy daily needs whilst feeling safe to do so. The most successful neighbourhoods are well connected – to employment centres, or places where people spend their leisure time. They are places where people can live at any stage of their lives – regardless of physical ability or social status. Successful neighbourhoods also tend to have a wide variety of things to do within them and have a strong connection to the area in which they sit – be it historical, cultural or visual.'

Urban Design Manual – A Best Practice Guide (2009)
Department of the Environment, Heritage and Local Government

Discuss the above statement in detail and propose **three** guidelines for best practice that would help create sustainable urban neighbourhoods.

2010 Higher Level Question 10

"In the increasingly urbanised world of the 21st century, a major challenge is to find solutions to the problems facing our towns and cities – the control of sprawl, sustainable growth, integrated transport systems and better-quality urban environments and public realms. Cities and towns that are diverse, varied in use, walkable, human scaled and identifiable by the high quality of their public realm can contribute to the process of creating sustainable urbanism. The challenge for all citizens is to make our towns and cities viable in the long term, environmentally and socially, as well as economically. There will be no sustainable world and no sustainable country without sustainable cities and towns".

Sustainable Urbanism: creating communities for the knowledge economy: by Anthony Reddy in The New Housing 2, Royal Institute of Architects of Ireland 2009.

Discuss the above statement in detail and propose **three** guidelines that would help create environmentally sustainable urban development in Ireland.

2008 Ordinary Level Question 5

(a) State **two** reasons why it is necessary to apply for planning permission to erect a dwelling house.

(b) Explain what is meant by **outline planning permission** and describe one situation where a person might wish to apply for outline planning permission.

(c) Discuss in detail **two** reasons why a planning authority might refuse to grant planning permission for a dwelling house in the countryside.

CHAPTER 3

SITE SELECTION, DESIGN AND PROJECT PLANNING

LEARNING OUTCOMES:

After studying this chapter students will:

- Identify the various stages involved in selecting a site to build on.
- Appreciate and understand the different factors that impact on the site, its selection and layout.
- Interpret various construction documents and represent graphically information relating to construction.
- Have an understanding of the people and skills involved in construction.

KEYWORDS:

- SITE • LOCALITY • ASPECT • ORIENTATION • SHELTER • PASSIVE BUILDING TECHNIQUES
- LAYOUT • TRADESPEOPLE • MORTGAGE • STAMP DUTY

INTRODUCTION

When choosing a site for a home, it is important to spend time considering the many factors that will influence the eventual building, and to plan for them. Some considerations relate to: the site, such as its location, aspect, terrain and soil type; access to services; and the local environment. Others relate to the building itself and where it should be located on the site. It is important to look at all these things at the outset, as they will impact on all aspects of the building process.

CONSIDERING A SITE

To identify a good site, the area must be looked at on three levels:

1. Locality
2. The plot of land
3. The location of the building on the site.

LOCALITY

A site can only be chosen after consulting the Area Development Plan for the region. Remember that different restrictions, which can influence the location and style of the building, apply in different urban and rural areas.

Consideration must be given to the land itself. For example, is it overshadowed by a mountain, or is it sloping? These topographic factors will determine the amount of light and shade on the site, as well as the methods of construction that can be used.

The impact of the house on the landscape has to be considered too. Development must be in keeping with the local landscape, and a development that has a negative impact on the landscape will not be approved for planning permission.

Other factors that will restrict the way a site can be used include the following:

- Architectural policies
- Heritage areas or sites
- Planning-restricted areas (e.g. green belt, coastal areas, rural housing control zone)
- Scenic amenity areas or trails
- Public rights of way.

It may be necessary to consult with several local bodies to get a full understanding of local conditions.

THE PLOT OF LAND

Once these issues are overcome, the site itself must be explored, bearing in mind:

- The aspect or orientation of the site
- Shelter on the site
- Orientation to the sun
- Light access to the site
- Road access to the site.

All of these elements will impact on the final build and may also impact on the efficiency of the dwelling once built.

Aspect/Orientation

Aspect refers to the direction in which a site or building faces. If the site sits on a slope, its aspect is the direction the slope faces. The site will have more or less sunshine during the day depending on its aspect. A south-facing aspect receives far more sun than a cold and bleak north-facing aspect. The south face will have sun all year round, though far more in summer than in winter, as Fig. 3.1 shows.

Aspect will also influence how much the prevailing wind affects the site, or how much shelter it gives. South-westerly winds are the most common in Ireland, but this can vary depending on the topography of the land in a particular area.

Certain measures can be taken to compensate for a site's aspect or orientation. Windbreaks, in the form of trees or vegetation, can be used to provide shelter

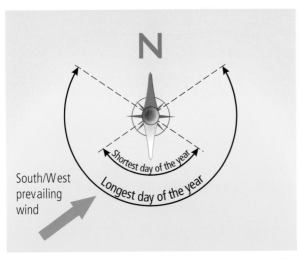

Fig. 3.1 Key weather factors that affect the direction of a site and orientation of a building. The south receives light all year round, though far more in summer than in winter.

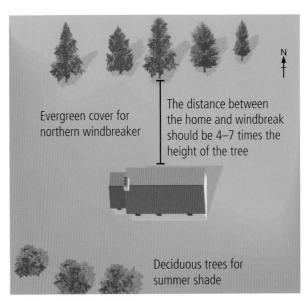

Fig. 3.2 Evergreen shelter provides year-round cover from harsh northern winds.

CHAPTER 3

from harsh winds. In Fig. 3.2 evergreen cover is used to lessen the impact of winds coming from the north. Northerly winds will almost always be cold, and evergreen trees will provide year-round protection. Deciduous trees have been planted to the south of the property, to provide summer shade from the high, glaring midday sun. Deciduous trees will allow more sunlight through in winter, when the trees lose their leaves. The lower branches can also be trimmed so as not to obscure the view.

Shelter

While houses in an urban area are sheltered by the surrounding buildings, in a rural setting natural shelter is vital. For this reason it is not advisable to build on an exposed site, as shown in Fig. 3.3. This home has no natural cover from the elements (e.g. wind and rain), which leads to higher heating costs. The building also has a high visual impact on the landscape and seems out of context with it.

Fig. 3.3 Building on a site exposed to the wind will lead to higher heating costs and more weathering.

Fig. 3.4 A site with natural cover helps to shelter the building.

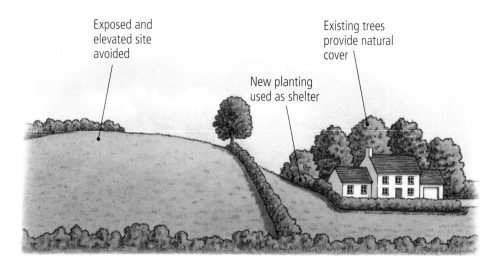

Exposed and elevated site avoided

New planting used as shelter

Existing trees provide natural cover

By using the natural landscape and vegetation, a site can be found and/or shaped to provide shelter from the elements. This will impact greatly on the cost of running the home, and the shelter will also protect the building against weathering. The house in Fig. 3.4 is sheltered by both the hill and the trees. In addition to shelter from the weather, this also means that the home will not have a big visual impact on the surrounding landscape.

Orientation to the Sun

Every living thing – including humans – relies on the sun. It provides warmth, energy and light, enabling plants to grow and humans and animals to survive.

It is important to consider where the sun will be in relation to the site and the building at different times of the day. Good orientation will help to heat the building naturally, so that it will not rely as heavily on artificial heating.

In a similar way, the sun will provide homes with natural light during the daytime, saving on the use of artificial lighting. For these reasons, it is best to find a site with a natural slope that is oriented to the sun.

Great energy savings can be made by considering light and shade when positioning the build. Light provides

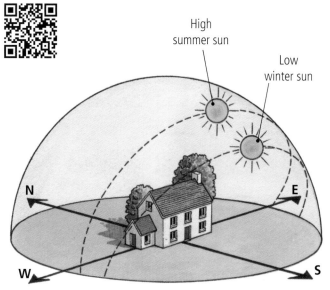

High summer sun

Low winter sun

N

E

W

S

Fig. 3.5 The path of the sun in summer and winter.

natural heat, and the building can maximise the solar gain from the sun if it is located correctly on the site. The sun rises in the east and sets in the west, as shown in Fig. 3.5. To gain from this, the ideal situation is to have the greatest amount of glazing to the southern aspect of the building or within 15 degrees either side of south.

While this will provide the maximum light for the internal space at the south, direct light may not be welcome. If this is the case, creating an overhang on the roof will help to make the most of available light and

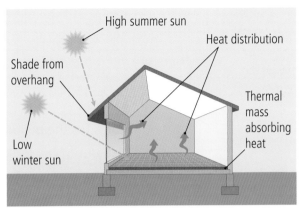

Fig. 3.6 A house can benefit from passive solar heating if it is sited correctly.

shade, providing natural heating in the winter and shade in the summer. The overhang acts as a solar block from the high summer sun, and in the winter allows the sun to heat the room (Fig. 3.6). This idea of designing a high-performance home is called passive home design. Using solar shading is just one element of these 'passive' building techniques, which will be discussed further in Chapter 24.

Road Access

Access to the site from a roadway is vital. It is important to note that it is not permitted to place road access to a site on a bend in the road. This is done for safety reasons. If a site is already accessed on a bend, further planning permission will not be granted unless the access point is repositioned.

THE BUILDING PLOT

Once the plot has been selected, it must be surveyed as a site, so that detailed plans can be drawn up for the builders. Surveying examines a number of factors, including soil type, site aspect/orientation, distance from the road, location of services, shelter, house location on the site and the site's boundaries, as well as any special features that the site may have. All of these factors can contribute to the design of the building and the building methods used.

At this stage of the build, the topography of the land – its heights, gradients, boundaries, etc. – are measured.

SITE SURVEYING

Site surveying or land surveying involves inspecting and drawing up plans of an area, including the height and contours of the land. The survey is used to calculate the cost of the construction project and to highlight any problems with the topography of the land. The survey first looks at the site as a whole and then analyses each section in turn.

There are many types of survey that can be carried out on a site. The main types look at:

- Boundaries
- Footings for the building
- Setting out of the building
- The surveyor's work (a check survey)
- Services.

In order to carry out the first four survey types, various types of measuring equipment are used. Measurements are taken from known points around the site, such as buildings, boundary lines, etc. Measurements from these known points can then be used to measure the distance and height of other areas of the site.

Measurement surveys follow a four-stage process:

1. **Planning.** It is important to plan before surveying an area. Setting points on or near the site as datums (reference points) helps to ensure accurate measurements.
2. **Collecting and recording measurements.** This involves using a theodolite, a piece of equipment rather like a telescope, which can measure angles from the horizontal and vertical (Fig. 3.7).
3. **Processing measurements.** Once the measurements have been recorded they are assessed and used for making calculations.
4. **Drawing up.** The calculations of various heights, angles and distances are used to draw up the topography of the site.

Some modern surveying instruments use GPS location to provide co-ordinates and datums for measurement.

Fig. 3.7 Surveying with a theodolite.

INTERNAL DESIGN

While we have dealt with the external layout, and will look at it further in Chapter 5, it is important also to consider the internal design of the home in relation to where it is sited. The layout of internal spaces will determine how the rooms in the dwelling are used. A home with a poor internal layout will feel unnatural and may be costly to run. There should be a good 'flow' from room to room. Heritage design, which was discussed in Chapter 1, includes some good design principles that maximise the efficiency of a home. For example, the vernacular cottages of Ireland commonly had a narrow depth in plan to benefit as much as possible from the amount of light coming through the windows, as can be seen in Fig. 3.8.

Good orientation and organisation of the living and functional spaces of the home will maximise how each room in the building is used. With this in mind, it is best to position living areas or areas that experience high use during daytime towards the southern face of the building. This allows these areas to be illuminated and heated by day. Fig. 3.9 shows an example of how rooms in a home are arranged to achieve this. We will look at different rooms and how they are best positioned in a dwelling.

Fig. 3.8 Traditional Irish cottage with thin depth in plan to maximise light.

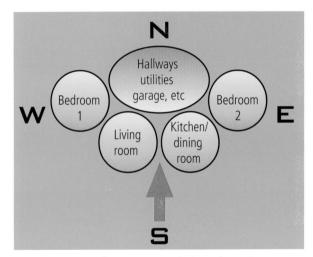

Fig. 3.9 Layout of rooms to maximise solar gain.

CHAPTER 3

KITCHEN LAYOUT

The kitchen is one of the most functional rooms in the home. It is important to spend time planning the layout of the various zones in the kitchen as a bad layout will make it more difficult to work in. Understanding the main functions of the kitchen makes it easier to design. These functions are:

- Food storage
- Food preparation and cooking
- Clean-up area.

The sink, cooker and fridge are grouped close together, creating a work triangle that reduces movement by the user (Fig. 3.10). For this triangle to be most effective, the length of each side must not exceed 6m and should not be broken

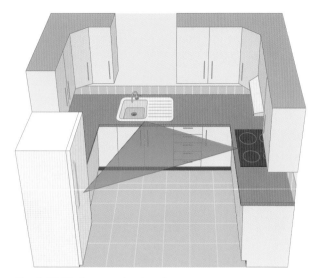

Fig. 3.10 Kitchen work triangle.

Fig. 3.11 Dining room.

Fig. 3.12 Living room.

by an access for people passing through. Work surfaces need to be supplied on either side of the cooker, and the distance between the sink and cooker must be less than 2m. These design features make the kitchen easier to use.

It is important to plan for the kitchen's appliances alongside the task area. Once it is decided where they will be positioned, the location of electrical outlets also has to be considered. (This will be dealt with in Chapter 22.)

DINING ROOM

The dining area follows on from the kitchen. It may be formal or informal. Formal dining rooms generally are furnished with well-finished furnishings and not for everyday use. In contrast to other rooms, the lighting in the dining room is focused on the table, rather than lighting the room as a whole.

LIVING ROOM

The living room, sitting room, lounge or family room is a multipurpose gathering area in the home. For the most part it is used in the evening, so the best position for a living room is where it will gain the maximum light from the evening sun.

Depending on the lifestyle of the occupants of the house, this room may have different uses. It can be used as a place to relax, study, watch television or talk. All of these activities will influence the many possible layouts of the living room. Traditionally, the fireplace or hearth acts as the focal point of the room.

BEDROOMS

Ideally, bedrooms will be situated where they receive the morning sun. This is not entirely necessary, though, as most of the time spent in this room is at night, and so direct sun may not be an issue. In most modern Irish homes, the master bedroom is en suite (it has a private bathroom connected with it).

Other factors affecting the location of the bedroom in the home may include:

- Proximity to children's rooms/bathroom
- Availability of sleeping area in attic space.

BATHROOM

It is important to plan the bathroom layout well in advance of the build. Sanitary ware such as toilet, sink and bath/shower all require at least one service (plumbing), which needs to be planned when constructing the walls of the room. Remember, unlike furniture in other areas of the home, these items cannot easily be moved later on.

HALLWAY

Most homes have a hallway, which can be seen as a transition space between the outside elements and the comfort of the home inside. The hall also gives access to the stairs and rooms on the ground floor.

UTILITY ROOM

This room may or may not be included in modern homes. It is a functional area, which will usually contain a washing machine/dryer, and so will require adequate ventilation (see Chapter 17) and services. The utility room may also include a water closet (WC) or bathroom.

PROJECT PLANNING

While there are some further practical issues that need to be examined to prepare the site for building, which we will look at in Chapter 5, once the site has been selected and surveyed it is time to consider the team who will build the dwelling.

A building site can be seen as a temporary factory that is set up to produce a house. There are many parts to this process, including manpower, money and materials.

As with any large-scale project, it is important to research the different factors involved in the build: this is called project management or project planning. It is important to spend time preparing for the build by planning where, when and how the structure will be constructed. Time spent in the planning stage allows the project to progress faster and more efficiently during the building phase.

CHAPTER 3

Fig. 3.13 Many skills, materials and processes go into constructing a house.

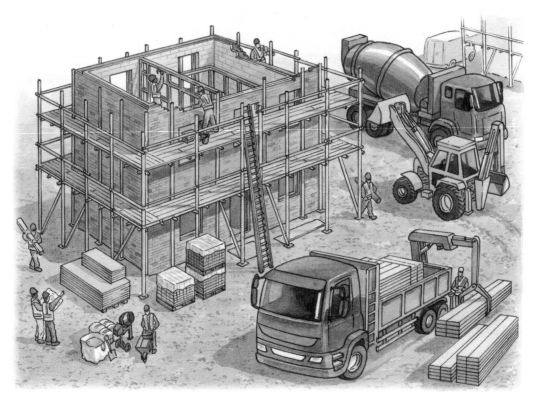

Good preparation can also save money at the building stage, for example by anticipating any difficulties that may arise and finding solutions or alternatives before they become a problem on site. It allows the builder to manage materials on site, making sure that materials are delivered only when they're needed, which helps to avoid overcrowding the site; and that they are delivered on time, which helps the work to progress efficiently. It is important to include all the major stakeholders in the build at the planning stage, as they will have different requirements once the work starts.

BUILDING DOCUMENTS

Before progressing with any build, all stakeholders must know what is being constructed. In times past, builders used local materials and built in traditional ways. Modern building methods now require a method that graphically communicates the plans to all members of the team.

Most of the graphical communication uses orthographic projection in the form of architectural drawings. These take different views and collate them into one set of drawings. The views include all elevation aspects, along with section views and floor plans. Examples of orthographic drawings are shown in Fig. 3.14.

Ground floor plan

Vertical section

Rear elevation

Side elevation

Front elevation

Side elevation

Fig 3.14 Sample house plans. These include elevations of the exterior and an internal layout plan.

THE IRISH CONSTRUCTION INDUSTRY

There have been great changes in the Irish building industry following the huge downturn in construction activity since its peak in the early years of this century. Fig. 3.15 shows the recent downward trend of ESB connections to the national grid, which is used as a key indicator of house completions.

New residential construction accounted for 3.4 per cent of the Irish economy in 2009, down from 7.3 per cent in 2008 and approximately 11.2 per cent in 2007.

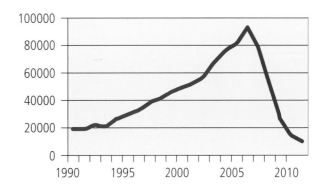

Fig. 3.15 Number of house completions based on ESB connections in the last two decades.

CONSTRUCTION OCCUPATIONS

As with any area of work, many different people make up the team on and off a building site. Below are some of the most common roles in the industry.

Professional Services

Architect: The architect is trained in design and planning and generally is in charge of the building site during construction.

Architectural Technologist: In charge of interpreting design concepts, typically from the architect, and relaying them in technical designs and working drawings.

Structural Engineer: Structural engineers are needed when a building must withstand large or unusual loads. It is their job to design the structure of the building.

Surveyor: In charge of setting out or laying out markers on the site for the building that is to be constructed.

Quantity Surveyor: This role is to analyse how much a build is going to cost. Quantity surveyors estimate the cost of labour and materials. They are also employed to survey properties for defects.

Health and Safety Consultants: Advise on health and safety matters on site. They establish safe work practices and site guidelines, including checking workers' safety certification and that the correct signage is displayed on site.

Mechanical and Electrical Engineers: Look after the services that come to the site, including electricity, water, etc.

Tradespeople

Steel Fixer: All the steel work on site is the responsibility of the steel fixer. This skilled worker cuts, bends and positions the steel that reinforces the building.

Scaffolder: Scaffolding on a site is very important. Only a qualified person with construction skills certification in scaffolding may construct the scaffolding.

Bricklayer/Blocklayer: Typically this tradesperson builds up the superstructure of the building, i.e. the walls.

Roofer: This tradesperson is a specialist who constructs the roof.

Carpenter: Works with wood. Typical jobs for carpenters include constructing shuttering, formwork, stud partitions, stairs, roofs, etc.

Plumber: The plumber's job is to look after all water services and heating systems in the building.

Electrician: A certified electrician on site looks after all the electrical work associated with the build.

Plasterer: Works with plaster and plasterboard to form a layer of plaster on walls or decorative plaster mouldings on walls or ceilings.

Painter and Decorator: Takes charge of the painting and decorating of the building.

LEGAL AND FINANCIAL ASPECTS

Once the ideal site has been chosen for the build, the financial and legal aspects of purchasing the site and building the home need to be dealt with. In most cases, a long-term loan must be obtained to finance the land purchase and the build. This is known as a mortgage and is available from most financial institutions.

A solicitor will need to be consulted to deal with legal matters. They will ensure that the land is registered in the purchaser's name once it is bought, and they can advise on the stamp duty that may be incurred in buying the site.

Stamp duty is a tax on land that is charged on the purchase of land or property. This cost needs to be taken into account when estimating the cost of the build.

INSURANCE

DURING THE BUILD

It is a legal requirement to have insurance on the site while the building is being constructed. This insurance will cover any damage or accidents that might happen on site. In most cases the builder or contractor will deal with this, though the developer may also secure insurance.

AFTER THE BUILD

Insurance is not legally necessary after the build has been completed. However, a mortgage lender will insist that the building is appropriately insured before they will grant a mortgage.

There are various types of insurance. One example is structural and defect insurance, which insures against any defects that may become apparent after the build is completed. To take out this kind of insurance, building standards and construction methods as laid out by the insurer must be complied with.

Other insurance sought for a house is commonly known as 'home insurance'. This covers the property and its contents against damage, loss or any other accidents. Different kinds of damage and loss may or may not be covered, depending on the type of insurance cover taken out.

CHAPTER 3

PRACTICE QUESTIONS

1. List some of the considerations involved in planning a build on a selected site.
2. How does aspect/orientation impact on building location?
3. Analyse the impact of shelter on the selection of a site for a home.
4. How can wind be counteracted on a site?
5. Why should glazing be located on the south face of the property?
6. The internal layout of a building is important and should be planned correctly. Discuss this statement with reference to the use of natural light.
7. Sketch a possible floor plan for a bungalow. Use notes to explain your reasoning for the room positions. The bungalow should contain as a minimum:
   - (a) Kitchen
   - (b) Dining room
   - (c) Living room
   - (d) Bathroom
   - (e) Four bedrooms
8. What is a work triangle and what is its importance?
9. Describe the occupation of each of the following:
   - (a) Architect
   - (b) Quantity surveyor
   - (c) Scaffolder
   - (d) Carpenter
   - (e) Plumber
10. Why is insurance necessary when building?

SAMPLE EXAMINATION QUESTIONS

2012 Higher Level Question 6

The elevation and ground floor plan of a house are shown. The house has a study / office as shown and also has three bedrooms and a bathroom upstairs. The external wall is of timber frame construction with a concrete block outer leaf. The house is designed to have low environmental impact, reflecting the sustainable ideal of doing more with less for longer.

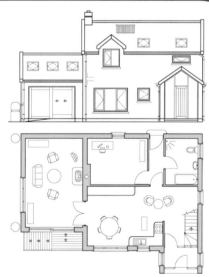

(a) With reference to the design shown, discuss in detail, using notes and freehand sketches, **three** features of the design that reflect the sustainable ideal of doing more with less for longer.

(b) Discuss in detail the importance of **each** of the following when designing an environmentally sustainable dwelling house:
- orientation of house
- flexibility of design
- sourcing of materials

SAMPLE EXAMINATION QUESTIONS

2011 Higher Level Question 6

The elevation and ground floor plan of a house are shown. The house has two additional bedrooms and a bathroom upstairs. The external leaf is of concrete block and cedar cladding construction, as shown. The house is designed to have low environmental impact.

(a) With reference to the design shown, discuss in detail, using notes and freehand sketches, **three** features of the design that ensure the house has low environmental impact.

(b) Discuss in detail the importance of **each** of the following when designing environmentally sustainable housing:

- Form of the house
- Materials and labour
- Design for lifetime use

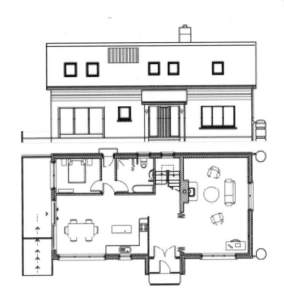

2010 Higher Level Question 6

The drawing shows the design of a timber frame house with an external wooden cladding and a flat roof. The house is designed to have low environmental impact.

(a) Discuss in detail, using notes and *freehand sketches*, **three** design features that contribute to reducing the environmental impact of the house shown.

(b) Discuss in detail the importance of **each** of the following when choosing materials for an environmentally sustainable house:

- renewable
- durable
- locally sourced.

CHAPTER **4**
HEALTH AND SAFETY ON SITE

LEARNING OUTCOMES:

After studying this chapter students will:

- Have a better awareness of safety and safe work practices on site.
- Be able to identify the different safety signs that can be seen on a building site.
- Be aware of the safe use of personal protective equipment (PPE).
- Appreciate the need for safe procedures of work on site.
- Show a greater knowledge of health and safety procedures, especially in specific risk areas.
- Be aware that there is training and certification involved in this area.

KEYWORDS:

- HAZARD • RISK • SAFETY • SIGNAGE • PPE • SPECIFIC RISK AREAS • ELECTRICAL
- EXCAVATIONS • SCAFFOLDING • CERTIFICATION • LEGISLATION

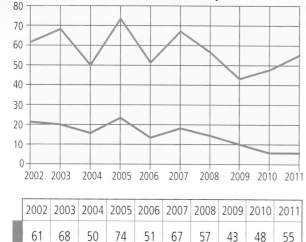

Fatalities in Irish construction industry versus total Irish industry

	2002	2003	2004	2005	2006	2007	2008	2009	2010	2011
	61	68	50	74	51	67	57	43	48	55
	21	20	16	23	13	18	15	10	6	6

■ Total industry fatalities   ■ Construction fatalities

Fig. 4.1 The fatality rate in construction highlights the need to follow health and safety practice on site.

INTRODUCTION

Building sites have hazards which workers and visitors must be aware of. Unlike other workplaces, large machinery, high-powered electrical tools and heavy materials are used regularly on building sites. Not surprisingly, building sites are classed as high-risk areas.

Accidents that occur on building sites include, among others, falls from heights, electrocution, crush injuries and injuries caused by construction vehicles. Fig. 4.1 shows graphically the number of fatalities in the construction industry compared to fatalities in industry as a whole in Ireland from 2002 to 2011.

Health and safety is everyone's responsibility, and everyone must follow health and safety instructions while on site. These might include, for example, wearing a hard hat or not entering a certain area of the site.

SAFE SYSTEM OF WORK PLAN (SSWP)

Under current health and safety legislation, the site manager must, by law, complete a Safe System of Work Plan (SSWP). The plan is a checklist that helps the site manager list all the activities taking place on site, determine possible hazards, and identify how to eliminate or reduce them. Risks can be reduced, or eliminated entirely, by finding alternative ways of doing the job, by using different materials, or by taking steps to protect workers who are involved in dangerous work.

HAZARD IDENTIFICATION AND PREVENTION

It is important that the SSWP identifies any hazards there may be on site. A hazard is a potential source of harm to a person and therefore is a major concern.

Building sites are dangerous places and very often there are many potential hazards. Some of these include:

- Working at heights
- Excavations
- Falling materials
- Electrical injuries
- High noise levels
- Dangerous materials
- Large plant machinery
- Heavy loads.

When a hazard is identified, there is a hierarchy which is followed to ensure the safety of those on site:

1. Eliminate the risk where possible.
2. Substitute the hazard with a lesser risk.
3. Isolate the hazard.
4. Use controls.
5. Wear personal protective equipment (PPE).

When weighing up a hazard, it is important to look at the likelihood of it occurring and the risk to the person carrying out the task. Take the case where water is spilled on a floor. Someone could slip on it and fall. If, however, the room is cordoned off, the hazard is still there but the risk is reduced. Anything that can be done to reduce or eliminate risk is called a control.

VISITING A CONSTRUCTION SITE

Workers are not the only people found on site. Visitors are permitted on building sites, but they must follow strict guidelines to protect themselves and others while they are there. To officially be allowed on site as a visitor, a person must have certification to confirm that they have attended a one-day training course as part of the Safe Pass programme.

CHAPTER 4

Visitors must obey all signs displayed at the entrance to the building site. They must wear proper protective clothing and any protective equipment that the site demands. All visitors must report to the site office. This ensures that the person in charge knows who is on site at all times. Visitors cannot just wander around a site – for their own safety they must always be accompanied by someone in authority. Finally, it is visitors' own responsibility to be aware of hazards while they are on site, whether these involve scaffolding, trenches, overhead loads, cables, or any other potential danger.

Fig. 4.2 Safety signage at the entrance to a site.

SAFETY SIGNAGE

Awareness of health and safety on site is the key to safe practice. For this reason, standard signs have been developed, and are erected on site where they can be seen clearly.

Signs are understood purely by the image they contain. They do not rely on text to accompany the sign – in fact, since 2007 new signs must not contain text. This helps to overcome language barriers and avoid misunderstanding. Text may be included on supplementary signage, but it must not adversely affect the safety sign.

Clearly marked safety signs, and signs signalling the general procedures that have to be followed on site, are posted at the entrance of the site. An example of entrance signage can be seen in Fig. 4.2. This signage sets out the basic safety requirements to be followed on site and gives notice to the general public that they must not enter for their own safety.

Signs use minimal colours, and illustrations are kept simple and direct so that they can be understood quickly and easily. Signs can be broken down into four categories according to their colour and shape.

RED: PROHIBITION SIGNS

These round red signs serve as a warning to show what you must not do in an area. Examples of prohibition signs are:

- No Entry
- No Smoking
- No Parking

Fig. 4.3 Prohibition signs show what must not be done in an area.

YELLOW: WARNING SIGNS

These triangular yellow signs warn about the risk of something happening. They help everyone in the area to become aware of the hazards that exist there. It is an individual's personal responsibility to take precautions with regard to these hazards, when they see signs such as:

- Chemical Irritant
- Trip Hazard
- Mind the Step
- Electrical Hazard
- Corrosive Chemicals

Fig. 4.4 Warning signs warn of hazards in an area.

BLUE: MANDATORY SIGNS

These round blue signs show people what they must do in a given situation. They illustrate the actions that people are required to follow, for example:

- Wear personal protection equipment – goggles, ear protection, hard hat, etc.

Fig. 4.5 Mandatory signs show what must be done in an area.

GREEN: SAFE CONDITION SIGNS

These square or rectangular green safety signs give information on emergency exits, first aid, escape routes or rescue facilities, for example:

- Fire Exit
- First Aid
- Fire Assembly Points

Fig. 4.6 Safe condition signs give useful information.

PERSONAL PROTECTION EQUIPMENT (PPE)

PPE is clothing, goggles, masks, and other garments or equipment used to protect the wearer from injury. Anyone working with loud tools should wear ear protection, for example. On a construction site, examples of PPE include:

- Safety helmet
- High-visibility jacket
- Goggles
- Gloves
- Hard-toed safety boots
- Dust mask
- Ear muffs
- Face shield.

The general PPE required on site is pointed out by mandatory blue signage at the site entrance. It is also important, when using tools or entering specialist areas, to be aware of signage about the particular tool or area and to take the necessary precautions with regard to PPE.

SPECIFIC RISK AREAS

TOOLS, MACHINERY AND EQUIPMENT

There are specific methods and procedures to follow when using tools, machinery and equipment. Only people trained in the use of a particular tool or machine should operate it. Training includes learning how to use a tool or piece of machinery safely, which reduces the chances of an accident while it is being operated. For some plant machinery, workers must have construction skills certification before they can operate it.

On a site, there is a variety of power tools, machinery and equipment for different uses, for example:

- Drills
- Generators
- Saws
- Pneumatic tools
- Excavators

- Cranes
- Loaders
- Paints
- Cleaning chemicals

Some power tools are battery operated, which means that they are portable, but have a shorter power and usage time. Using battery power tools reduces the risk of electric shock, but these tools are still potentially dangerous and must be handled as such.

Fig. 4.7 Portable battery drill.

Other power tools are operated at a voltage of 110 volts. This is a step down from mains power (240 volts). These tools are individually connected to a 110 volt step-down transformer, similar to that shown in Fig. 4.8, so as to reduce the voltage.

As well as stepping down the voltage from 240 volts to 110 volts, most 110 volt tools split this further between two wires to the tool. This is a safety precaution which further reduces the likelihood of a fatal shock. Only 110 volt tools may be used on site. Fig. 4.9 shows a diagram of how voltage is stepped down and split. These safety features allow the tool access to the full 110 volts available.

Fig. 4.8 Safety step-down transformer.

There are a few standards and checks which need to be looked at when using power tools:

- Insulation from operator shock
- Quality standards.

Power tools should not be used in wet conditions. The leads must be checked regularly for kinks, splits and other damage. The tool must be double insulated, so that no part of the outer casing of the tool touches any live parts inside, reducing the risk of electrocution. The tool must carry the CE mark. This mark shows that it complies with European health, safety and environmental protection legislation. It is a legal requirement across the European Union for certain tools to carry this mark. These symbols can be seen in Fig. 4.10.

Where possible, cordless tools are used on site to prevent trailing cables causing accidents. All tools on site must only be used by skilled operators who have been trained on how to use them properly.

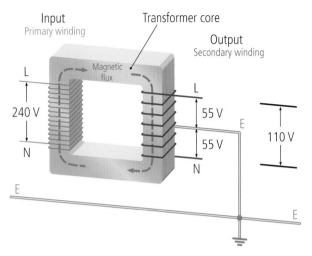

Fig. 4.9 How a safety step-down transformer works. The input (240 volts) is reduced to 110 volts by the transformer. The safety device in this circuit is that the 110 volts is centre tapped to earth to reduce the risk of shock.

Fig. 4.10 LEFT: Double insulated symbol: RIGHT: CE mark.

CHAPTER 4

OVERHEAD CABLES

When planning for a build, it is vital to consider services that cross the site, including sewerage, electricity, gas, telecoms, etc. Services can travel over or under ground.

Large machinery will be used on site, so overhead cables must be made obvious to the drivers of large vehicles. Gates are erected to direct vehicle access under overhead services like power lines, and bunting is hung out as a further warning. The bunting must be at a height of 3–4.2m so that it can be easily seen by operators of tall machinery.

Working under power lines is restricted to necessary personnel only, and a hazard zone of 10m either side of the power lines is outlined. This lessens the chances of accidents occurring related to power lines.

Fig. 4.11 Overhead lines and machinery are both protected by providing gateways for machinery to use.

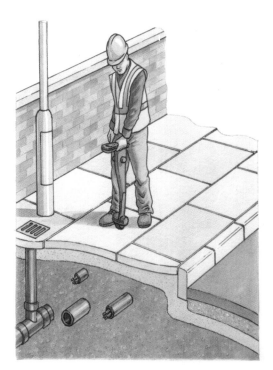

Fig. 4.12 Scanning the surface for underground services.

EXCAVATIONS

It is equally important to be able to identify hazards below ground. Underground services include telecom lines, electricity, gas, water mains and sewers, which are laid using cables and pipes. Locating these potential hazards is obviously more difficult than identifying services above ground. While some plans may show where underground services are located, they are not always accurate or exact, and other services or underground objects may not be on the plans at all.

When carrying out excavations on a site, the builder must know what is below the surface before they start digging. The ground must be scanned, and any findings marked on the surface prior to the dig. Fig. 4.12 shows a worker scanning and marking the area where a pipeline is located.

Service providers must also be contacted before any work takes place. They will provide information in relation to safe excavation near their service lines. Bord Gais, for example, provides free maps of its gas line locations for those intending to excavate near them. The flow to these services must be turned off before any excavation can take place.

When excavation begins, measures must be taken to prevent the trench that is being dug from collapsing. The trench is dug in layers rather than in large gauges. Removing material in layers lessens the risk of the side walls collapsing.

Any trench deeper than 1.25m must have its sides supported to give it stability and prevent subsidence. In Fig. 4.13 sheeting is placed along the walls of the trench and propped up with vertical and horizontal supports; this makes the walls secure and provides a safe area for people to work in. Another method used to make a trench safe is known as 'battering back'. Here the sides of the trench are sloped, or 'battered back', to a safe angle, stabilising the trench and preventing it from collapsing.

Suitable access to the trench must be provided to allow workers to enter and exit safely on foot. Workers operating in or near a trench must wear protective

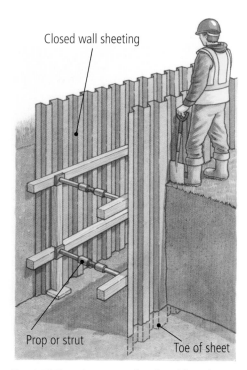

Closed wall sheeting

Prop or strut

Toe of sheet

Fig. 4.13 Trench support for the sides of an excavation.

footwear and headgear, as well as high-visibility jackets to ensure that they can be seen at all times. Vehicles must be kept back from the edges of the dig as they could compromise the strength of the sides and cause collapse. When machinery is removing material from a trench, workers must stay out of the danger zone. Eye contact with the driver is essential before making a move towards or across the work area.

Due to the high risk involved, excavation work carries one of the largest incident rates, so it is vital that it is managed, co-ordinated and carried out safely. These activities relate back to the SSWP, which should be prepared by the person in charge of the site.

SCAFFOLDING

Scaffolding is a working platform erected temporarily around the perimeter of a build. It provides a safe working platform at a convenient height. Scaffolding is required whenever work is to be carried out above a height of 1.5m, though of course scaffolding can be much higher. Working at the heights where scaffolding is used is dangerous, and a number of safety precautions must be observed while it is being erected.

Scaffolding must not sink or slip. Before putting up the scaffolding, the ground needs to be checked to ensure that it is firm, solid and capable of supporting the structure, as well as any loads imposed on it.

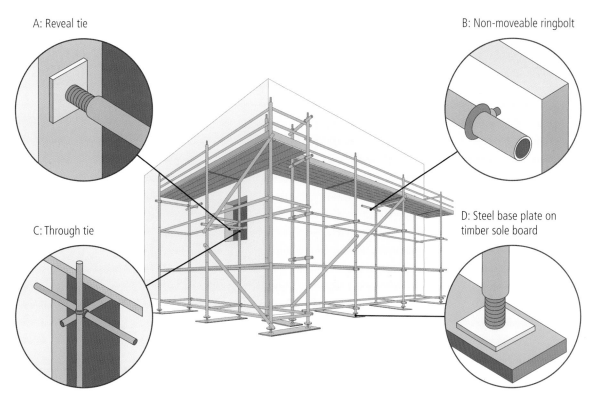

Fig. 4.14 Common components of an independent tied system scaffold, including the most common scaffold ties.

Spirit levels and adjustable jacks are used to make sure that the scaffolding is set level. If it is not level, the parts will not fit together firmly or correctly.

Timber is used under each leg of the scaffolding to distribute the load evenly. This is because soil has poor impact load-bearing ability.

As the scaffolding is put together, braces and ties are fitted to create a rigid framework that prevents the scaffolding from collapsing.

The scaffolding must be tied to the building at various points to prevent it from falling away from the building. It can be tied at window or door openings, or to special ringbolts fixed to the wall, as seen in Fig 4.14, detail B.

The scaffolding must have uninterrupted walkways to allow easy access for workers and minimise the risk of accidents. For this, platforms are fully boarded. Guard rails and toe boards must be used on scaffolding that is above 2m in height. These elements must be placed at every point at which a person could fall while working. Guard rails prevent workers falling from the scaffolding and are fixed at a height of 950–1200mm. Toe boards, which prevent loose material falling from the scaffolding, must be a minimum of 150mm high. The walkway must be unobsructed and set up as in Fig 4.15.

Finally, diagonal bracing and triangulation are used to strengthen the overall structure of the scaffolding. Triangles are a strong, stable shape, and triangulation means using triangular structures to improve rigidity.

Ladders, which provide access to different levels of the scaffolding, must be properly secured at both ends to prevent accidental movement. The top of the ladder must extend at least 1m above the platform and be at a slope of 1:4 to ensure optimum safety.

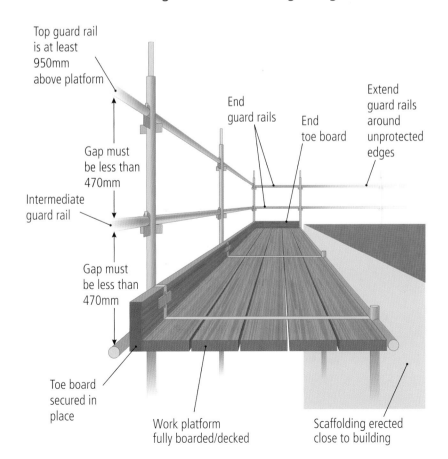

Top guard rail is at least 950mm above platform

Gap must be less than 470mm

Intermediate guard rail

Gap must be less than 470mm

Toe board secured in place

Work platform fully boarded/decked

End guard rails

End toe board

Extend guard rails around unprotected edges

Scaffolding erected close to building

Fig. 4.15 A working platform, which must have a toe board and guard rails for protection.

Scaffolding comes in many forms, depending on the system employed on site and the situation it is needed for. Two common types of scaffolding are:

- **Fabricated frame scaffold:** This uses prefabricated sections to allow users connect the pieces to form a full scaffold system.
- **Tube and coupler scaffold:** This type of system offers the flexibility of creating scaffolds which can be customised for the build.

YOUNG WORKERS

Ireland has a great tradition of young people finding work on building sites, both at home and abroad. This is part of the construction industry's culture, and long may it continue.

From the point of view of health and safety, one must consider the risks involved, both for the young person and for other workers on site. Young people, because they are inexperienced, are more prone to accidents.

Fig. 4.16 Young workers on site.

They are also more likely to take risks, and their enthusiasm often leads them to ignore advice. Lack of training and lack of familiarity with tools and plant machinery are also major factors in the dangers posed to young workers on building sites.

A number of strategies can be employed to reduce accident rates among young workers. For example, they can be paired with more experienced workers in a buddy system; this offers the young worker supervision and mentoring. Frequent site safety meetings, appraisal of work carried out, and provision of training are other steps that can be taken to improve the safety of young workers on site.

SAFETY CERTIFICATION

Health and safety is important in any industry, but particularly in the construction industry, which has such high-risk operations going on every day. For this reason it is important that adequate training in health and safety is carried out and that workers are certified.

SAFE PASS

The aim of Safe Pass is to increase the level of safety awareness in the construction industry. Safe Pass serves as a standard that ensures all site personnel have undergone some form of health and safety training, and a Safe Pass card must always be carried on site. It is the duty of the National Training and Employment Authority to administer the Safe Pass course and to keep a register of personnel who have received health and safety training.

In order to keep up to date with the latest health and safety practices, construction workers are required to complete the test every four years.

The Safe Pass programme is divided into 12 sections:

1. Promoting a safety culture
2. Duties and responsibilities at work
3. Accident reporting and prevention
4. Working at heights
5. Excavations and confined spaces
6. Working with electricity, underground and overhead services
7. Personal protective equipment
8. Use of hand-held equipment and tools
9. Safe use of vehicles
10. Noise and vibrations
11. Manual handling
12. Health and hygiene.

CONSTRUCTION SKILLS CERTIFICATION SCHEME (CSCS)

While the Safe Pass course looks at general on-site safety, the Construction Skills Certification scheme deals with specific areas where health and safety measures are required. These include the safe use of large plant machinery, scaffolding, and other specialist areas on construction sites. This certification confirms that workers are trained in specialist jobs and know how to carry out these tasks in a safe manner.

LEGISLATION

In Ireland, there is a great deal of health and safety legislation and regulation that must be adhered to. These laws and regulations are updated regularly as new hazards become apparent or safer practices come on stream. The major Acts that deal with health and safety in workplaces are:

- Safety, Health and Welfare at Work (General Application) Regulations 2007
- Safety, Health and Welfare at Work (Construction) Regulations 2006
- Safety, Health and Welfare at Work Act 2005
- Safety, Health and Welfare at Work (Confined Spaces) Regulations 2001

PRACTICE QUESTIONS

1. List some of the hazards of a construction site.

2. Why is safety signage necessary?

3. Explain the safety signs below. Could someone who has not seen them before understand what they mean, in your opinion?

4. Explain with the aid of notes and neat freehand sketches the different safety signs that can be found on site.

5. Explain the function of the PPE devices listed below:
   (a) Safety goggles/glasses
   (b) Face shields
   (c) Hard hats/helmets
   (d) Safety boots
   (e) Gloves
   (f) Reflective vests.

6. Why must tools on construction sites be double insulated?

7. What is the CE mark and why is it used?

8. What are the risks of having young workers on a construction site and how can these risks be reduced?

9. Comment on the importance of safety certification for workers in the construction industry.

SAMPLE EXAMINATION QUESTIONS

2012 Ordinary Level Question 6

(a) List **two** specific safety precautions that should be observed in **each** of the following situations and give **one** reason for each safety precaution listed:

- manually lifting a load from a floor
- placing concrete in a foundation trench from a ready-mix truck.

(b) Using notes and neat freehand sketches, describe **two** items of personal protective equipment that must be worn on a building site and discuss the importance of **each** item to ensure the personal safety of workers on a building site.

2011 Ordinary Level Question 6

(a) List **two** specific safety precautions to be observed in each of the following situations and give **one** reason for each safety precaution listed:

- fitting a precast concrete window cill at ground floor level in a house
- working at height when renovating an old house.

(b) Using notes and neat freehand sketches, describe **two** specific safety precautions that should be observed when using a wood turning lathe in school. Give **one** specific reason why each safety precaution listed should be observed.

2010 Ordinary Level Question 6

(a) List **two** specific safety precautions to be observed in **each** of the following situations and give **one** reason for each safety precaution listed:

- using a ladder when painting an external wall
- using a veneering knife to cut veneers
- using a jig saw to cut a wooden panel.

(b) Using notes and *neat freehand sketches*, describe **two** specific safety precautions that should be observed when using electrical tools out-of-doors.

2009 Ordinary Level Question 6

(a) List **two** safety precautions to be observed in each of the following situations and give **one** reason for **each** safety precaution listed:

- placing ready-mix concrete in a foundation trench
- cutting a pre-stressed concrete lintel.

(b) Workers can be in danger when slating a pitched roof. Using notes and *neat freehand sketches*, describe **two** safety precautions that should be observed when slating such a roof.

SAMPLE EXAMINATION QUESTIONS

2008 Higher Level Question 2

(a) Identify **two** possible risks to personal safety associated with **each** of the following:
- (i) fitting a concrete window cill on the second storey of a dwelling house;
- (ii) laying pipes in a deep trench;
- (iii) excavating in an area where there are underground electrical cables.

(b) Using notes and *freehand sketches* as appropriate, outline **two** safety procedures that should be observed to eliminate **each** risk identified at **(a)** above.

(c) Discuss in detail two reasons why younger workers are more vulnerable to accidents on construction sites and suggest three strategies to encourage a safety culture in younger workers.

2008 Higher Level Question 7

(a) List **two specific** safety precautions to be observed in **each** of the following situations:

- using a pillar drill in the Construction Studies room;

- fitting a double-glazed unit in a wooden window frame;

- using a contact adhesive to fix veneer to a wooden panel.

(b) Sketch **two** safety signs that should be displayed at the entrance to a construction site, as shown in the accompanying sketch, and explain the purpose of each safety sign.

2007 Higher Level Question 2

(a) Identify **two** possible risks to personal safety associated with **each** of the following:
- (i) Slating a steeply pitched roof of a two storey house;
- (ii) Working around a stairwell prior to having the stairs fitted;
- (iii) Placing a ladder against a scaffold.

(b) Using notes *and freehand sketches*, discuss in detail **two** safety precautions that should be observed to eliminate **each** risk outlined at **(a)** above.

(c) Discuss in detail **three** reasons that make a construction site a high risk area for accidents at work.

CHAPTER 4

CHAPTER 5
SITE PRELIMINARIES

INTRODUCTION

Site preliminaries cover much of the preparatory work that must be done before starting the build. This involves planning, research and preparing the site.

It is important at this stage to gather as much information as possible about the site so that the build will progress smoothly once it starts. All of this information will have an impact on where, how, with what materials and at what cost the building can be constructed.

In general there are two stages to the research that has to be carried out. These are the desk study and field study.

While they can be classed as two separate elements, results from each complement the other. Both can be carried out at the same time.

DESK STUDY

A desk study is a means of gathering information that has been recorded about the area. Information is obtained from a variety of sources, such as Ordnance Survey maps, historical documents, heritage documents, planning records and environmental documents. These offer detailed information about the topography, land use and land type of the area, as the maps opposite show.

Fig. 5.1 Historical map of Limerick.

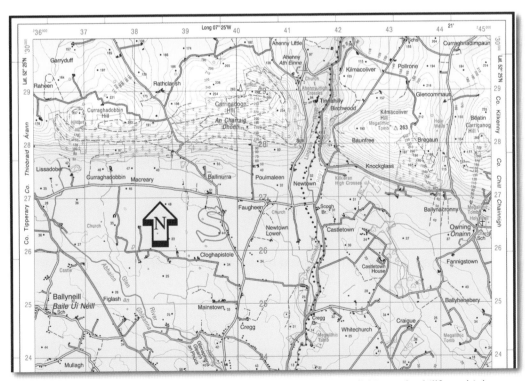

Fig. 5.2 Ordnance Survey map showing historic sites, including megalithic tombs, hillforts, high crosses and holy wells.

MAPS AND HISTORICAL DOCUMENTS

Maps give a graphical representation of a land area. They provide vital information about infrastructure, the topography of the land, and local landmarks and settlements, all of which helps us gain a greater understanding of the site.

It is useful to note that both historical maps, like the historical map of Limerick shown in Fig. 5.1, and modern maps can be used to conduct research. Both types of map are available from the national mapping agency, Ordnance Survey Ireland.

Modern maps do not include all historical elements, but they show the modern zoning or use of land. Maps also show the topography of the area, so that low-lying areas that are susceptible to flooding, or high areas that are prone to strong winds, can be identified.

The landmarks, historical sites and placenames noted on maps provide us with evidence of past settlement, which can sometimes pose problems when trying to obtain planning permission, or when carrying out works at the excavation stages. For example, if the site is situated in a region which has a high concentration of ringforts, raths, castles or historical ruins, it will be necessary to investigate whether there are any of these on the proposed site, because planning legislation does not as a rule allow a person to develop near them.

Where a developer is unsure of the implications of historical features, an archaeological survey can – and sometimes must – be carried out to see if any historical features are located on the site or nearby.

PLANNING RECORDS

Modern planning records are available free of charge from local authority websites. These give details of previous planning applications for the site and surrounding sites. This record of past applications helps to show whether or not there might be difficulty acquiring permission to build in this area.

Planning permission records are particularly useful for looking at:

- Acceptable styles of building
- Exclusion zones for building
- Sewage treatment used in the area (if required).

TECHNICAL AND ENVIRONMENTAL DATA

The technical and environmental aspects of the desk survey set out to identify the site's geological and environmental characteristics. Carrying out this research at an early stage helps the developer to position the building on the site, choose an efficient method of construction, and look at any remedial works that need to be done to the site before work commences.

The study provides, in particular, an indication as to which type of foundations can be used in building. For this part of the research it is important to consult the Geological Association of Ireland, which produces maps that show the geological features of the country. More local, county level geological maps are also available. This gives an idea at the desk research stage of what to expect on site, but it does not give the full picture. On-site investigations will examine the ground in more detail. Fig. 5.3 shows a detailed view of Ireland's soil types.

FIELD STUDY

Armed with the information gathered from the desk study, the researcher next investigates the site itself. This part of the research provides confirmation of the desk study – or it shows whether something in the desk study has been overlooked.

The field study gives a realistic, physical picture of the site. It is important to walk around the land. Simple things to note, for example, are areas that need to be cleared of vegetation or other obstacles before the build. More detailed parts of the study will require measurement and testing.

LOCAL KNOWLEDGE

Local people can often provide valuable insight into an area. This should be kept in mind when visiting a site. Talking with local people can uncover information about:

- Drainage
- Foundations typically used in the area
- Planning permission
- Land use of the area
- Historic elements of interest.

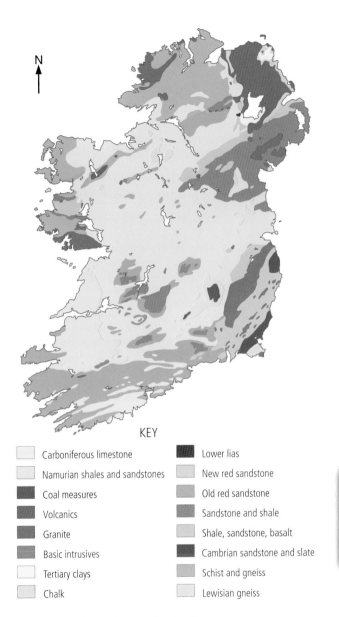

N

KEY

Carboniferous limestone		Lower lias
Namurian shales and sandstones		New red sandstone
Coal measures		Old red sandstone
Volcanics		Sandstone and shale
Granite		Shale, sandstone, basalt
Basic intrusives		Cambrian sandstone and slate
Tertiary clays		Schist and gneiss
Chalk		Lewisian gneiss

Fig. 5.3 Geological map of Ireland.

Fig. 5.4 Architect in the field.

CHAPTER 5

It is useful to find out how the land has been used previously, for example whether there has been mining or quarrying there, or hazardous waste disposed of to a landfill. This kind of information saves time and resources when it comes to the build.

SOIL INVESTIGATION

A house must be built on solid foundations, so it follows that the ground on which the foundations stand is of crucial importance. The type of soil found on the site must be examined very carefully.

The main elements of the build that are affected by soil type are:

- The foundations
- Septic tank accommodation (if required)
- Drainage of surface water from the site.

Where septic tanks are going to be installed, the soil is checked to make sure that the site can treat the wastewater (sewage) adequately, that there is sufficient run-off of treated wastewater, and that the minimum site separation distance can be accomplished. A percolation test is carried out to check that the soil can cope with this.

SOIL TYPE

It is possible to make some observations about the soil while doing a walk-round inspection of the site. In general, on a greenfield site poor soil types can be identified by the type of vegetation growing there. For example, the presence of thistle, bracken and ragwort is a sign that the soil is good, while alder, iris and rushes all indicate that the soil is in poor condition.

Generally speaking, soil in the north and west of Ireland tends to be poorly drained, while in the south and east soils are richer and well drained.

Fig. 5.5 Soil can be loose or compacted, and this will determine whether or not it is a suitably solid base to build on.

Soil density

A

B

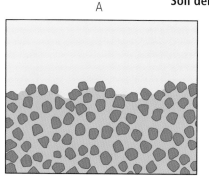

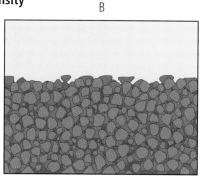

Loose soil
(poor load support)

Compacted soil
(improved load support)

The type of soil found on the site has a great impact on the viability of building there, and of course the selection of the type of foundation to use. For this reason, a professional land surveyor is employed to carry out a number of tests to check the soil type. It is particularly important that this kind of soil survey is carried out on a new site.

The land surveyor compiles a report detailing the load-bearing capacity of the soil on the site. Bearing capacity is the ability of the soil to withstand a load placed upon it. The surveyor's report will also indicate the type of foundations suitable for the building, which may restrict the size and height of what can be built. The result is based on a number of factors, including how compacted the soil is.

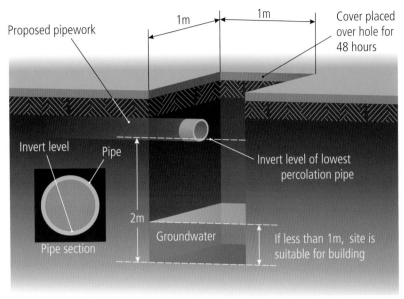

Fig 5.6 Trial hole.

To check the soil, the surveyor sinks trial holes at different places throughout the site. For a typical dwelling, a trial hole is 1m by 1m and between 2.5m and 4m deep. This ensures that the layers of subsoil can be easily seen and identified. By excavating a number of trial holes, an overall assessment of the soil contained in the site can be made. Fig. 5.6 shows a trial hole and Fig. 5.7 shows the typical layers of soil in the ground.

Limestone, sandstone, shale, clay and slate are typical rock and soil types found in Ireland. It is worth considering these local raw materials when it comes to deciding on the finish for a building, so that it can match well with the local landscape.

Rock and soil types can be classified into six categories for building purposes:

- Rock
- Sand
- Gravel
- Clay
- Silt
- Peat.

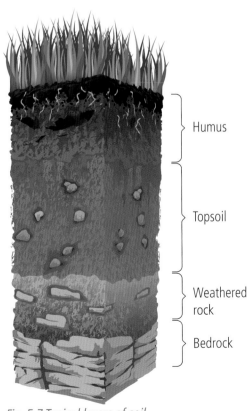

Fig. 5.7 Typical layers of soil.

It is important to know which type – or combination of types – of soil are present on site, because each category has a different bearing capacity. The load-bearing capacity is the weight that the land can sustain over a certain area. It is measured in kN/m² (kilonewtons per square metre). At a bearing capacity of under 150kN/m² the soil can be moulded by hand. This applies to the lowest of the categories, for example peat, silt and some clays. An outline of bearing capacity against type of soil is shown in Table 5.1.

TABLE 5.1 SOIL TYPES

Category of soil	Types of subsoil	Bearing capacity	Description
1. **Sand** & 2. **Gravel**	Compacted sand	>600kN/m²	Hard to work. Must be excavated with a pick.
	Compacted gravel	>300kN/m²	
	Loose gravel	>200kN/m²	Easy to work. Can be excavated with a spade.
	Loose sand	>100kN/m²	
3. **Clay** & 4. **Silt**	Hard clay	300–600kN/m²	Pick needed for excavation – cannot be moulded by hand.
	Stiff sand/clay	150–300kN/m²	
	Firm clay	75–150kN/m²	Can be excavated with a spade and moulded with fingers under substantial pressure.
	Soft clay	75kN/m²	Easily excavated and easily moulded by hand.
	Soft silt/clay		
	Soft sand/clay		
	Very soft clay	75kN/m²	When squeezed, this soil will ooze from between the fingers.
	Very soft silt		
5. **Peat**	Soft/firm	<75kN/m²	Not suitable to build on.

DRAINAGE AND GROUNDWATER

The site's groundwater level can be discovered by digging trial holes. This information is essential to any build because there can be problems with flooding and excavation in areas where the natural level of water in the soil – the water table – is high. It is important to note that the level of the water table can rise and fall throughout the year.

A trial hole is dug to find the groundwater level on the site, as well as to test whether the site is suitable for use as a percolation area (Figs 5.6 and 5.8). This hole measures 1m square and goes down to a depth of 2m below the invert level of the proposed percolation pipes. The invert level of a pipe is a horizontal level taken from the lowest part of the pipe as it lies in place. The top of the hole is covered and left for at least two days, and then the level of water in the hole is measured. If the level of water is more than 1m deep, the site has failed, as such land is deemed unsuitable to build on.

PERCOLATION TEST

A percolation test is needed if a proposed building is to have its own septic tank on site. Septic tanks are a big issue in Ireland, and are becoming a big issue in planning. They are dealt with in further detail in Chapter 23.

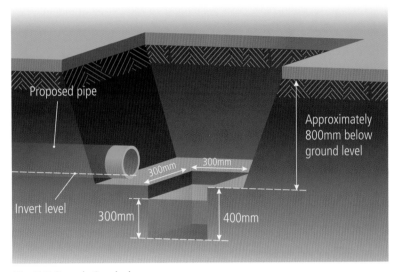

Proposed pipe

Approximately 800mm below ground level

300mm   300mm

Invert level   300mm   400mm

Fig. 5.8 Percolation hole.

The percolation test is used to measure the rate at which the soil allows liquid to filter through. The test determines how quickly or slowly water will drain from different areas on a proposed site. If this rate is too fast or too slow, a standard septic tank is not suitable and another method of waste disposal will have to be used. Certain percolation planning and environmental requirements must be met in relation to the drainage of private sewage.

The trial hole dug earlier to determine the groundwater level can also be used for the percolation test; however, it must be situated where the septic tank will be built. Like the groundwater test, the percolation test also takes place over at least two days. A minimum of two percolation holes must be dug in order to corroborate results.

Experiment: To test the percolation of a site
CONTEXT OF EXPERIMENT:
A site must have effective percolation to satisfy planning and environmental regulations.

EQUIPMENT NEEDED:
Measuring tape, stopwatch, spade, large quantity of water.

PROCEDURE:
STEP

At the bottom of the 2m deep trial hole in the area of the proposed septic tank, dig a 300mm-square hole down to a depth of 400mm.
Leave the sides of the hole rough to the touch so that the natural surface is exposed.

STEP ②

Note the time and pour water into the hole until it is filled to the top. Leave it for seven hours to percolate (filter through the soil).
After seven hours have passed, fill the hole with water again and leave it overnight.

STEP ③

The following day, fill the hole with water again, at the same time as in step 2.

STEP ④

Wait as the water level drops from 400mm to 300mm.
Using a stopwatch, record the time it takes for the water to drop from 300mm to 200mm.

STEP ⑤

Refill the hole with water to a depth of 300mm and record the time it takes for the water to drop from 300mm to 200mm. This is done a total of three times.

STEP ⑥

The percolation value of the hole is measured in units of time, t. It is calculated by taking the average value of the three readings and dividing it by four. This equates to the time taken for the water to drop 25mm.

STEP ⑦

All of the above steps are repeated in the second percolation hole and compared to the first set of results.
In order to pass the test, the value of t must fall within the range of 5 and 60. Any value above or below this range is deemed to have failed the test, in which case an alternative method of waste disposal will have to be found.

LAYOUT AND LANDSCAPING

When looking at the site, it is useful at an early stage to consider the potential of the space surrounding the home, which can be developed to give shelter and privacy. In rural areas, it is best to use natural landscaping so that the building fits into the local environment. Landscaping around the house should embrace existing wildlife habitats, and natural features such as wildflower meadows or small woodland areas should be respected.

If work needs to be done on the ground around the building, or the area needs to be replanted, native species of plants and trees should be chosen in order to harmonise with the natural rural scene. In the urban landscape more modern approaches, such as clean-cut lines in hedges and lawns, are acceptable.

While landscaping is considered at the start of the build, landscaping work usually doesn't start until after the structure is complete. This is to ensure that all construction machinery, vehicles and workers have free rein to complete their tasks without being impeded by landscapers.

Fig. 5.9 Inappropriate landscaping of a rural site. Manicured lawns, non-native plants and picket fences should be avoided in the countryside.

Fig. 5.10 More sympathetic landscaping, using natural features to integrate the dwelling into the landscape.

CHAPTER 5

SITE ENTRANCE

Having looked at the natural features of the site and the best place to build on it, and thought about the landscaping that will surround the build, the entrance to the finished site must now be considered. In order to be deemed safe, the entranceway must have a sightline of 45m in each direction. In some cases hedgerows may need to be removed in order to create these sightlines, but hedgerows should not be disturbed any more than absolutely necessary.

Normally the original entranceway to a site is retained, but where this entranceway is deemed unsafe another must be created. Fig. 5.11 shows how the sightline is achieved while maintaining a hedgerow at the entranceway.

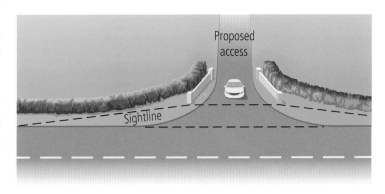

Fig. 5.11 Site entrance sightline.

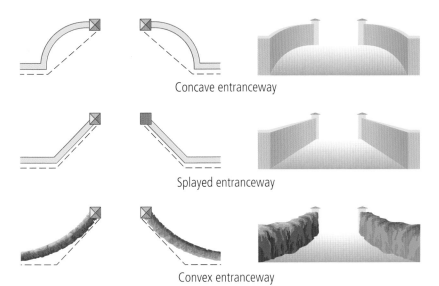

Fig. 5.12 Site entrance types.

Concave entranceway

Splayed entranceway

Convex entranceway

Fig. 5.13 Landscaping that retains existing road and site boundaries helps integrate the dwelling into its surroundings.

The basic design requirements for entranceways include a 45-degree splay, a minimum distance from the road of 5m and a 3m minimum width at the narrowest point. These requirements do not mean that all entranceways must look the same. Fig. 5.12 shows different design layouts that fit the requirements.

Roadsides and existing boundaries should be maintained to help integrate the development into its surroundings. This is most often relevant in a rural location. The different effects of landscaping at roadside boundaries is shown in Fig. 5.13. In the first illustration, the dwelling stands out imposingly on the landscape. The natural hedgerow has been removed, disrupting the natural line of the roadside. In the second illustration, the building is integrated into its surroundings with the aid of natural cover. This provides a buffering effect from the road, with the aid of added planting.

PRACTICE QUESTIONS

1. What is a desk study and how is it carried out?

2. How does a field study differ from a desk study?

3. Why does the soil on a site need to be surveyed and classified?

4. Name two indicators of good-quality soil.

5. Name two indicators of poor-quality soil.

6. What is a percolation test used for?

7. Describe the steps taken to carry out a percolation test.

8. Explain using notes and neat freehand sketches the requirements for entranceways.

9. Explain using notes and neat freehand sketches how landscaping at boundaries can integrate a building into the landscape.

CHAPTER 6
STRUCTURAL FORMS

INTRODUCTION

In order to understand how buildings stand upright, we need to understand the natural laws that govern structural form and the forces that act on structures. The structure of a building is similar to the skeleton of a person: the structure holds the weaker elements together and gives them stability.

The structural part of the building system is a complex one. There are four aspects to consider:

- The types of loading a building undergoes
- The types of forces that impact on a building

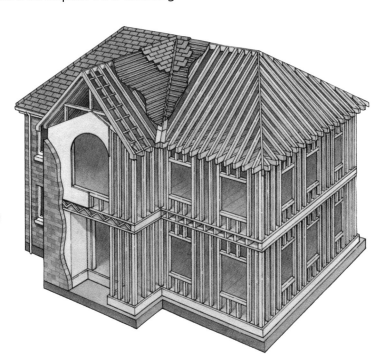

Fig. 6.1 Structure of a house underneath the external envelope.

- The reactions of components when subjected to forces
- The properties of materials.

The first three considerations will be looked at in this chapter. The properties of materials will be covered in Chapter 7.

By understanding the behaviour of different elements of a building under loadings, the designer can counteract the results of these forces.

STRUCTURAL INTEGRITY

It is important that structures are designed to be rigid and stable. For this to happen, the forces – or loadings – which buildings are subjected to must be considered. Structural loads are transferred through the building's structural system down to the foundations and into the ground. Loadings are directed to the foundations using structural walls, beams and columns.

There are two different types of load that a building is subjected to:

- Static loads
- Dynamic loads.

STATIC LOADS

Static loads are forces that are applied slowly and do not change rapidly. They are also referred to as vertical loads or gravity loads. These loads can be seen as the day-to-day forces a building will be put under. They can be further divided as follows.

Dead Loads

This is the force exerted on the building's structure from the weight of the structure itself, including all permanent fixings in the structure. This force works with gravity and so the direction of the force is vertically downwards, as shown in Fig. 6.2. It includes the plaster panels on the ceiling, weight of the floor joists, etc.

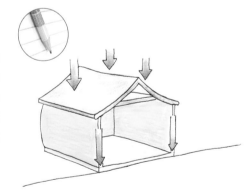

Fig. 6.2 Dead loads on a building.

Live Loads

Live loads are the loads imposed as a result of the occupancy of the building, as well as weather loads. These include the forces exerted on the building from all unfixed items, such as the people in the building and furniture, as in Fig. 6.3, or collected water and snow on the roof, as shown in Fig. 6.4.

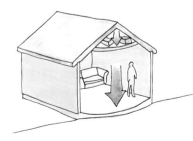

Fig. 6.3 Live loads on a building, including the building's contents.

Fig. 6.4 Water and snow collected on roofs contribute to live loads.

CHAPTER 6

Fig. 6.5 Environmental loads can bear on the foundations.

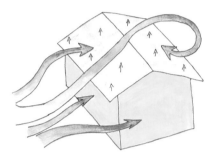

Fig. 6.6 Dynamic wind loads cause push and pull forces.

Fig. 6.7 Dynamic earthquake loads occur at the base of the building.

Environmental Loads

Environmental loads are static loads that are constantly acting on the building, such as the pressure placed on the foundations or the force which the soil places on vertical elements of the structure below the finished ground surface. Environmental loads are shown graphically in Fig 6.5.

DYNAMIC LOADS

Dynamic loads change the force they apply to a building, sometimes quite suddenly. The loads are called dynamic as they vary in intensity and point of force. They work laterally or horizontally on the structure. There are two main dynamic loads:

Wind Loads

Wind loads are the forces placed on a structure, or any element of a structure, by horizontally travelling masses of air. Wind loads can produce both positive and negative forces on the structure. These act as either push or pull forces on the elements of the building, as shown in Fig. 6.6.

Earthquake Loads

Earthquake loads are forces exerted horizontally at the base of a building (Fig 6.7). In extreme circumstances an earthquake load can cause failure of parts of the structure, which can lead to collapse. In areas prone to earthquakes, builders use methods and materials that counteract these forces by allowing the building to move with them.

RESULTS OF LOADS

Loads cause stresses, deformations and displacements in structures. Excessive loads or overloading can cause structural failure. Buildings must be designed so that the structure is able to cope with the variety of loads that will be placed on it in normal conditions.

In order to understand how materials fail or deform under loads, we need to look at the stresses placed on the individual elements, and the internal structure of the materials these elements are made from.

STRUCTURAL FORCES

Structural engineering looks at a building and the forces involved in its complex structural system, and calculates the ability of those structures to withstand both its own and external forces. A force is a pushing or pulling, twisting or shearing action, and has a direction and intensity associated with it.

On earth, gravity is a force which pulls objects towards the earth's centre. Isaac Newton's experiments in the area of force and gravity found that:

> **Force = Mass (weight in kg) x Acceleration (m per sec^2)**

The equation shows that the greater the mass or weight of an object, the greater the amount of force required to move it. Due to Newton's work in the area of forces, force is now measured in newtons.

> **1 Newton = 1kg x 1m/sec^2**

STRESS AND STRAIN

Understanding how materials react under forces allows us to gauge what materials work well in different applications. For this reason, materials are tested to gauge their attributes and tolerances. This is done by analysing the way materials are stressed and strained by the pressure of forces acting on them.

Stress

Forces can act on materials in four ways:

1. Push force (compression)
2. Pull force (tension)
3. Twist force (torsion)
4. Sliding force (shear).

These forces are known in physics as stress. Stress (f) is defined as a force (P) per unit area (A).

> $$f \text{ (stress)} = \frac{P \text{ (force)}}{A \text{ (area)}}$$

Take the example of a brick wall. The bricks that are higher on the wall put stress on the bricks beneath. The weight, however, is distributed evenly through the structure, as shown in Fig. 6.8. The load is distributed through the wall bond, which is one reason for offsetting the bricks in a bond, a fact we will cover in a later chapter.

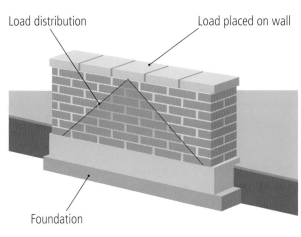

Fig. 6.8 Load distribution of the top brick on a wall.

CHAPTER 6

Lifting weights offers another example of how stress is distributed. The weights that are lifted above the weightlifter's head place stress on the area holding them. Much like what happens in building structures, the weight is distributed down the weightlifter's body structure to the ground.

Strain

Strain refers to the internal displacement of a material due to stress. The internal structure of a material resists the force placed on it. However, if the stress is great enough it will change the material's structure or form. That is how the material reacts to the force. Each material has a threshold of forces it can withstand without permanent deformation, but forces greater than those will change its shape.

Fig. 6.9 A weightlifter distributes the load down through his body structure.

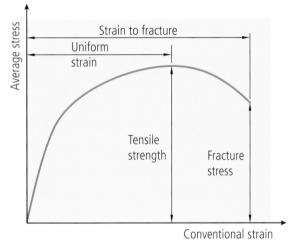

Fig. 6.10 Stress versus strain. As the material is placed under stress, it will maintain shape (uniform strain) until it reaches tensile strength. After this it will deform until fracture. The stress at the point of fracture is known as fracture stress.

Stress and Strain Curve

The more stress that is applied to a material, the more it will deform. There is a relationship between the two. The curve in Fig. 6.10 shows the relationship graphically.

Studying the graph, it can be seen that as stress is added strain increases. Maximum strain occurs when the material can no longer resist the stress placed on it and begins to deform. Beyond this point, the material begins to lose strength and will eventually break.

TYPES OF MATERIAL STRESS

Stress can act in many directions in a building material.

Compression

Compression is a pushing force that presses towards the centre of a member. Squeezing a sponge is an example of compression. As the hand closes around the sponge, the material compresses towards the centre.

The shorter the member is, the more compression it can undergo. Compression on longer elements can cause deflection.

Look at how it works in relation to beams, an important element in the structure of a building.

A beam is a horizontal member in the system that is longer than it is wide or deep. Most beams are supported at each end. Compression on such a beam can cause it to bend in the direction of gravity. The distance that the beam moves from a horizontal position once the compression load is placed on it is called deflection. Compression is shown graphically in Fig. 6.11.

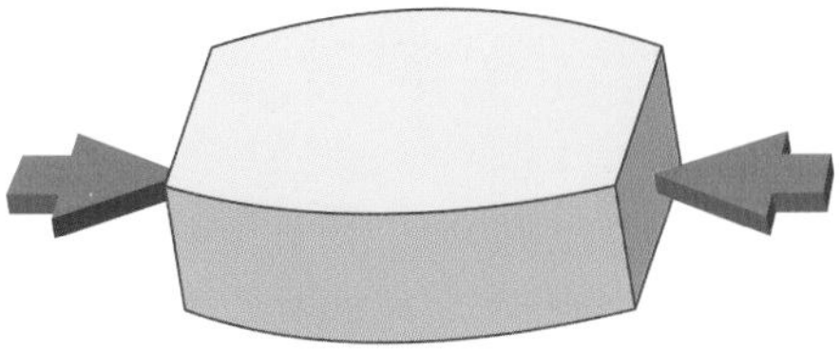

In a building, a structural member which is put under compression is referred to as a strut.

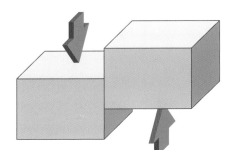

Fig. 6.11 Compression force – the force on the element pressing towards its centre.

Tension

Tension is a pulling force. It pulls a member in opposite directions along its length. It tries to stretch the material of the member away from its centre. Tension is the opposite of compression.

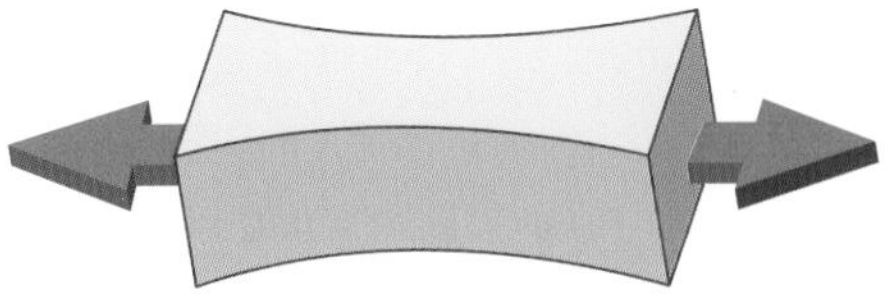

In construction, guide wires and cables in tension are used to support features. Tension is shown graphically in Fig. 6.12.

A structural member that is placed in tension is referred to as a tie. A tie can be either a cable or a solid beam.

Fig 6.12 Tension force stretches the member away from its centre.

Shear

Shear is the result of two forces pressing in opposite directions on one point of a member. If the force is strong enough, it will cause the member to fracture at that point. The two parts of the fractured member will then move in the direction of each force. This is shown graphically in Fig. 6.13.

Shear forces are at work in most buildings, for example where sheet material is fastened to a wall. The screws or bolts holding the sheets are pulled down by the weight of the sheet, but kept from moving by the wall.

Fig 6.13 Shear force – pressing in opposite directions.

Torsion

Torsion is a twisting force placed on a member. It occurs along its longitudinal axis (longest span) and is caused by two equal forces of opposite rotation. It's like wringing water from a cloth by twisting in opposite directions. Torsion is shown graphically in Fig. 6.14.

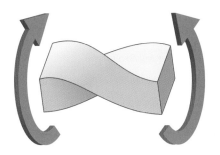

Fig 6.14 Torsion force – a twisting action on a member, pushing in opposite directions.

CHAPTER 6

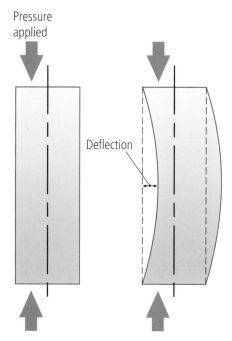

Pressure applied

Deflection

Fig 6.15 Eccentric force – offset from the centre of a member.

Eccentric Force

An eccentric force is a force applied parallel to the longest axis of the member, but off centre to its axis. The load is therefore unevenly distributed on the member, causing deflection as seen in Fig. 6.15.

REACTION TO FORCES

Every member used in construction is chosen for the characteristics of its material and the situation or force it will face. All members experience force, so selecting the right material to withstand this pressure is very important. Excessive force can cause a material to bend, crack, buckle or crumble.

Materials react to the forces placed on them. They counteract the force imposed on them by changing their internal structure. This change can be temporary or permanent, depending on the material and the force it experiences. The material's properties determine the way it reacts. Some are strong under one type of stress and weak in response to others.

ELASTICITY

Elasticity is the term used to describe a material's ability to return to its original shape once the force it is under is removed. Elastic materials readily deform and change their internal structure when a force is applied to them. They can change shape, and then return to their original form. An example is a rubber band. When the band is stressed by stretching it will accept its new shape. Once the force is removed it will return to its original form.

The formula for calculating a material's elasticity (λ) uses values for stress and strain:

$$\lambda \text{(elasticity)} = \frac{\text{stress}}{\text{strain}}$$

Using this formula, it is possible to calculate the elasticity of materials under various force loadings.

If a force is great enough, it can cause permanent deformation to the internal structure of a material. This is known as plastic deformation. Plastic deformation is not to be confused with the material plastic. Plastic, in this context, means that the material is malleable or capable of being shaped or formed.

DEFLECTION

Deflection is the amount by which a member will deform or bow when put under force. Take the beam shown in Fig. 6.16. The length of the beam between the two supports is called the span. If a vertical pressure is put on the beam at its centre, the beam will bow downwards: this is called deflection. The amount of deflection which a beam will undergo increases with the length of the span and the amount of force placed on the centre of the beam.

Where there is deflection in a beam, there are both tension and compression forces at work. The top surface of the beam is compressed, while the bottom surface is in tension, as shown in Fig. 6.17. The middle of the beam can be said to have neutral force.

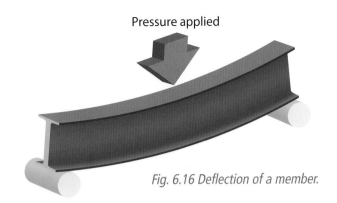

Pressure applied

Fig. 6.16 Deflection of a member.

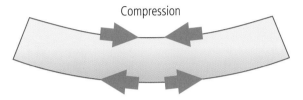

Compression

Tension

Fig. 6.17 Top surface in compression, bottom surface in tension.

Because the stresses are greater on the top and bottom surfaces, beams can have a thinner cross section. Beam designs take advantage of this to save on material costs, and so the midsection of the beam uses less material. Examples of such beams are shown in Fig. 6.18.

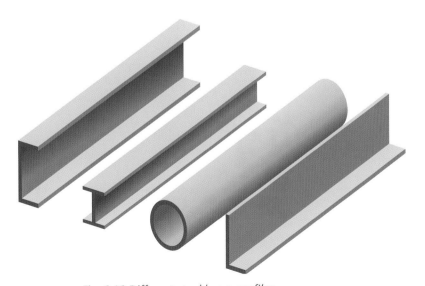

Fig. 6.18 Different steel beam profiles.

CHAPTER 6

Experiment:

To test the effects of an applied load on a simply supported beam

CONTEXT OF EXPERIMENT:

Support is very important in buildings. Beams are used where there are open spans that need to be supported. Deflection in beams must be considered when choosing materials for these beams.

EQUIPMENT NEEDED:

Two supports (high enough to hang weights from samples with clearance), clamps, metre stick, weights, samples of wood.

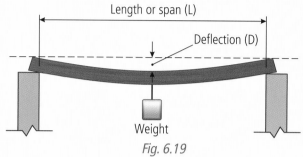

Fig. 6.19

PROCEDURE:

STEP 1

Prepare three samples of different types of wood of equal length and cross section.

STEP 2

Label each sample.

STEP 3

Measure and mark 1m on each sample (leaving extra space at each end of the samples). Also mark the centre point of the metre.

STEP 4

Place a length of wood between two supports, ensuring that the metre marks are at the edge of each of the supports.

STEP 5

Measure any initial deflection, if there is any, without any weight being applied. This deflection is measured with the metre stick.

STEP 6

Hang a known weight (for example 3 newtons) from the sample, at the centre of the metre mark.

STEP 7

Measure the deflection of the sample by placing a metre stick or other sample (without weight) behind it.

STEP 8

Record your results in a table.

STEP 9

Repeat the experiment for all samples.

ADDITIONAL EXPERIMENT:
The same experiment can be carried out using a cantilever set-up (one side of the sample can be clamped to a support). Weights can be hung at the 1m mark along the sample. This will test the deflection of this style of beam.

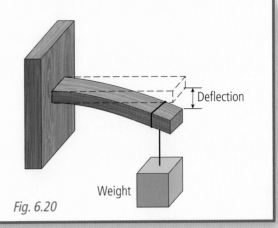

Deflection

Weight

Fig. 6.20

FORCE EQUILIBRIUM

All forces must be in equilibrium if a structure is to remain standing. Take the example of a person leaning against a wall. They are, in fact, applying a force to the wall. The person, however, does not fall over, and the wall doesn't fall down, so the wall must be exerting an equal force opposing the force of the person. This does not mean that the wall is pushing back, rather that the force applied by the person is counteracted by the mass of the wall. This is one of Newton's laws of motion, which says that equal strength and opposite force will balance one another:

'For every action there is an equal and opposite reaction.'

STRUCTURAL LOGIC

Structural logic is the term given to the way the elements of a structure are organised. This includes the design of the cavity wall to take the weight of the roof and the design of the foundations to spread the load evenly through the ground. The structural system of a building is the combination of all of the elements that bear the loads placed on the building. In very simple terms, these systems can be classified in three ways:

- Solid structures
- Skeletal structures
- Surface structures.

These classifications show the path that forces in the structure follow, i.e. through solid mass, a skeleton frame or along the surface of a structure.

Some structures use two or more types of system in order to resist more intricate forces.

CHAPTER 6

STRUCTURAL SYSTEM FORCES

While a building may have more than one type of structural system in place, buildings can be divided into three types:

- Compressive or compression structures
- Tensile structures
- Truss structures.

We have looked at the forces that are placed on elements in a building. Now we look at how these loads travel through the structure as a whole. Generally, it can be said that the forces are what keep the building upright.

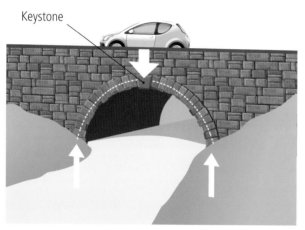

Keystone

Fig. 6.21 Compression structure. The weight of the car is the load placed on the bridge. This load is transferred to the arch. The reaction load is transferred up the arch in equal measure.

COMPRESSIVE STRUCTURES

Compression or compressive structures stay together through the application of compression to the building elements; that is, the ends of the elements are pushed towards one another. This force can be applied either horizontally or vertically. An example is shown in Fig. 6.21.

In compressive structures, the main forces acting on the elements are compressive. This does not mean that there are no tensile forces at work; these will be discussed below. There are various types of compressive structure, including:

- Two-dimensional repetitive shapes
- Three-dimensional surfaces.

Two-dimensional repetitive shapes use a simple shape and repeat it to form a building. Many simple shapes can form these structures. Examples include:

- Post and beam
- A-frame
- Arch structures.

Post and Beam

The post and beam structure is the simplest in form. It has two upright pillars and one cross member that spans between them. Its use can be traced back thousands of years, to the earliest built structures in Ireland (Fig. 6.22).

Fig. 6.22 Two upright pillars support a beam: the Poulnabrone Dolmen, Co. Clare.

A-Frame

This type of structure makes use of the triangle. Triangles are a stable shape, and when repeated in constructions add strength to the building.

Arch Structures

Arch structures may be curved (Romanesque) or pointed (Gothic). A curved arch has continuous compressive forces which are distributed through its shape. The weakest points of arches are at the base, as the loading is intensified in this region and may require extra support (such as the flying buttresses for Gothic arches).

Vaults and domes can be included in these types of structure as they are the meeting points of arched chambers.

TENSILE STRUCTURES

As the name suggests, tensile structures work with forces of tension. Here the majority of the elements of the structure are placed in tension. An example of this is shown in Fig. 6.23.

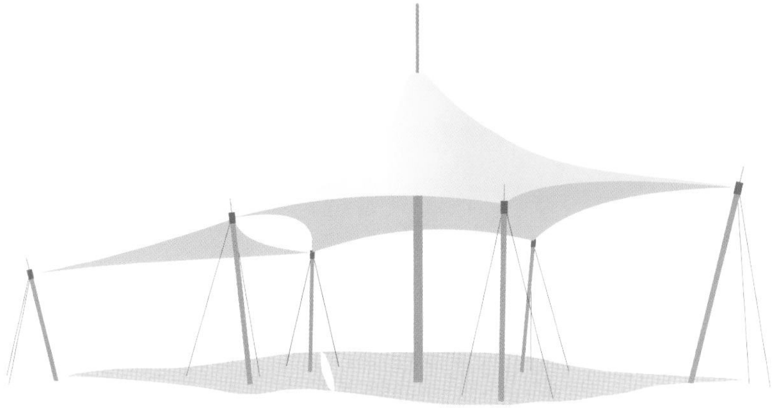

Fig. 6.23 A tensile structure. The supporting posts stretch the fabric to form a rigid roof.

TRUSS STRUCTURES

A truss is a structure made up of straight elements arranged in triangles. The truss responds to dynamic loads, as each element can be subjected to compression, tension, or both. Truss structures are economical to construct due to their efficient use of materials. A perfect example is the Eiffel Tower, the most famous truss structure in the world.

Fig. 6.24 The Eiffel Tower, Paris: a famous truss structure.

Form Active Systems

These systems are non-rigid, flexible matter whose form is of a certain shape and is secured at the ends. These structures have many applications and can be divided into:

- Cable structures
- Tent structures
- Pneumatic structures
- Arch structures.

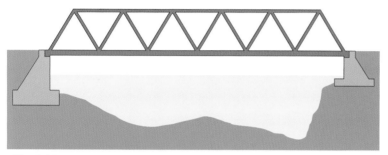

Fig. 6.25 A vector active system, with the trusses supporting a bridge.

Vector Active Systems

These structural systems consist of short, straight, solid elements that redistribute forces. These forms use the strength of triangular arrangements to divide the forces into tensile and compressive forces. This means that the elements of the structure may be under tension or compression.

These structures are the simplest forms and are the basis for many structural designs, including bridges. Fig. 6.25 is a simple triangular truss, and shows how the truss supports the bridge below it.

Vector active structures can be divided into:

- Flat trusses
- Curved trusses
- Space trusses.

Section Active Systems

Like the other active systems, these systems have many groups of elements (rigid, solid and linear), in which parts of the structure are able to move, redirecting the forces acting upon them. Examples include:

- Beam structures
- Frame structures
- Slab structures.

Surface Active Systems

These are systems of flexible or rigid planes that are able to resist tension, compression and shear. These parts of the structure have the ability to move and redirect forces. Examples include:

- Plate structures
- Folded structures
- Shell structures.

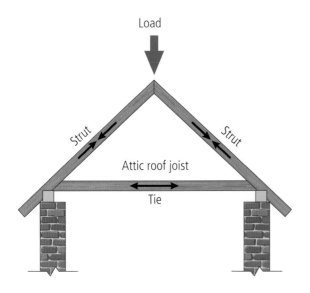

STRUTS AND TIES

Struts and ties are elements that help to support a building. A structural member that is placed under a compression force is referred to as a strut. A member that is placed in tension is referred to as a tie. The image in Fig. 6.26 shows both struts and ties. The horizontal member of the truss is in tension and so is referred to as a tie. The sloped members are in compression, so these are the struts in the structure.

Fig. 6.26 Struts and ties. All structures have forces acting on them. All elements with a tensile force acting on them are called ties and those with compressive force acting on them are known as struts.

PRACTICE QUESTIONS

1. Where are structural loads directed?

2. Name and describe, using notes and neat freehand sketches, the different types of loads that can act upon structures.

3. Name the four types of force and give an example of where each is seen.

4. What is elasticity?

5. How does an eccentric load cause deformation?

6. What is deflection?

7. Using notes and neat freehand sketches, describe struts and ties and the properties associated with each.

SECTION

B

SUBSTRUCTURE

CHAPTER 7
BUILDING MATERIALS

LEARNING OUTCOMES:

After studying this chapter students will:

- Understand the properties of the main materials used in construction, where they come from and how they are used.
- Understand how cement and concrete are manufactured and used.
- Explain how timber is converted from trees, how it is deemed structurally suitable and the necessary moisture content for individual tasks.
- Identify rot in timber, and its treatment.
- Appreciate man-made materials, including manufactured boards, steel and plastics.

KEYWORDS:

- STONE • BRICK • CEMENT • AGGREGATE • CONCRETE • REINFORCEMENT • PRE-TENSION
- POST-TENSION • TIMBER • MOISTURE CONTENT• MANUFACTURED BOARDS • STEEL • PLASTICS

INTRODUCTION

Whether building a small dwelling or a skyscraper, the materials used are vitally important. Building materials all have their own characteristics and properties. Some common materials used in Ireland, both historically and today, include:

- Stone
- Brick
- Concrete
- Timber
- Metal
- Plastics

STONE

Stone is a fundamental building material. It has been used for many centuries all around the world. In Ireland stone is used for two main applications: to make walls and to provide a decorative finish to a building. Stone is recyclable, and crushing and grading stone is a successful, cost-effective and sustainable way of reusing this material. Stone, the bedrock of this island, provides some of the basic material for the buildings we live in and look at every day.

BUILDING IN STONE

Granite is a hard, durable stone with characteristics suitable for building. It generally has a grey or pink colour, and on close inspection it glistens with minerals and crystals. Granite is found in the mountainous regions of Dublin and Wicklow, in Galway, and in the Mourne Mountains, Co. Down. Granite can be used as dimension stone (it can be accurately cut and retains its quality). It is a very hard rock, and wearing on tools used to cut it. Some of Ireland's major public buildings, like the GPO, Dublin, are made of granite (Fig. 7.1).

Fig. 7.1 The GPO, Dublin, constructed of hard-wearing granite.

Limestone is hard, durable and tough. Most famously in Ireland it is found in the Burren, Co. Clare. A fine example of a limestone building is Cork City Hall, shown in Fig 7.2.

Sandstone is thermally resistant and so is a suitable building material for fireplaces. Sandstone is a hard rock that resists erosion. It is found in the southwest, where an example of a building with sandstone detailing is Muckross House, Killarney, Co. Kerry (Fig. 7.3).

Fig. 7.2 Cork City Hall, reconstructed in 1920 using limestone.

Marble comes from limestone. It is an expensive, decorative stone, used more often indoors than outdoors as it does not weather very well. The most common uses of marble in a home are for fireplaces or kitchen worktops (Fig. 7.4).

Slate is a hard, durable stone and is often used for roofing. Slates are made by splitting the stone, which breaks off and is then graded. Thicker slates are used at the base of the roof (over the eaves) and thinner slates are used at the top. Valentia, Co. Kerry, is home to the last working slate quarry in Ireland.

Fig. 7.3 Muckross House, Killarney, Co. Kerry, built with local sandstone.

Stone has been fundamental in shaping our built heritage. It is a common feature of the Irish landscape, with its traditional stone walls, and of towns and villages, with their old, unplastered stone buildings. The development of these structures evolved from simply stacking stones on top of one another to shaping the layers of stone to

Fig. 7.6 Old slate roof tiles.

Fig. 7.4 Marble counter-top.

Random stone uncoursed

create pleasing designs. The considered placing of stone in layers is called coursing. Common styles seen in Ireland are random stone uncoursed, random stone coursed, and square rubble coursed (Fig. 7.6).

Square rubble coursed

Random stone coursed

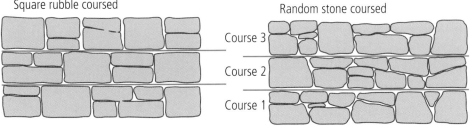

Course 3

Course 2

Course 1

Fig. 7.6 Basic patterns of building with stone.

BRICK

Red brick buildings are a familiar sight around the country. Particularly popular in the Georgian period, bricks provide a desirable façade to a building, wall or footpath. Bricks are recyclable; they can be salvaged and reused many times over. Bricks are made from clay. The clay is mixed with water and pushed into moulds, which are then placed in a kiln, where they are heated until the bricks are hard. Bricks are available in different colours, and different coloured bricks are often used to create patterns in walls. Some common brick patterns are shown in Fig. 7.7.

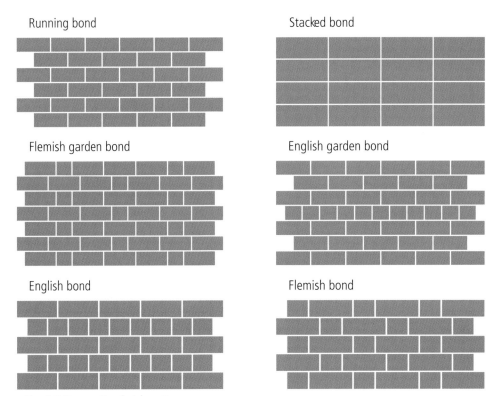

Running bond

Stacked bond

Flemish garden bond

English garden bond

English bond

Flemish bond

Fig. 7.7 Decorative brick patterns.

CEMENT

Cement is used in many construction products, including mortar, plaster and concrete. Portland cement is the cement most commonly used in Ireland. It is made by heating limestone (calcium) and clay, which produces clinker. The clinker is then ground with gypsum to form a fine powder. Fig. 7.8 shows the process of cement manufacturing.

Cement is a very fine, grey powder that reacts chemically when mixed with water. This reaction is known as hydration and it happens in two stages. First, the cement begins to stiffen, then it gains strength. The chemical reaction continues while the cement and water remain in contact. Although logic would suggest that the more water is added, the stronger the end product will be, this is not the case. Adding too much water to cement leaves air pockets in the final product, which weakens it. The strength of the finished product is based on the water/cement ratio: too much weakens the product and too little does not allow the full reaction to take place.

The hydration of cement mixed with aggregates results in a hard, durable building material known as concrete.

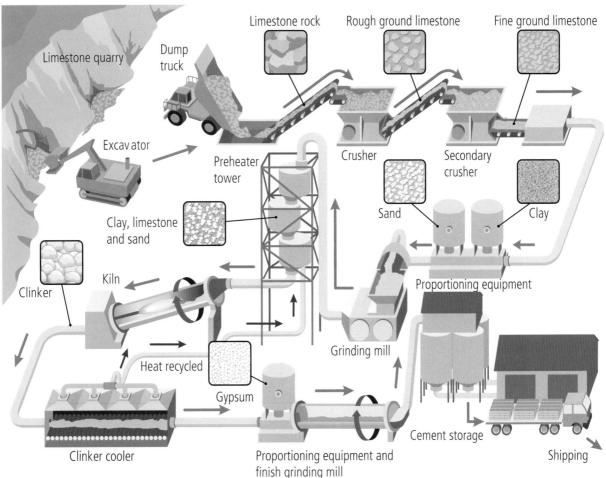

Fig. 7.8 The cement manufacturing process.

CONCRETE

Concrete is the product formed when cement, water and aggregates are combined. Aggregate is any granular material used in construction, particularly sand, gravel and stone. Aggregates are graded to different sizes. Coarse aggregates include natural gravel, crushed rock and stones that are larger than 5mm in diameter. Fine aggregate is material that can pass through a 5mm sieve. Concrete is used to make foundations, floor slabs, walls and a multitude of pre-cast products.

Fig. 7.9 Pre-mixed concrete being loaded into a truck for transportation to a site.

The process of measuring the materials before mixing the concrete is called batching. Batching can be done by weight or volume. In weight batching, the materials are weighed individually before mixing. Most ready-mix systems use this method as it is very accurate. Batching by volume is more commonly used for small amounts or in domestic mixers.

When mixed, the water and cement react chemically and begin to form a paste. The paste coats the aggregates in the mix, and binds everything together. The mix sets and hardens over time.

Concrete is often mixed off site and brought to the site in trucks. It is important that the concrete is mixed correctly for the purpose it is to be used for on site.

Concrete Mix

A mix of 1:2:3 cement:sand:gravel gives a high-strength concrete suitable for most applications.

The Portland cement content of a mix must be properly proportioned to produce concrete that can be easily poured and finished, and will have adequate strength and durability. Mixtures with low Portland cement content:

- Result in harsh concrete and slabs
- Bleed excess water to the surface
- Are difficult to finish
- Have poor surface characteristics.

Too much Portland cement content in a mix can result in increased drying and shrinkage.

Not all concrete is the same. If the ingredients are mixed in different ratios, they will produce material with different structural properties. Different structural properties are needed in different situations – for example, a dwelling will use different mixes for foundations and walls. Whatever the mix used, it is important that it is mixed thoroughly to produce a product of uniform strength.

Workability

Concrete must be able to take the shape of any mould it is poured into. Good workability means that the concrete can be formed into a mould, compacted and screeded without trouble. Workability is determined by the amount of water and aggregates contained in the mix. As outlined earlier, too much water reduces the strength of the concrete.

An easy method for determining the workability of fresh concrete is the slump test, which measures the shape the concrete takes on when its support is taken away. The test is widely used for on-site checks. The test is outlined below.

Experiment: The slump test

CONTEXT OF EXPERIMENT:

Concrete must be workable. This test aims to analyse the workability of concrete.

EQUIPMENT NEEDED

Three concrete samples

- Mixing tray
- Truncated cone
- Steel tamping rod
- Metre stick
- Smooth surface

METHOD:

STEP 1

Take three samples of concrete from different parts of the concrete batch produced (i.e. ready mixed concrete). Do not test the first or the very last sample.

STEP 2

Empty sampling buckets onto the mixing tray, ensuring that each sample bucket is scraped clean.

STEP 3

Re-mix the sample fully on the tray, shovelling it into a heap, turning the heap over to form another.

STEP 4

Ensure that the cone and level surface are clean and damp.

STEP (5)

Fill the cone in three layers and rod each layer 25 times. Ensure the blows are spread equally across the cone. Only rod the layer you are working on.

STEP (6)

Once all three layers have been added, top up the cone if necessary, and level off the top of the cone.

STEP (7)

Turn upside down and then carefully lift the cone straight off while ensuring that all excess concrete outside the cone has been removed.

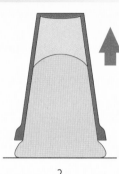
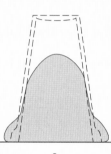

Fig. 7.10

1   2   3

STEP (8)

Lay a rod across the top of the upturned cone as in Fig. 7.11, and using a metre stick measure the difference between the height of the slump and the cone top.

Fig. 7.11

Results of this test must show a true slump, as the diagrams below illustrate.

Results

0–50mm slump = low workability

50–75mm slump = medium workability

Types of slump

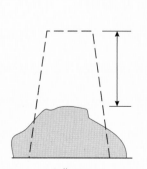
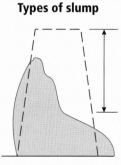
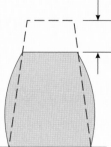

Fig. 7.12

Collapse   Shear   True slump

Placing and Compacting

When the desired mix has been made, the concrete is ready to be poured on site. As the concrete is still liquid, it needs to be contained within a frame, or formwork, to allow it to set. While it is in this formwork, it is tamped and vibrated to remove air bubbles.

Formwork is the boarding or sheeting used to hold the wet concrete in place as it sets. Formwork is generally made from timber and is reusable. Fig. 7.13 shows the formwork required for a concrete wall.

Curing

Curing is the process used to achieve the best strength and hardness of concrete. Concrete is cured by spraying water either directly onto the concrete or onto mats placed on the concrete. The water protects the concrete from extreme temperatures and a dry atmosphere, which are detrimental to the curing process. Properly cured concrete is strong with minimal chances of cracking.

Fig. 7.13 Formwork for a concrete wall.

The strength of concrete varies from batch to batch. The strength of hardened concrete is tested using the concrete cube test.

Experiment: The concrete cube test

CONTEXT OF EXPERIMENT:

The strength of concrete is crucial to a build. This test aims to determine whether concrete meets the British Standard or not.

EQUIPMENT NEEDED:

- Cast iron cube moulds
- Samples of concrete
- Spanners
- Oil

- Tamping bar
- Float
- Damp cloths
- Plastic sheets

METHOD:

STEP 1

Ensure that all moulds are clean. Fill each with concrete samples in 50mm layers. Each layer of 50mm must be tamped to compact the concrete. Fig. 7.14 shows the cube used in the cube test.

Fig. 7.14 Cast iron mould.

STEP 2

Smooth off the top of the cubes, removing all surplus concrete.

STEP 3

Cover the moulds with a damp cloth and plastic sheet and store inside for 24 hours at 15–25°C.

STEP 4

Remove the moulds by unbolting the sides. Handle the cubes carefully.

STEP 5

Store the cubes for 28 days to allow them to harden.

Fig. 7.15 Batch samples.

STEP 6

Send cubes to lab for testing. Fig. 7.16 shows a cube being tested in the machine. The results are taken at this point.

RESULTS:

The results sent back from the lab will state the compressive strength of the samples as well as their compliance with the British Standard.

Fig. 7.16 Computer monitors the pressure and fracture of the sample.

REINFORCED CONCRETE

Concrete has high strength properties when it is under compression, but concrete under tension will not last long. Concrete is reinforced so that it can withstand tensile loads. Steel, which is stronger in tension than compression, is an ideal reinforcement material. Steel reinforcement is commonly known as rebar (reinforcing bar), and can either be placed in the concrete in lengths or made up into a mesh or cage. In concrete foundations, the cage is positioned in the excavated area, held up with rebar chairs, and the concrete is poured around it, holding all in place. This type of reinforcement is not under any stress. Fig. 17.17 shows this detail.

Concrete can also be reinforced by pre-tensioning and post-tensioning it. This practice, known as pre-stressing, results in:

- Larger loads being carried
- Wider spans being achieved
- Reduced weight of components – materials are stronger so fewer are needed
- Materials being connected together to create large areas of high strength.

Fig. 7.17 Steel mesh added to the base of the foundation to strengthen its weaker underside.

There are some drawbacks when pre-stressing concrete:

- Special steel is required
- It is expensive – added cost of steel
- High level of control and finish required
- Specialist equipment necessary.

Pre-tensioning

A steel wire tendon is stretched between two anchors. Concrete is poured and allowed to set. When the concrete has hardened sufficiently, the wire is freed from the anchor. When the wire is freed, the concrete element has a tendency to buckle upwards in the middle. This is not usually seen as clearly as it is shown in Fig. 7.18. However, the concrete will straighten out again when it is placed in its final position with a load on top. Lintels and suspended concrete floors are generally pre-tensioned.

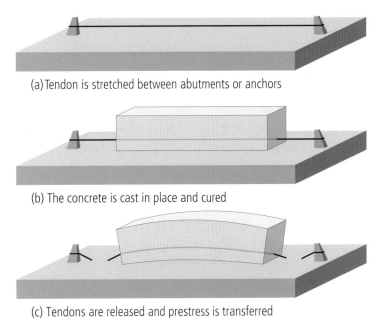

(a) Tendon is stretched between abutments or anchors

(b) The concrete is cast in place and cured

(c) Tendons are released and prestress is transferred

Fig. 7.18 Pre-tensioning concrete.

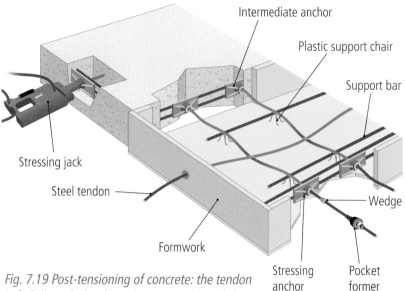

Fig. 7.19 Post-tensioning of concrete: the tendon is fed through the duct, shown in red, and left limp while the concrete is forming. Once cured it is tensioned with the stressing jack.

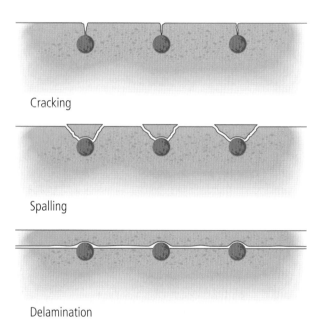

Fig. 7.20 Cracking, spalling and delamination of reinforced concrete.

Post-tensioning

Here the concrete is allowed to harden before the steel is tensioned. A flexible duct is placed loosely before the concrete is poured. When the concrete has set, steel tendon is fed through the duct and anchored at one end. A stressing jack is used to apply tension to the required degree. The space left between the steel tendon and ducting is filled in with grout to prevent moisture reacting with the steel. The pocket creates a void in the poured concrete that allows the stressing jack access to the anchor. The wedges clamp on to the steel tendon when the jack releases, thereby holding the tension. Post-tensioning is used on large-scale projects such as bridges and roads. Fig. 7.19 shows the process of post-tensioning.

Reinforced concrete is an incredibly strong building material, but if moisture and air come into contact with the steel, they can cause it to rust. Steel with rust occupies more space than steel on its own, and this expansion can cause problems such as cracking, spalling and delamination of the concrete, as can be seen in Fig. 7.20. These can lead to the reinforcement failing.

CONCRETE BLOCKS

Concrete blocks are precast and sold in bulk. They can be solid or hollow. Solid concrete blocks have many applications, including cavity wall construction. Hollow blocks are more commonly used in buildings like garages and large outdoor sheds. Both types of block have a rough surface, which helps render to bond easily.

Fig. 7.21 Solid concrete block.

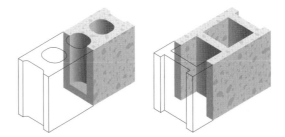

Fig. 7.22 Two different types of hollow block.

Solid block: used in the construction of cavity walls and for other domestic purposes.

Hollow block: generally used in uninsulated buildings such as garages and large sheds. When they are used in a dwelling, they must be located on a south-facing wall and cannot be load-bearing. The cavity inside the block reduces heat gain.

Fine texture block: often seen in schools, offices and other public places. These blocks have a smooth finish and can be painted directly.

High-strength block: made with a higher cement content than a normal concrete block.

Aerated block: a lightweight product suitable for use in general construction.

TIMBER

Timber is a popular natural renewable material. The construction industry relies heavily on timber, both native and imported.

Species of trees grown in Irish forests include pine, willow, birch and oak. Exotic timbers, such as ebony, rosewood and teak, are imported. Timber is a very useful building material because it is easily processed and has a relatively high load-bearing capability. It has many applications in the structure of the building.

Fig. 7.23 Felled trees ready to be transported to a sawmill.

CLASSIFICATION OF WOOD

Timber is classified into two basic categories: softwood and hardwood. This does not mean that the wood is 'soft' or 'hard'. In general, the softwoods are the coniferous, cone-bearing trees (spruce, cedar, firs), while the hardwoods are deciduous, fruit-bearing trees (oak, mahogany, teak). The difference between softwoods and hardwoods lies in the cellular structure of the material.

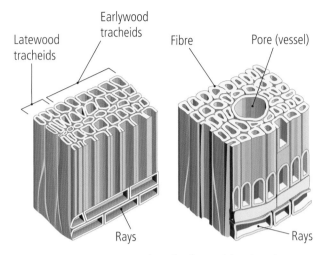

Fig. 7.24 Microscopic samples of softwood (LEFT) and hardwood (RIGHT).

STRUCTURE AND GROWTH

Wood, like other plants, is made up of fibres or cells that resemble an irregular honeycomb. The tight structure of these fibres gives wood its rigidity. The tube-like structures in the wood that carry nutrients and water through the fibres are shown in Fig. 7.24. Felling the tree does not disrupt the ability of the fibres to soak up water. For this reason, timber is described as hydroscopic. Due to this hydroscopic property, timber in its natural form will not remain structurally sound in wet conditions.

PARTS OF A TREE

Trees are made up of many parts and each part has a purpose. The parts of the tree are:

Bark: The rough exterior of the tree. The bark protects against insect attack and retains moisture.

Bast: A layer just under the bark. Contains the phloem cells which carry nutrients to all parts of the tree.

Cambium layer: This layer produces new cells.

Medullary rays: Radiating from the centre of the log, these allow sap to travel through the trunk of the tree.

Growth rings: A collection of light and dark growth rings of the once-living cambium layers. Counting the rings is a well-known method of determining the age of a tree.

Sapwood: This part of the tree carries nutrients through the trunk to the leaves.

Heartwood: This part of the trunk is made up of inactive cells, which make the tree more rigid. Structurally, the best timber is found here, because it contains minimal moisture.

Pith: The centre of the log. This is where the tree began life as a sapling.

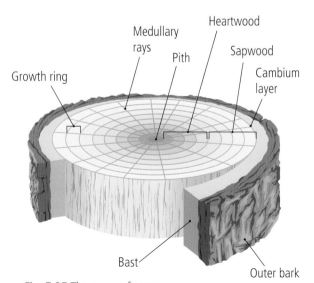

Fig. 7.25 The parts of a tree.

LOG SELECTION

Rough-sawn logs are taken to a sawmill, where they are converted into cut boards. On arrival they are fed into a grading machine, which sorts the wood by thickness and length. Machines stack similarly sized logs in piles so that they can be processed together. Timber must be cut to standard dimensions and regular shapes if it is to be used in construction.

Fig. 7.26 Feeding a timber grading machine.

TIMBER CONVERSION

There are three ways in which a log can be sawn to provide lengths of timber. These different types of cuts produce lengths that are either tangential or radial to the centre of the log, which can affect the properties of the length of timber. Cutting the log in the wrong way can lead to defects in the finished product. Common sizes for structural timbers are widths of 150–250mm with thicknesses ranging from 38mm to 50mm.

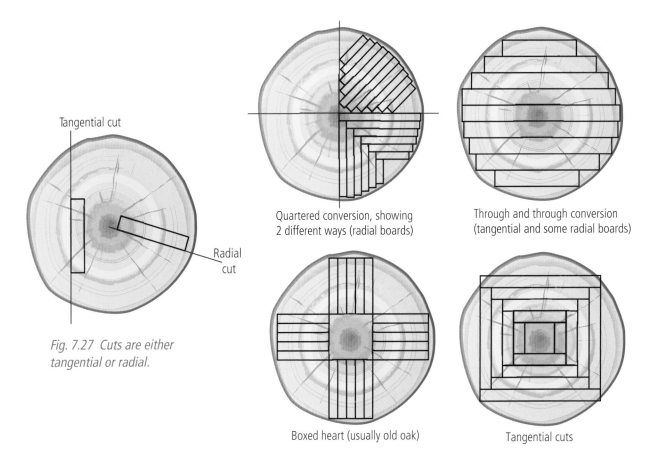

Tangential cut

Radial cut

Fig. 7.27 Cuts are either tangential or radial.

Quartered conversion, showing 2 different ways (radial boards)

Through and through conversion (tangential and some radial boards)

Boxed heart (usually old oak)

Tangential cuts

Fig. 7.28 Four different methods of cutting logs into lengths.

Check
Shake
Knots

Fig. 7.29 Checks, shakes and knots are all natural wood defects which can affect the suitability of wood for certain uses.

Twist
Bowing
Splitting

Fig. 7.30 Wood conversion defects include twisting, bowing and splitting.

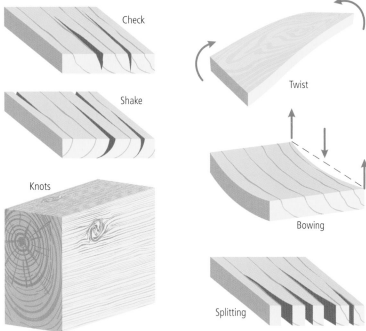

Defects in timber can occur naturally or as a result of the conversion process. Natural defects include checks, shakes and knots (Fig. 7.29). Defects relating to the conversion of the timber include twisting, bowing and splitting, which are shown in Fig 7.30.

STRUCTURAL CLASSIFICATION OF TIMBER

In Ireland, timber suitable for building is subject to European Union standards, specifically IS EN 1995. Timbers are stamped with their classifications. The stamp includes information regarding the species, its structural strength, the standard to which it belongs, and the National Standards Authority of Ireland (NSAI) logo. The species and structural strength are given in short codes, such as:

- WE/SG1 – Western Europe, Species group 1 (pine, douglas fir, sitka and Norway spruce) sourced in Ireland
- WE/SG2 – Western Europe, Species group 2 (larch, Scots pine) sourced in Ireland.

The timber's structural strength is classified with a 'C' followed by a number. The higher the number, the greater the strength, e.g. C18, C24, C27. The strength class is determined by the species and grade of the timber, e.g. GS (General structural grade – graded visually), SS (Special structural grade – graded visually). In order to comply with European Union regulations, structural timber must carry a stamp indicating both its strength class and its strength grade.

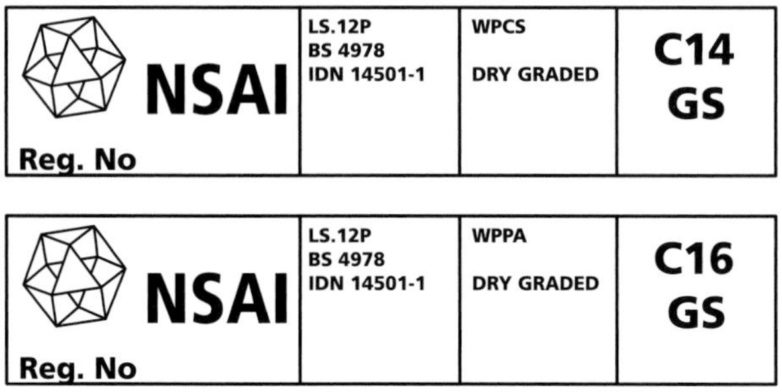

NSAI
Reg. No
LS.12P
BS 4978
IDN 14501-1
WPCS
DRY GRADED
C14
GS
NSAI
Reg. No
LS.12P
BS 4978
IDN 14501-1
WPPA
DRY GRADED
C16
GS

Fig. 7.31 Examples of the stamps used to classify timber.

MOISTURE CONTENT

Timber is hydroscopic, which is to say that it absorbs moisture. After it is kiln dried, timber's moisture content drops to between 8 and 10 per cent, but its hydroscopic nature means that this does not last if the timber is not stored correctly. Fluctuations in moisture content cause timber to expand and contract. To be suitable for structural work, the moisture content of the timber at the time of construction must not be more than 24 per cent, but should ideally not be higher than 20 per cent. After construction, the moisture content of structural timber must not exceed 20 per cent.

Typical Moisture Contents	
15–20%	External joinery, windows, structural timber
10–15%	Internal joinery, furniture
8–10%	Internal joinery in rooms which are continuously heated

ROT IN TIMBER

Timber is a natural material and will decay over time, particularly if it is exposed to damp or humid conditions. Rot attacks timber when mould grows and spreads over its surface, and if it is left unchecked will lead to the degradation and eventual failure of structural timbers in a build. The two types of rot that attack timber are wet rot and dry rot.

Wet Rot

Wet rot attacks timber that has a constant moisture content of 30 per cent or more. Wet rot is caused by a fungus. It starts when spores land on the wet timber, where they germinate. The fungi then feed off the timber, their source of food, eroding the wood and eventually destroying it. Wet rot is identified by a number of characteristics, including:

Fig. 7.32 Wet rot causes wood to deteriorate.

- A musty smell
- Split grain, with evidence of white fungal strands
- Spongy, wet wood
- Weakening of the timber.

Wet rot cannot be reversed, but its spread can be stopped. First, the source of the moisture dampening the timber must be eliminated. Next, the rot is cut out completely, leaving only solid, healthy timber. This healthy timber is treated with preservatives and finished with a water-repellent finish.

Fig. 7.33 Dry rot in timber.

Dry Rot

Dry rot is much more severe and damaging than wet rot. Its name comes from the appearance of the wood, which is left dry and powdery. Dry rot occurs in timber with a moisture content above 20 per cent. The fungus that causes this rot originates as spores, which land and germinate on the timber. The fungi then send out thin roots, which bore into the wood in search of food. Warm, humid conditions allow a fruiting body (like a mushroom) to form. When the fruiting body is fully grown it sends out more spores, infecting surrounding timber.

Dry rot can spread to dry, healthy wood, and does so extremely quickly. Dry rot is identified by a number of characteristics, including:

- The appearance of fruiting bodies
- Dry, crumbly wood
- The presence of red dust
- Deep, cube-like cracks
- A strong musty smell.

Dry rot is much harder to eliminate than wet rot. As with wet rot, the supply of moisture to the timber must be eliminated. Then the infected timber is cut away, along with a minimum of 600mm of healthy timber. The infected timber must be burned to prevent the fungus spreading, and nearby brick and concrete should be treated with fire too. All of the timber removed is replaced, and three coats of preservative are applied to the wood.

PRESERVING TIMBER

Outdoors, timber experiences a wide range of temperatures and physical conditions. To make it suitable for use outdoors it needs to be pre-treated to protect it against weather, insect and fungal attack.

Timber can be preserved in a number of ways. Most commonly, oils or paints are applied to seal the material.

Preservatives are applied in the following way.

1. The surface is sanded and cleaned, and knots are treated with knotting varnish.

2. Primer is applied to all surfaces and allowed to dry.

3. Holes, cracks and dents in the timber are filled, allowed to set, and sanded.

4. The surface is cleaned once more before the undercoat is applied.

5. Two coats of undercoat are applied and allowed to dry.

6. The surface is lightly sanded before applying the final coat. The brush used must be of good quality and coats must be applied evenly and in the direction of the grain.

Preservative can also be applied using pressure. The timber is put into a machine that creates a vacuum around it. When the preservative is then introduced, the vacuum serves to pull the preservative into the fibres of the timber, creating an even and deep coverage.

Internal timber members can also be treated, depending on their function. Common applications for preserving internal timber include wax, varnish and polish.

MANUFACTURED BOARDS

Manufactured boards are used where natural timber products will not meet the requirements of a build, or where price is an issue, as manufactured boards are less expensive than solid timber. Manufactured boards are constructed by gluing strips and pieces of wood together. There is a wide range of manufactured boards available, and each has properties desirable for different situations. The most common manufactured boards used in construction are plywood, oriented strand board (OSB) and chipboard.

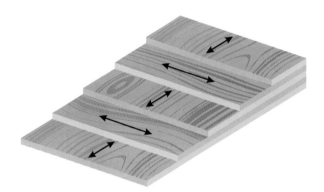

Fig. 7.34 Plywood is made by laying each layer in a different direction.

Plywood is made up of thin layers, each laid at a 90-degree angle to the previous layer. There is always an odd number of layers in plywood so that both outer layers show the same grain direction; they also allow for even shrinkage. Common uses for plywood include floors, walls, roofs and concrete formwork. Plywood is also available in a waterproof version known as marine plywood, which is ideal for bathroom applications.

Oriented strand board (OSB) is made using chips, which are oriented in layers and glued together with resin and wax. OSB is very distinctive due to its surface pattern. It is often used as sheeting on upper floors before carpet or other flooring types are laid. It is also used in walls, flooring and roofing.

Chipboard is made from small particles of timber. Chipboard is weaker than plywood and OSB. It is usually covered with a veneer for aesthetic purposes and

Fig. 7.35 Oriented strand board (OSB).

is commonly seen in kitchen cabinet construction. It is also used in fire doors, kitchen worktops and flat-pack furniture.

Medium-density fibreboard (MDF) is a manufactured board made from sawdust particles. Like other manufactured boards, it is produced using glue, heat and pressure. There is a range of fibreboard products, including hardboard and particleboard, which are used for decorative purposes and cabinet making. Like chipboard, MDF can be covered with a veneer to make it resemble hardwoods.

Fig. 7.36 Chipboard.

Fig. 7.37 Medium-density fibreboard (MDF).

METALS

Steel is the most common metal used in building. Steel has a high iron and low carbon content (usually less than 2 per cent). The iron gives the steel its strength. However, with greater strength comes less ductility – that is, it is not malleable or easily shaped. Steel is used widely in the construction industry. Its main uses include:

- Structural (beams for internal and external balconies)
- Lintels
- Fittings, e.g. socket boxes, hinges, taps, etc.
- Reinforcement of concrete.

Steel is susceptible to rust. A more expensive form of steel known as stainless steel can be made by adding chromium to the metal. Stainless steel is expensive, and therefore not used for structural purposes. Stainless steel is most commonly found in kitchens and bathrooms, where the chromium provides protection against the moisture in the area.

Where steel is used for structural purposes, there are a number of standard sections to choose from. Fig. 7.38 shows a number of steel sections. Structural steel components are produced by rolling hot steel through the shape of the desired cross section. The term used to refer to these components is RSJ (rolled steel joist).

There are a number of ways of preventing structural steel from rusting. Two of these are:

Galvanising: This method involves coating the metal with zinc, either by dipping or electro-plating it.

Painting: When painting steel it is important to use a suitable paint type. The paint prevents air and moisture penetrating through to the metal and consequently stops rust from forming.

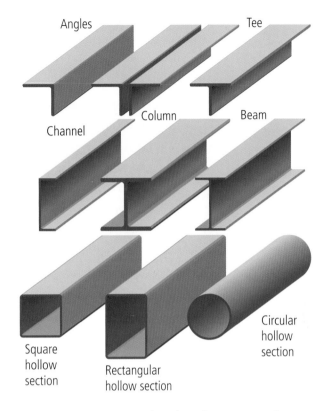

Fig. 7.38 Various types of steel sections seen on site.

PLASTICS

Plastics are a man-made material, and are becoming used more frequently in building, particularly as they are recyclable. Plastics are used in preference to other materials for a wide range of reasons, not least because they are:

- Easy to manufacture
- Easy to install
- Resistant to water
- Resistant to rot
- Resistant to rust

- Thermally insulating
- Electrically insulating
- Rigid or flexible
- Opaque or transparent
- Recyclable.

Plastics are used in various applications around the house, including plumbing fixtures, piping, windows, doors and electrical ducting.

Although there are many advantages to using plastics, there are some drawbacks too. These include:

- Discolouration
- Brittleness
- Not all are recyclable
- Toxic gases produced during processing.

POLYMERS

'Polymers' is the correct term for plastics. In construction, two groups are particularly relevant:

1. **Thermosetting polymers:** Once they are moulded, they keep their new shape. Examples include:

   - Epoxy resins – used in combination with a hardener to form a hard plastic. Also used in fibreglass as the material that holds the glass fibres in place.

   - Polyurethane – used as foam to insulate hot water storage tanks. Also used in its liquid form as a varnish for wood.

2. **Thermoplastic polymers:** Can be reheated and remoulded repeatedly into various shapes. Examples of thermoplastics include:

   - Acrylic – used in sheets as a substitute for glass; also poured into moulds to form bathtubs.

   - Polythene/polyethylene – used in packaging, and as damp proofing material. It can also be used to make 'hard plastic' objects such as paint trays, storage boxes, etc.

   - Polystyrene – used to make foam for insulation.

   - Polyvinyl chloride (PVC) – used to make doors and windows, and to insulate electrical cables.

   - Polypropylene – used in ropes and carpets.

PRACTICE QUESTIONS

1. Name and describe three kinds of stone and explain how they are used in construction.

2. Describe how cement is made.

3. What is concrete made of?

4. Describe each of the following terms as they relate to concrete:
   (a) Batching
   (b) Water:cement ratio
   (c) Workability
   (d) Formwork.

5. Explain how you would carry out a slump test on fresh concrete.

6. Describe, using notes and neat freehand sketches, both pre-tensioning and post-tensioning of concrete.

PRACTICE QUESTIONS

7. Explain how timber is structurally graded. Make reference to the stamp in your answer.

8. What is the difference between wet rot and dry rot?

9. Describe two methods of applying preservative to timber.

10. Name three manufactured boards and describe how they are made.

11. What is galvanising?

12. Name and describe the two groups of synthetic polymers used in building.

 SAMPLE EXAMINATION QUESTIONS

2007 Ordinary Level Question 6

(a) List **two** situations where ready-mixed concrete is usually used in the construction of a dwelling house and discuss **two** advantages of using ready-mixed concrete in preference to concrete mixed on site.

(b) Using notes and *neat freehand sketches*, show how a slump test is carried out on a batch of concrete.

(c) Using notes and *neat freehand sketches*, show the correct position of the reinforcing steel in a concrete lintel.

CHAPTER 8
FOUNDATIONS

LEARNING OUTCOMES:

After studying this chapter students will:

- Understand the functions of a foundation.
- Be able to identify different types of foundations.
- Select suitable foundation types for different categories of soil.
- Draw neatly annotated sectional diagrams of various foundation installations.

KEYWORDS:

- FOUNDATION • SETTLEMENT • BULB OF PRESSURE • STRIP FOUNDATION • RAFT FOUNDATION
- PILE FOUNDATION • PROFILE BOARDS • REINFORCEMENT • REBAR CHAIRS • SCREEDING

INTRODUCTION

The foundation is the most important structural element of a building because it takes all the building's loads and guides them into the ground. Foundations have a number of functions. They:

- Transmit building loads directly to the earth
- Limit the amount of settlement of the building
- Provide a level platform for the building
- Anchor the structure against wind
- Resist pressure imposed by surrounding soil.

As discussed in Chapter 6, the loads affecting foundations are both static and dynamic, and the foundation, therefore, must be solid enough to withstand these forces.

Settlement is the term given to the movement of a building when the volume of soil underneath the foundations changes after it is built. Put simply, the building sinks into the ground. The job of the foundation is to allow settlement to occur evenly, so as to prevent strain and cracking in the building structure.

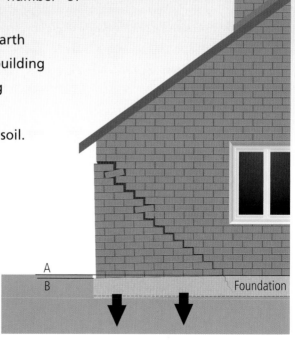

Fig. 8.1 Subsidence in the ground can cause the walls of a building to crack. A: shows the original level of the foundation. B: shows its level after settlement.

Uneven settlement is called subsidence. This is a serious problem when it occurs. Here the movement of the ground can distort the building's shape. When a foundation fails to provide support, the ground appears to fall away from under the building, leading to the kind of damage shown in Fig. 8.1. Settlement, which is a major concern in building, is discussed more fully later in this chapter.

Because the entire building rests on the foundation, it is essential that the foundation is level. Any mistakes will be amplified as the building takes shape. The foundation must be strong enough to 'hold' the building in place and to stop it sliding or, in extreme cases, overturning when the building is exposed to strong winds. This applies to high buildings more than typical domestic dwellings.

Soil surrounding the base of a building can exert huge pressure on it. The foundation structure of buildings with basements, in particular, must be able to withstand the pressure that the surrounding soil will place on this area.

SELECTING A FOUNDATION

The kind of foundation to be used in a building is governed by a number of factors. First, the load-bearing capacity of the soil must be determined: this is discussed in Chapter 5. Where a site contains more than one soil type, with differing load-bearing capacities, the foundation must be made to suit the soil of lowest load-bearing capacity. Next, the topography of the site is looked at. If the site is not level, a stepped foundation may be required. Finally, the depth of good strata must be determined.

Fig. 8.2 shows the bulb of pressure under a foundation. The bulb of pressure is a concept that helps us to measure the vertical stress that a building imposes on the ground. The pressure that the building exerts on the ground spreads out and down in the shape of a bulb. Lines that share an equal amount of pressure

CHAPTER 8

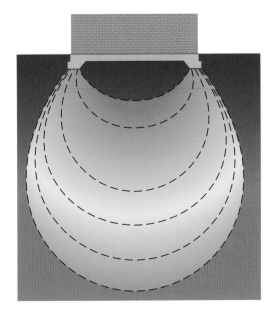

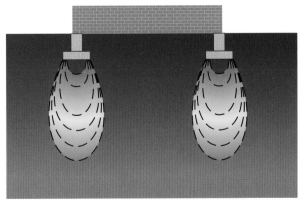

Fig. 8.2 Bulb of pressure underneath the foundations: raft foundation (LEFT); and strip foundation (RIGHT). The greatest bulb pressure is shown in red.

can be joined to form bulb shapes within the strata of soil. All points on each line represent the same pressure at that point, regardless of depth.

Wider foundations have a larger depth of 'bulb', but it contains very low pressure the further down the bulb goes. Narrower foundations exert more vertical force and therefore have higher values on the outer rings of the 'bulb', though they do not extend down as far.

FOUNDATION TYPES

There are three main foundation types used in the Irish building industry:

- Strip foundations
- Raft foundations
- Pile foundations.

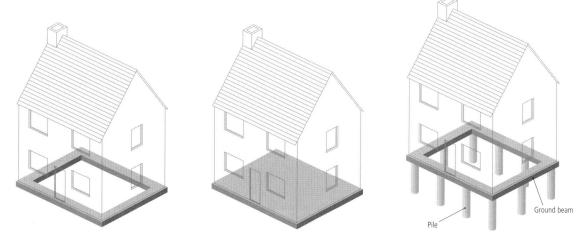

Fig. 8.3 The three most common foundation types: strip, raft and pile foundations.

STRIP FOUNDATIONS

Strip foundations are used where the soil is of average to good bearing capacity. This type of foundation supports the building's load-bearing walls, using 'strips' of concrete. Strip foundations are particularly suitable for house building, due to the relatively low load pressure exerted by the structure. They are also more economic to build than other kinds of foundations.

There are a number of design features associated with strip foundations, in particular:

- The depth of the foundation must be greater than or equal to the width of the wall to be built on top of it.
- The width of the foundation must be three times the width of the wall being built on top of it.

Fig. 8.4 shows these design features graphically.

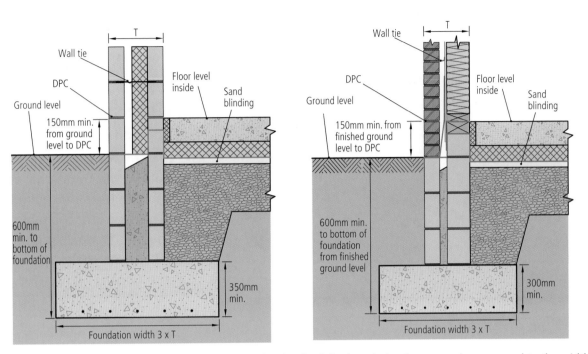

Fig. 8.4 Key features of strip foundations. Note that the depth of the foundation is greater than or equal to the width of the wall, and the foundation is three times as wide as the wall built on top of it.

These design features are based on the fact that the load that the wall places on the foundation travels at 45 degrees from the point of contact between wall and foundation. Any foundation that is more than three times as wide as the wall to be built on it will suffer from shear failure, because it will contain redundant zones. A redundant zone is an area of the foundation which is surplus to the needs of the forces placed on the foundation. It can be seen in Figs 8.5 and 8.6, which show how shear failure can affect a strip foundation.

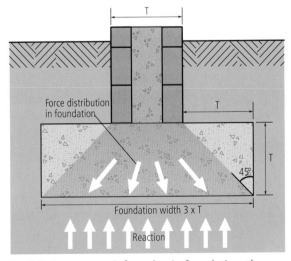

Fig. 8.5 For a non-reinforced strip foundation, the width of the foundation should be three times the width of the wall to avoid shear failure.

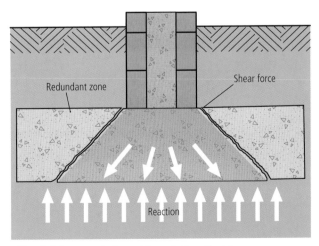

Fig. 8.6 A non-reinforced foundation that is more than three times the width of the wall will create a redundant zone and suffer shear failure.

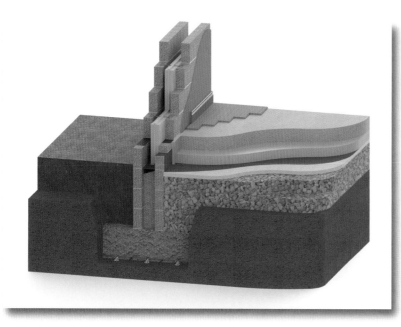

Strip foundations can be further divided into three categories: traditional strip, wide strip and deep strip.

Traditional Strip Foundations

Of the three types of strip foundation, the traditional strip foundation is the most commonly used. This type is not suitable for building on soft clay, silt or peat. Figs 8.7 and 8.8 show the details of a traditional strip foundation.

Fig. 8.7 Strip foundation.

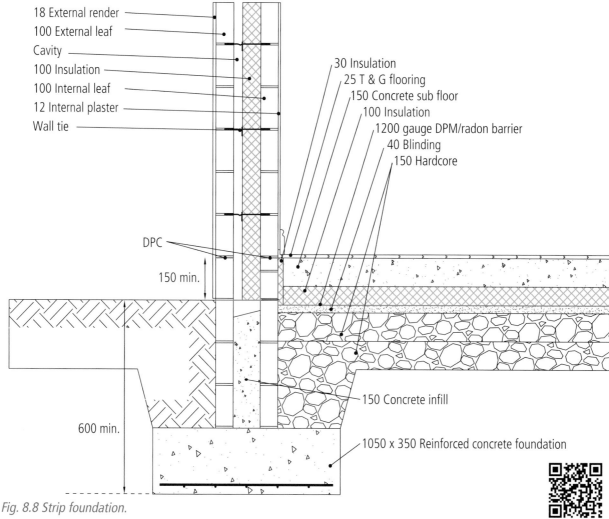

18 External render
100 External leaf
Cavity
100 Insulation
100 Internal leaf
12 Internal plaster
Wall tie

30 Insulation
25 T & G flooring
150 Concrete sub floor
100 Insulation
1200 gauge DPM/radon barrier
40 Blinding
150 Hardcore

DPC

150 min.

600 min.

150 Concrete infill

1050 x 350 Reinforced concrete foundation

Fig. 8.8 Strip foundation.

The strip foundation can be 'stepped' to suit a site with sloping ground. Where this stepped strip foundation is used, there are a number of design features to be aware of:

- The depth of the step is usually made to suit the height of the blocks used to build the wall.
- The horizontal overlap of the step must be either twice the height of the step, or the width of the foundation, or 300mm, whichever is the greater.
- The length of each step must be a minimum of 1m.

Fig. 8.9 shows details of these design features.

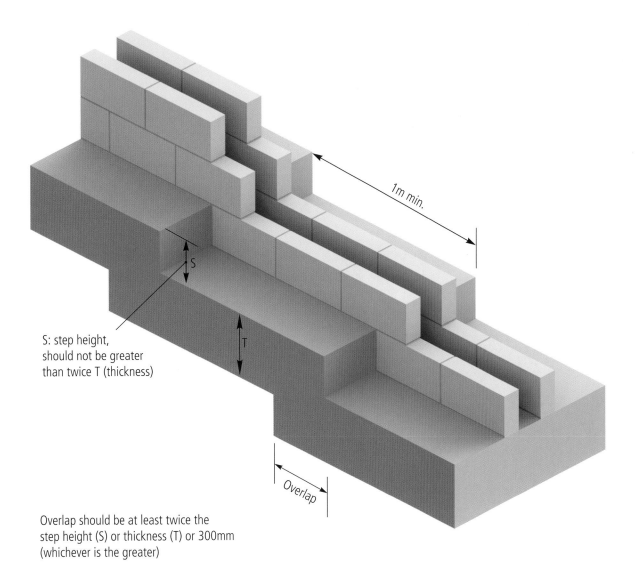

S: step height, should not be greater than twice T (thickness)

Overlap should be at least twice the step height (S) or thickness (T) or 300mm (whichever is the greater)

Fig. 8.9 Stepped strip foundation.

Wide Strip Foundations

Wide strip foundations are used where the load-bearing capacity is not suitable for a traditional strip foundation.

A wide strip foundation can be used on soils with a low bearing capacity, such as soft clay and silt. The depth of a wide strip foundation is the same as a traditional strip foundation. The width, however, is greater.

In order to support itself, reinforcement must be positioned across the transverse axis of the foundation (that is, across the width). Fig. 8.10 shows the details of a wide strip foundation.

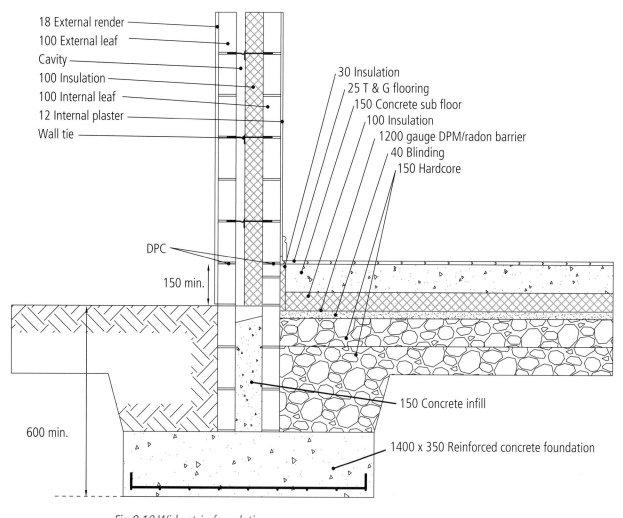

18 External render
100 External leaf
Cavity
100 Insulation
100 Internal leaf
12 Internal plaster
Wall tie

30 Insulation
25 T & G flooring
150 Concrete sub floor
100 Insulation
1200 gauge DPM/radon barrier
40 Blinding
150 Hardcore

DPC

150 min.

600 min.

150 Concrete infill

1400 x 350 Reinforced concrete foundation

Fig 8.10 Wide strip foundation.

Deep Strip Foundations

A deep strip foundation is used when the depth down to good strata is 900mm or more. As the depth of this foundation is so large, it is possible to decrease its width. The top of the foundation must be 150mm below the surface of the soil. Fig. 8.11 shows the details of a deep strip foundation.

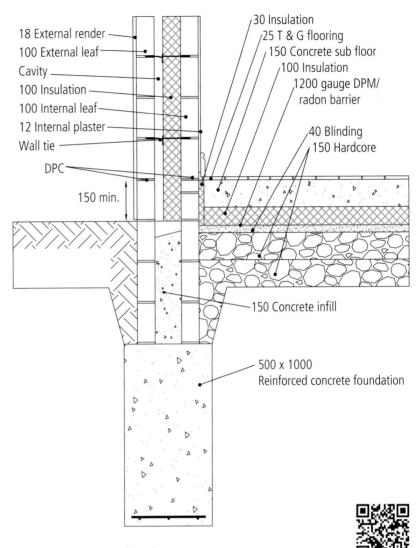

18 External render
100 External leaf
Cavity
100 Insulation
100 Internal leaf
12 Internal plaster
Wall tie
DPC
150 min.

30 Insulation
25 T & G flooring
150 Concrete sub floor
100 Insulation
1200 gauge DPM/ radon barrier
40 Blinding
150 Hardcore
150 Concrete infill
500 x 1000 Reinforced concrete foundation

Fig 8.11 Deep strip foundation.

RAFT FOUNDATIONS

A raft foundation is a large slab of concrete that covers the whole ground floor plan of a building. This type of foundation is suitable for use on soils that have a low bearing capacity. All the loads of the building are transferred to the raft, which in turn transfers them to the soil below. Because the soil is of poor bearing capacity, it is likely that a lot of settling will occur under the building. By building the house on a raft, the whole load can move as one, preventing any settlement damage.

Raft foundations are not confined to use on soils of low bearing capacity. They can also be used on soils of average to good bearing capacity. This practice, however, is uncommon, due to the financial and time implications that are involved.

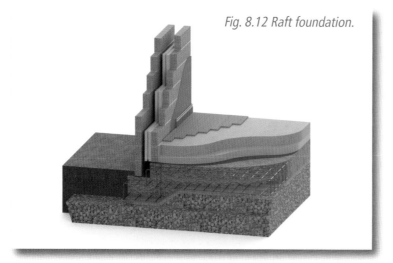

Fig. 8.12 Raft foundation.

The raft itself is reinforced with steel rebar and cage construction and can be up to 300mm thick – and the thickness is increased under load-bearing walls in order to fully support the load. The details of a raft foundation are shown in Figs 8.12 and 8.13.

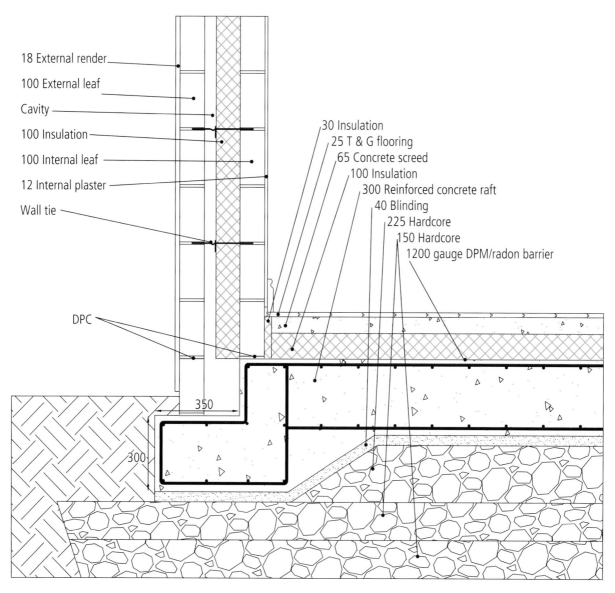

18 External render
100 External leaf
Cavity
100 Insulation
100 Internal leaf
12 Internal plaster
Wall tie

30 Insulation
25 T & G flooring
65 Concrete screed
100 Insulation
300 Reinforced concrete raft
40 Blinding
225 Hardcore
150 Hardcore
1200 gauge DPM/radon barrier

DPC

350

300

Fig. 8.13 Raft foundation.

PILE FOUNDATIONS

Pile foundations are used where the soil is of low bearing capacity, or where a good stratum of soil lies beneath a stratum of inferior bearing capacity.

This type of foundation is similar in a way to a strip foundation. However, instead of the strip resting on the soil below, it is supported by piles driven or poured into the ground. The top of each pile is tied into the bottom of the strip with reinforcing steel. The 'strip' used in a pile foundation does not need to be as wide as it is in a strip foundation; this is because the load is being transmitted to the piles rather than straight to the soil. The 'strip' poured for this type of foundation is more commonly referred to as the ground beam.

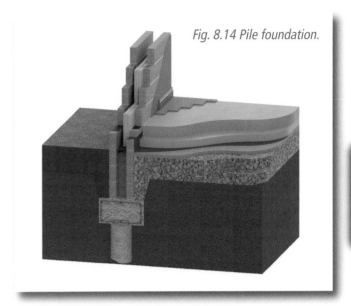

Fig. 8.14 Pile foundation.

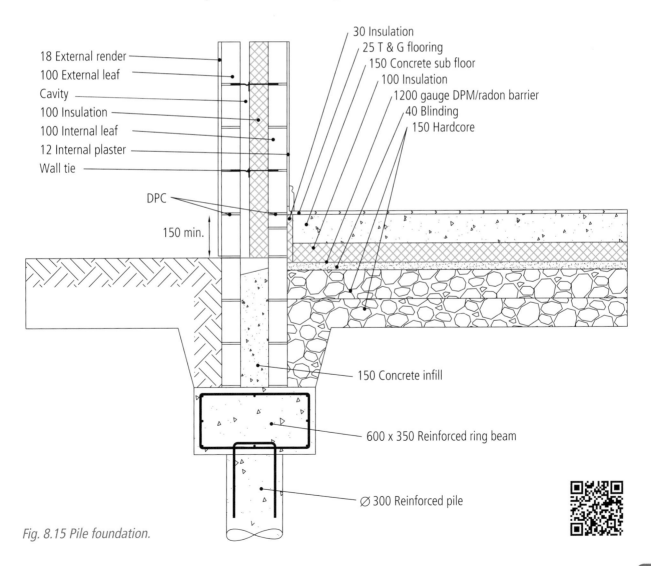

18 External render
100 External leaf
Cavity
100 Insulation
100 Internal leaf
12 Internal plaster
Wall tie

DPC
150 min.

30 Insulation
25 T & G flooring
150 Concrete sub floor
100 Insulation
1200 gauge DPM/radon barrier
40 Blinding
150 Hardcore

150 Concrete infill
600 x 350 Reinforced ring beam
Ø 300 Reinforced pile

Fig. 8.15 Pile foundation.

It is important to note that with pile foundations the piles cannot be placed under window or door opes (openings in the blockwork or panel). They must be placed on either side of prospective opes in order to prevent failure in the structure.

Detailed diagrams of a pile foundation are shown in Figs 8.14 and 8.15.

There are three types of pile foundation:

- End-bearing piles
- Friction piles
- Short-bored piles.

End-bearing piles are driven down until they hit a stratum of solid soil. The ground beam is then poured around the tops of the piles. Fig. 8.16 shows an end-bearing pile.

Friction piles are driven into the ground until the friction between the surface of the pile and the surrounding soil reaches a point where the pile can no longer be moved. Each of these piles is a different length. The tops of the piles are cut and the ground beam is then poured. Fig. 8.17 shows a friction pile.

Both the end-bearing pile and the friction pile are driven into the soil using heavy machinery. The piles are precast, and the top of each pile is capped with steel to prevent damage as it is driven into the ground.

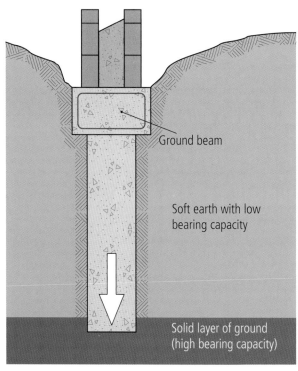

Fig. 8.16 End-bearing pile.

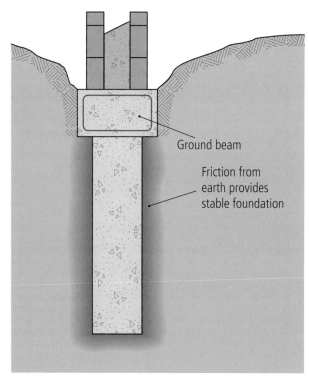

Fig. 8.17 Friction pile.

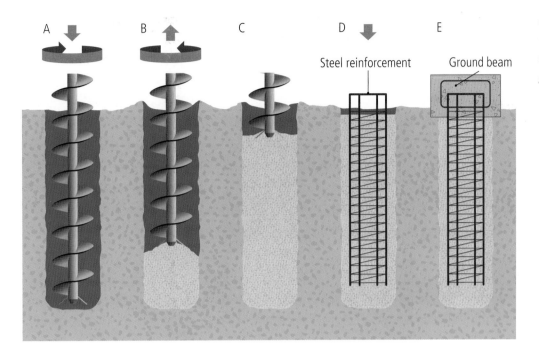

Fig. 8.18 Construction of a short-bore pile.

Short-bore piles are made on site to a maximum depth of 4.5m. A hole is drilled through the ground and concrete is poured in. Steel reinforcement is pushed down through the wet concrete, reinforcing the pile. Reinforcing bars are left protruding from the top of the pile. The ground beam is then tied to the pile with more reinforcing bars.

This type of pile foundation is suitable for house building as loadings placed on the piles are not as large as those of bigger buildings. Further advantages of this type of foundation are that it can be constructed quickly, it wastes very little material, and the work can proceed in bad weather. Fig. 8.18 shows the process by which the short-bore pile foundation is created.

SETTING OUT FOUNDATIONS

Setting out the foundations is an important job and must be done accurately.

First the building line is located; this is the line that contains the front face of the build. A 90-degree line is set up from the building line; this line gives the position of the side walls. The location of the corners of the build are measured and marked with steel pegs. These markings are compared to the building plans to ensure that the measurements match. Once the measurements are verified, profile boards are made up. Profile boards are used as a guide in setting out the foundations. The boards mark the location and width of the foundations. Setting-out lines are used in conjunction with the boards to provide a template to keep foundation lines straight and walls in line.

The boards are kept back from the building in order to allow room for machinery later on. Fig. 8.19 shows profile boards at a later stage of the build.

The width of the foundation as well as the width of the wall is marked on the board using saw cuts or nails.

Fig. 8.19 Profile board.

DIGGING FOUNDATIONS

Before excavating the foundations, all topsoil is removed from the entire site. Foundation trenches are dug using heavy plant machinery. The profile boards are used as a guide for the operator as they dig the trench down to the required depth. The base of the deepest part of the trench must be below the frost line to prevent freezing and thawing of the foundation.

The bottom of the trench needs to be clean, dry, compacted and level before the concrete is poured. Pegs are stuck into the base of the trench to show the finished height of the foundation.

Fig. 8.20 Rebar chairs, steel mesh and concrete in the foundations.

REINFORCING FOUNDATIONS

Concrete is strong in compression but weak in tension. This means that when the weight of walls is applied to a concrete foundation, it will crack and fail at the underside face. However, steel is a material that is strong in tension, and combining the two materials creates a foundation that is strong both in compression and in tension. The steel is placed where the tensile strength of the concrete is weakest, which is at the base of the foundation.

The steel used to reinforce foundations takes many forms. Most commonly it is made up as separate bars, grids or cages. The reinforcing process starts by placing reinforcing bar chairs along the base of the trench. The steel mesh or cage is placed on top. The chairs keep the steel off the ground, which ensures that the cage is completely surrounded by concrete. Surrounding the steel with concrete not only prevents the steel from corroding as a result of rust, it also optimises the strength of the base of the foundation.

POURING FOUNDATIONS

With the trench dug and the steel in place, it is time to pour the foundation. Lorry-loads of ready-mixed concrete are brought on site and poured into the trenches. The concrete is poured until the level rises to the top of the pegs installed earlier. Then the top surface is screeded. This is done using a screed – a straight edge held by two people — which is pushed along the surface of the concrete, levelling the concrete and removing any air bubbles trapped in it. The screeding must be done immediately after the concrete is poured, because the concrete begins to set after two to three hours. The foundation should be left for at least seven days to set properly and become hard and strong enough to support weight.

SETTLEMENT OF FOUNDATIONS

Settlement is the downward movement of the building to a point below its original position. This is generally caused by a change in the condition of the soil where the foundation is placed. Settlement can happen over many years. It is not something that only affects new buildings.

There are generally two different types of settlement:

- **Total settlement:** This is where the building uniformly settles to a point below where it began when constructed.

- **Differential settlement:** This is where an element or part of the structure settles or moves below the rest of the structure. This type of settlement can cause distortion and structural defects in the building.

No settlement   Total settlement   Differential settlement

Fig. 8.21 Settlement of a building: no settlement, total settlement and differential settlement.

Settlement can be caused by a number of factors:

- **Consolidation of soil:** The soil underneath the structure becomes more dense as the water that was in the ground is squeezed out by compression pressure.

- **Removal of water from the soil:** Water can also be displaced from soil by nearby trees (see Fig. 8.22 below).

- **Plastic flow of soil from under the building:** As a result of pressure from the building, a solid mass (such as clay) is formed under the structure.

- **Cohesive soils bulging:** The weight of a buildling can cause silty soils to bulge.

- **Soil erosion by wind or water:** Erosion on the side of a foundation can weaken the structure.

- **Frost heave:** The freezing and thawing of water in the ground causes the soil to shift, which can cause settlement.

BUILDING NEAR TREES

Trees are an attractive element of many sites, and preserving mature trees helps a new build blend with its surroundings. Wherever possible, trees should be retained.

However, although they are aesthetically pleasing, trees are not welcome too close to a house. Trees absorb large amounts of water from the soil around them. When a tree is too close to a house, its roots suck moisture from under the foundations, causing shrinkage, which can make the structure unsound and lead to cracks on the façade of the building.

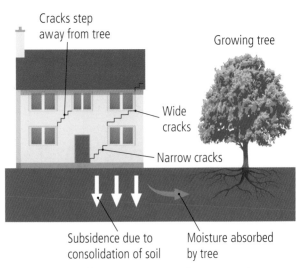

Fig. 8.22 The effect the presence of a tree can have on a building's foundation.

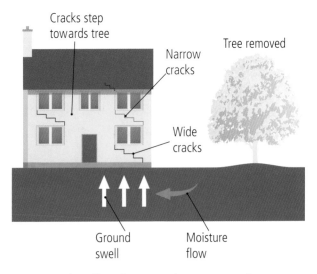

Fig. 8.23 The effect that removing a tree can have on a building's foundation.

Removing the tree is not always the best solution, as the area where the tree stood can now fill with water, which causes the ground to swell. This effect, which is called heave, can lead to cracks on the building's façade.

Where a developer wants to keep existing trees or plant new ones, there is a simple rule of thumb to follow. In order to prevent the problems of swelling or shrinkage, the mature height of the tree (the height it will be when fully grown) is researched. The minimum distance from the building to the tree must be equal to its mature height.

EFFECTS OF FROST

Water beneath the surface of the ground can freeze in cold weather and form ice. When the ice expands, it forces the soil apart. Over the course of a cold season, this movement of the soil can lift the foundations. When the ground thaws the foundations may settle, though not necessarily in their exact original position. If this process, known as frost heave, continues for a number of seasons, the action can cause major structural problems.

PYRITE

Pyrite is a mineral that may be found in the hardcore of a foundation. When exposed to moisture it reacts to form sulfuric acid, which in turn reacts with calcium carbonates in the hardcore. Over time this leads to swelling and results in the lifting of internal floor slabs and the interior structural supports resting on them.

PRACTICE QUESTIONS

1. List the functions of a foundation.
2. Describe what is meant by the term 'bulb of pressure'.
3. What are the main foundation types used in the Irish construction industry?
4. Using notes and neat freehand sketches, describe the different types of strip foundation.
5. Sketch a neat freehand diagram of a raft foundation, and indicate the typical dimensions on your diagram.
6. Using notes and neat freehand sketches, describe the difference between an end-bearing pile foundation and a friction pile foundation.
7. Describe the steps involved in constructing short-bored piles for foundations.
8. List the steps involved in setting out foundations.
9. Why are foundations reinforced and how is this done?
10. Name three factors that can affect a foundation years after it has been poured.

SAMPLE EXAMINATION QUESTIONS

2012 Ordinary Level Question 4 (a)

A strip foundation is designed to support a 350 mm external wall of a dwelling house. The wall is of concrete block construction with an insulated cavity, as shown in the sketch.

(a) Describe, using notes and neat freehand sketches, the design of a typical strip foundation for the above external wall under the following headings:
- width and depth of trench
- finished level of concrete in foundation
- reinforcement of foundation
- position of wall on strip foundation.

2009 Higher Level Question 2

(a) Discuss in detail **two** functional requirements of a foundation for a dwelling house.

(b) Using notes and *freehand sketches* show **three** different foundation types suitable for a dwelling house. Show the position of the reinforcing and indicate typical dimensions of each foundation type.

(c) Discuss **two** factors that must be taken into account to ensure the maximum strength of concrete in a foundation.

2008 Ordinary Level Question 2

Strip foundations are widely used for modern dwelling houses.

(a) Using notes and neat freehand sketches, show the construction of a strip foundation for the external wall of a dwelling house.
Include the following in your sketch:
- depth of trench;
- width of foundation;
- thickness of foundation;
- position of a 300 mm wall on the foundation.

(b) On your sketch, show one design detail to ensure that the foundation is strong enough to support the external wall and the roof of the house. Include two typical dimensions.

FLOORS AND RADON

LEARNING OUTCOME:

After studying this chapter students will:

- Understand what radon gas is, where it occurs, and name and describe the methods of protecting against it.
- Illustrate various ground floor types, describe their advantages and disadvantages and graphically describe how they are constructed.
- Describe how upper floors are constructed and the different methods used.

KEYWORDS:

- RADON • URANIUM • RADIUM • RADIOACTIVE • BARRIER • FLOORS
- SUSPENDED • SOLID • CONCRETE • TIMBER • INSULATION • DPM • DPC
- SUB FLOOR • HARDCORE • DWARF WALL • WALL PLATE • JOISTS
- SOLID BRIDGING • HERRINGBONE STRUTTING

INTRODUCTION

Floors have many functions. They distribute loads as well as protecting from:

- Radon gas
- Dampness
- Cold
- Draughts.

They must be level, durable and relatively maintenance free. Floors must be built bearing all these elements in mind. Most building systems deal with each of these issues separately.

RADON

Uranium is a radioactive material that generates radium as it decays. Radon gas is a product of this decay. Radon is a naturally occurring radioactive gas, and it is tasteless, odourless and colourless, making it extremely difficult to detect without specialist equipment. Radon testers provided by the Radiological Protection Institute of Ireland (RPII) are used to test for the build-up of radon in homes. Fig. 9.1 shows an image of radon testers.

Fig. 9.1 Radon detectors.

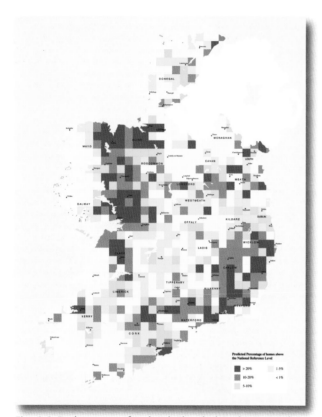

Fig. 9.2 Radon map of Ireland. The darker the area, the greater number of homes above the Reference Level.

Fig. 9.3 A large plastic layer is laid out over the base of the building to provide an airtight ground envelope.

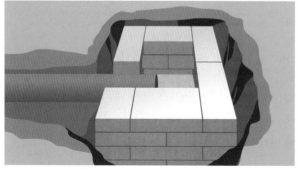

Fig. 9.4 A void can be made up with loosely stacked blocks, which are subsequently covered over.

When radon is allowed to rise through the earth's surface, it is diluted in the atmosphere and poses little or no danger. However, when radon builds up in an enclosed space, such as a house, it can cause severe health problems. It has been linked to an increased risk of developing lung cancer, for example. Radon levels vary throughout the country. The most up-to-date records are kept by the RPII, which monitors radon levels in existing buildings. Fig. 9.2 shows a map of radon concentration in Ireland.

Radon typically enters a building through:

- Cracks in walls and floors
- Gaps in floors and around any service pipes protruding from the floor
- Junctions between floors and walls.

There are two methods of protecting a new house against radon build-up. These are:

- **Passive system:** The whole ground floor plan of the building is sealed with an airtight polythene sheet installed by a specialist. Because the sheet is airtight it prevents the entry of radon gas. This radon barrier is usually 4µm gauge (Fig. 9.3).

- **Active system:** A sump is installed in the hardcore during the early stages of the build. The sump is a void or container set deep in the hardcore of the foundations, as in Fig. 9.4. Because it has lower pressure than its surroundings, the void draws gases into the sump. The gases can then flow through ventilation pipes or cavities connected to the sump which lead outside the building (Fig. 9.5). A fan can also be installed to increase ventilation (Fig. 9.7). As well as a sump, the active system also uses the airtight polythene sheet described under 'Passive system'.

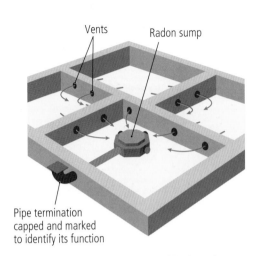

Vents
Radon sump

Pipe termination capped and marked to identify its function

Fig. 9.5 Cavities or vents in the blockwork are used to direct radon gas out of the building.

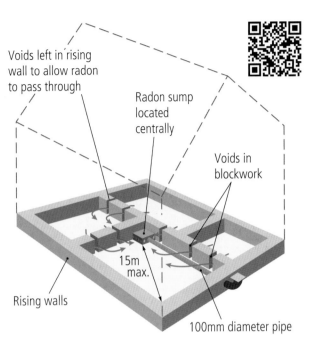

Voids left in rising wall to allow radon to pass through

Radon sump located centrally

Voids in blockwork

Rising walls

15m max.

100mm diameter pipe

CHAPTER 9

Fig. 9.6 Typical location for a sump in a single home. Note that this method uses voids in the blockwork. Each home must have its own sump and means of extraction if needed.

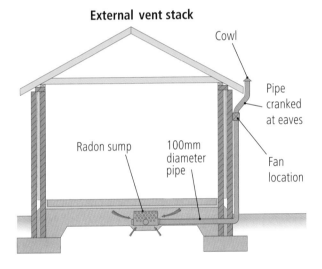

External vent stack

Cowl

Pipe cranked at eaves

Radon sump

100mm diameter pipe

Fan location

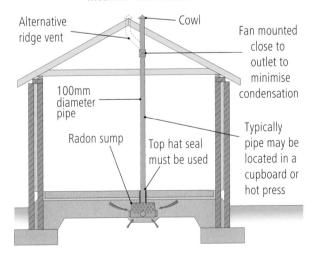

Internal vent stack

Alternative ridge vent

Cowl

Fan mounted close to outlet to minimise condensation

100mm diameter pipe

Radon sump

Top hat seal must be used

Typically pipe may be located in a cupboard or hot press

Fig. 9.7 Typical layouts if a fan is required for the system.

A National Reference Level of 200 becquerels per cubic metre (200Bq/m³) has been established as a guideline. Levels above this require remedial action, such as fitting an active system in a home. The active system is recommended because it incorporates mechanical ventilation as well as using the polythene sheet described under 'Passive system'.

It is much harder to protect against radon gas in existing buildings. First, all cracks, gaps and junctions must be sealed to prevent the gas entering the building. A construction-grade silicone sealant is suitable as it sticks to most surfaces, is easy to apply and allows for movement without breaking. A sump can also be installed as close to the building as possible. This large, empty space draws the radon, which is then ventilated as described earlier. It is even more effective to install the sump as if the building were a new build. To do this in an existing dwelling, the cavity wall is broken from the outside, creating an

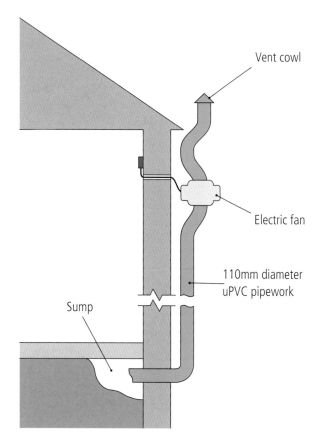

Fig. 9.8 Integrating a sump into an existing building.

Fig. 9.9 Top hat seal – an adjustable clip around the outside needs to be added to ensure a gas-tight seal.

empty space where the radon can build up, and a pipe is installed to ventilate the gas. Fig. 9.8 shows how a radon sump can be integrated into an existing building.

Where any service pipes or cables pass through the radon barrier, a proprietary 'top hat' seal should be used. Double-sided sealing tape is placed around the service pipe, and the top hat is then installed, and tightened with an adjustable clip around the circumference of the pipe. This provides a gas-tight seal between the membrane and the top hat seal (Fig. 9.9).

GROUND FLOORS

The ground floor rests at the level of the soil surrounding the house. Floors at this level have several requirements. They must:

- Resist damp
- Prevent heat loss from inside to outside
- Be hard-wearing
- Be level
- Be durable
- Be maintenance-free.

Experiment: Resisting damp

CONTEXT OF EXPERIMENT:

It is important that water is not able to travel up from the underlying soil to the inside fabric of the house. Dampness rises through capillary action. Capillary action is the ability of liquid to flow through narrow spaces without being hindered by gravity. In order to see capillary action and how it works, do the following experiment.

EQUIPMENT NEEDED:

Plastic tray, food colouring, three drinking straws of different diameters.

STEP 1

Fill a small transparent tray with water. Add food colouring to make the water levels easier to see.

STEP 2

Take three straws of different diameters. Hold each straw in the tray of water.

STEP 3

Note the height of water in each straw in relation to its diameter. Your results should be similar to those in Fig. 9.10.

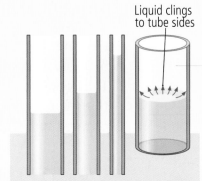

Fig. 9.10 Note the different levels the water reaches in the straws. This demonstrates capillary action.

OBSERVATIONS:

- The water in the tray climbed upwards in all three straws.
- The water climbed highest up the straw with the smallest diameter.
- The water climbed least in the straw with the largest diameter.

From the results outlined above, it can be determined that the less air made available (thinnest straw), the higher the water will climb; and the more air made available (largest straw), the lower the water climbs. Therefore, if there are large air gaps in the hardcore filling, moisture will not be able to climb as high as if there were many small gaps. Fig. 9.11 shows the same process of capillary action as it affects concrete blocks.

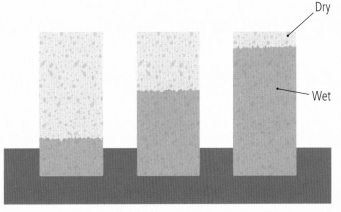

Fig. 9.11 Over time the block soaks up more and more water through capillary action.

CHAPTER 9

PREVENTING HEAT LOSS

Heat loss is a major problem in buildings. Heating a dwelling of any kind is costly, so designing a floor to prevent heat from escaping through to the ground beneath saves money in the long run. Insulation is used in floors (as well as other locations in the build) to prevent heat loss. Insulation is discussed in detail in Chapter 17.

HARD WEARING

Because it has to deal with a lot of traffic, the ground floor needs to be hard wearing. The kitchen, in particular, which is usually on the ground floor, is a high-use area and therefore needs to have a suitable finish, for example tiles. The living area is associated with comfort, and although a lot of time is spent in this room, the level of traffic passing through is lower, so a soft finish like a carpet is suitable.

CONSTRUCTION OF GROUND FLOORS

The ground floor is an important construction. Ground floors must be built on a solid base. The base consists of several layers and materials. The main features of the base depend on the type of floor being constructed.

The two main types of floor are solid floors and suspended floors.

SOLID FLOORS

Solid floors are cast on site and are finished with a smooth concrete surface. The layers that make up a solid concrete ground floor are:

Hardcore: This is the section that lies directly on top of the soil. It consists of compacted stones of the same grade (size). Hardcore must be clean and free from gravel, clay and mud. This layer is a minimum of 150mm. Where the depth is to be larger, layers of a maximum of 225mm are compacted to finished depth. Each layer must be no deeper than 225mm or the bottom of the layer will not be compacted.

Blinding: Blinding is a layer of sand (usually 40mm deep) placed on top of the hardcore. It is used to fill any surface voids in the hardcore and to prevent any sharp stones tearing the radon barrier or damp proof membrane (DPM).

Radon barrier/DPM and DPC: A radon barrier is needed to prevent radon gas from entering the building. A damp proof membrane (DPM) is used in the same way to prevent any moisture seeping up from the foundations to the floors of the building, and a damp proof course (DPC) is used to prevent moisture travelling upwards through block walls. A DPC is installed into the blockwork as the wall is constructed. It is provided in rolls of varying width to a thickness of 0.375mm. A DPM and radon barrier can essentially be the same membrane product. They are: a 4µm gauge polythene sheet, which is both airtight and watertight. It is essential that there are no rips or tears in this membrane.

The sheet (membrane) acts to prevent damp rising from the ground to the inside floor of the building. It is laid on the blinding and over the walls so that it is lapped by the DPC, which is built into the blockwork of the inner and outer leaves of the cavity wall. Not only does this prevent moisture from climbing to the inner leaf, it also prevents any radon building up within the cavity of the wall. The DPC must be a minimum height of 150mm above the ground level around the building.

Insulation: Rigid insulation is placed on top of the radon barrier/DPM. This prevents heat escaping through the finished floor into the ground. Under current building regulations, there must be at least 100mm of rigid insulation in a solid concrete ground floor. Insulation is also placed vertically along the internal leaf of cavity walls to prevent heat being lost through the blockwork.

Sub floor: The sub floor is a layer of concrete poured over the top of the insulation and levelled. The sub floor is 150mm thick.

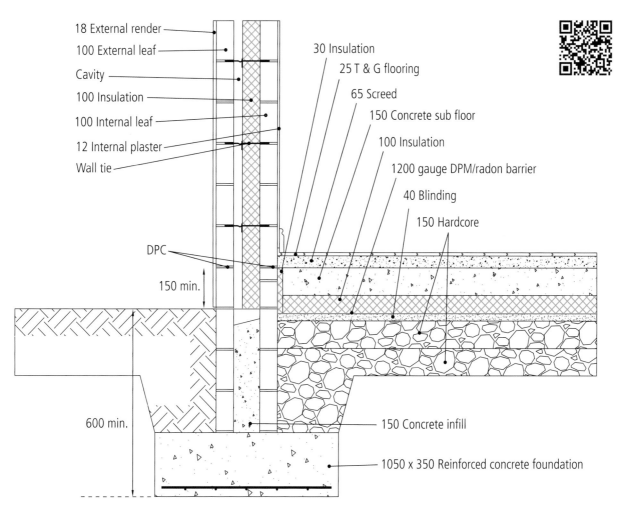

Fig. 9.12 Solid concrete floor.

Screed: The screed is the final layer of the ground floor. It is optional: some builders use the sub floor as the final layer. The finished surface – tiles, wooden floor, etc. – will be laid on top of this. The screed is generally a thin layer of concrete, and because it is so thin it is often reinforced with steel mesh at the base. The mix for the screed is 1:3 cement:dry sand.

Where underfloor heating is used, the pipes are clipped to the rigid insulation and the screed is poured straight on top of the pipes, with no reinforcement necessary. The screed must be a minimum thickness of 50mm where it meets the wall. Where the screed is floating and meets the insulation lining the wall, it must be a minimum thickness of 65mm.

Figs 9.12 and 9.13 show the elements of solid concrete floors in detail.

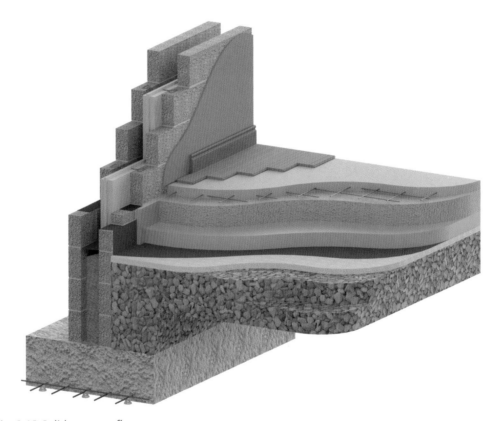

Fig. 9.13 Solid concrete floor.

SUSPENDED FLOORS

A suspended floor is used where it is not practical to construct a solid floor. This may happen because too much fill is needed, because a solid floor is prone to cracking when the fill is not compacted enough. Too much fill can also be costly.

A suspended floor is supported by a number of dwarf walls, hangers, or the inner leaf of the cavity wall. Suspended floors make it easier to install services

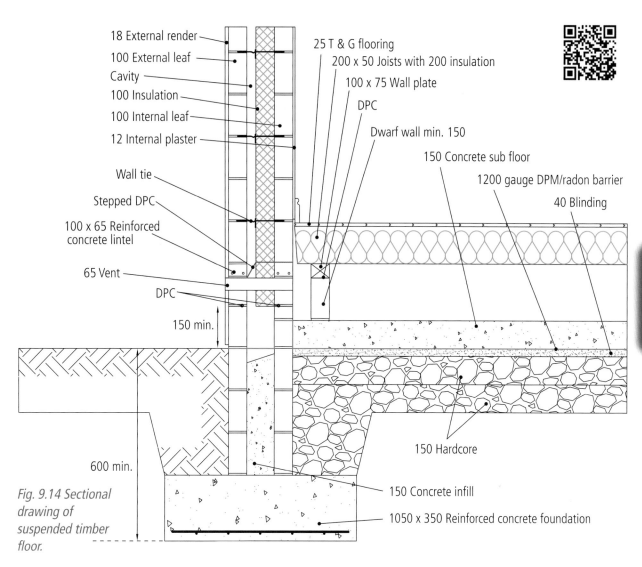

18 External render
100 External leaf
Cavity
100 Insulation
100 Internal leaf
12 Internal plaster

Wall tie
Stepped DPC
100 x 65 Reinforced concrete lintel
65 Vent
DPC
150 min.
600 min.

25 T & G flooring
200 x 50 Joists with 200 insulation
100 x 75 Wall plate
DPC
Dwarf wall min. 150
150 Concrete sub floor
1200 gauge DPM/radon barrier
40 Blinding
150 Hardcore
150 Concrete infill
1050 x 350 Reinforced concrete foundation

Fig. 9.14 Sectional drawing of suspended timber floor.

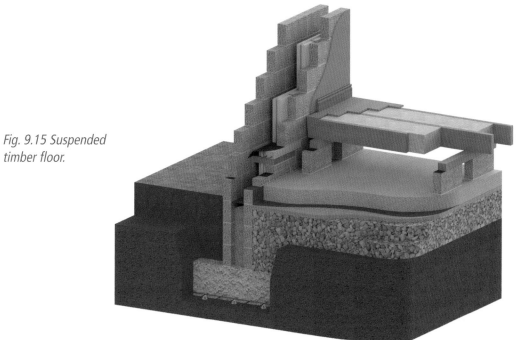

Fig. 9.15 Suspended timber floor.

as they will not be encased in concrete, as they would be in a solid floor. There are a number of types of suspended floor: the main ones are discussed below.

Suspended Timber Floor

A suspended timber ground floor sits on joists (lengths of wood 200 x 50mm) spanning the width of the ground floor of the building. Traditionally the joists were supported at intervals of 2m by dwarf walls, low walls that the planks rest on. Nowadays, metal hangers are more commonly used. They are built into the inner leaf of the cavity wall at the height set for the joists. Using hangers to hold the joists is both cheaper and quicker than providing walls to support them.

The layers involved where dwarf walls are to be used are as follows:

Hardcore: Hardcore is laid as for a solid floor. A maximum of 900mm of hardcore may be used where a suspended ground floor is to be constructed. The hardcore must be well compacted.

Radon barrier: A radon barrier is required in order to prevent a build-up of radon gas underneath the floor. The specifications for this barrier are the same as for a solid floor (described earlier).

Concrete slab: A 150mm concrete slab is poured on top of the compacted hardcore. This slab provides a level surface on which to construct the dwarf walls. The top of the concrete slab must be higher than the ground level around the dwelling. If the slab is below ground level, the area inside will fill with moisture, which will never have an opportunity to drain away.

Dwarf walls: Dwarf walls, sometimes called sleeper or tassel walls, are used to support the joists that span the width of the dwelling. They prevent the joists sagging and allow air to circulate underneath the floor. The walls are built in a honeycomb fashion, leaving space between blocks to provide ventilation. The area underneath the floor must be ventilated to prevent the timber developing rot. The minimum height of a dwarf wall is 150mm.

Damp proof course: The damp proof course (DPC) is similar to the damp proof membrane (DPM), but rather than being a large sheet it is bought in thin rolls, slightly wider than a block. It is used for the same purpose as the DPM – to prevent moisture rising into the fabric of the house. DPC is rolled out across the top of the dwarf wall, and a layer is also built into the outer leaf of the cavity block.

Wall plate: The wall plate is a piece of timber (75 x 100mm) that is skew nailed (nailed at an angle) into the dwarf wall. The floor joists rest on the top of the wall plate.

Joists: The joists rest on the wall plate, at a perpendicular angle, and are not built in to the inner leaf of the cavity wall. The ends are sawn at an angle to prevent damage and are treated with preservative. They are placed at 400mm centres – that is, the distance from the centre of one joist to the centre of the next one is 400mm.

Vents: Vents are used to allow air to circulate underneath the floor. They are positioned strategically around the building to allow maximum air flow. Generally a 100mm diameter pipe or plastic grid is used across both the inner and outer leaf to allow air to flow in and out of the space (Fig. 9.16).

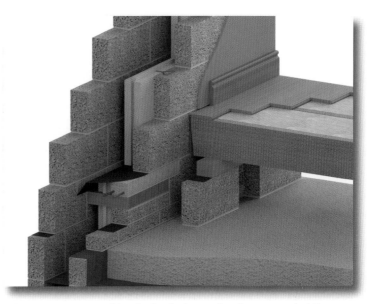

Fig. 9.16 Vents provide air circulation under the suspended floor.

Insulation: There are two methods of insulating a suspended timber floor. The first method is to hold quilted insulation in place using netting. The second method is to fix battens to the sides of the joists to support rigid insulation boards. Both methods are shown in Fig. 9.17. Whichever method is used, the insulation must conform to current building regulations.

Floorboards: 25mm tongue-and-groove floorboards can be fitted straight on to the joists, as in Fig. 9.17 (left).

Carpet: Where a carpet is to be laid on a suspended timber floor, the floor must first be sheeted with manufactured boards to provide an even, level surface, as in Fig. 9.17 (right).

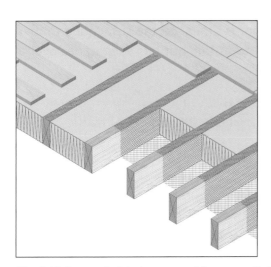
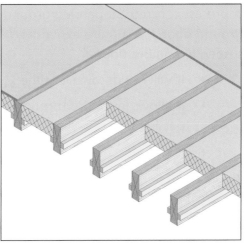

Fig. 9.17 Suspended timber ground floor. LEFT: Quilted insulation held in place by netting stapled to the joists. RIGHT: Rigid insulation boards supported on battens nailed to the joists.

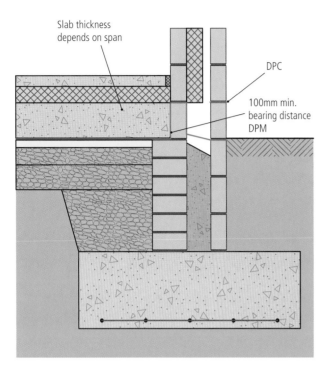

Fig. 9.18 Vertical section of suspended concrete slab with floating screed. The slab is cast on site and is suspended over the rising walls.

Suspended Concrete Slab

A suspended concrete slab ground floor is a lot heavier than a suspended timber floor. Because of the weights and stresses involved in suspending a concrete slab, the supporting members (i.e. the rising walls – the blockwork between the foundation and ground level) must be reinforced. The inner leaf of the rising wall is under more pressure than it would be with a lighter floor. For this reason the inner leaf of the rising wall is constructed with the blocks lying flat. This gives the suspended slab more surface area to come into contact with, spreading the downward pressure.

The construction of a suspended concrete slab ground floor follows exactly the same layers as the solid floor up to the insulation layer. The insulation is laid directly on top of the slab, with an infill piece against the internal leaf of the cavity wall. Reinforcement is positioned where the bottom of the slab will be, and the slab is then poured. Where a load-bearing wall is to be built on top of the slab, additional reinforcement is necessary at both the top and bottom of the slab to prevent it cracking and even failing. Fig. 9.18 shows the details of a suspended concrete slab floor.

Precast Concrete Suspended Floors

A precast concrete suspended ground floor is similar to the suspended timber ground floor. It is a more expensive floor to install, but has advantages over a suspended timber floor:

- It will not decay over time
- It allows less noise through, for example the rumble of traffic passing by
- It excludes draughts.

The finished floor will leave a void underneath the house, which must be vented as described earlier. When using a floor of this type, insulation is usually placed on, between or around the supporting beams. Some different examples of precast concrete suspended ground floors are shown in Fig. 9.19.

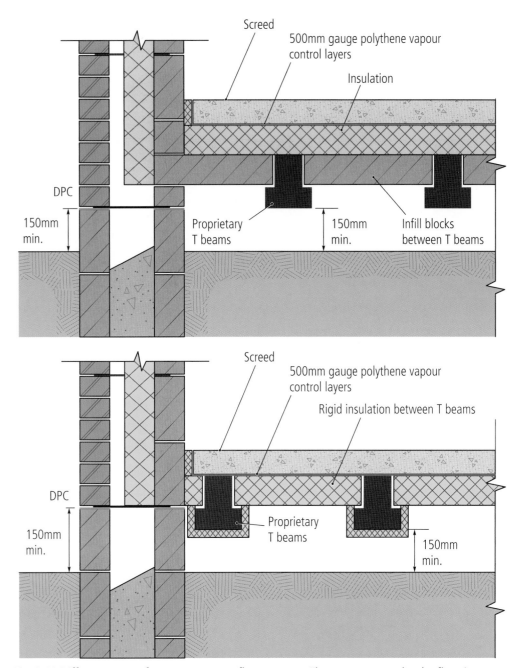

Fig. 9.19 Different types of precast concrete floor systems. The open area under the floor is vented in the same way as a suspended timber floor.

LINKED FLOORS

On a site with different levels, it is possible that both types of floor described above – a suspended timber floor and a suspended concrete slab – are used, and linked together. At the construction stage, 100mm-diameter pipes are installed in the solid concrete floor side, to allow the cross-ventilation of the suspended floors. It is important to ensure that the finished floors are the same level. The thickness of each floor layer is planned before construction to ensure that they are flush when they are built. Details of how these floor types are linked are shown in Fig. 9.20.

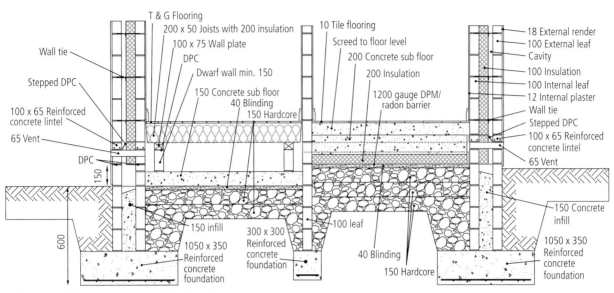

Wall tie

Stepped DPC

100 x 65 Reinforced concrete lintel

65 Vent

DPC

150

600

T & G Flooring
200 x 50 Joists with 200 insulation
100 x 75 Wall plate
DPC
Dwarf wall min. 150
150 Concrete sub floor
40 Blinding
150 Hardcore

150 infill

1050 x 350 Reinforced concrete foundation

300 x 300 Reinforced concrete foundation

10 Tile flooring
Screed to floor level
200 Concrete sub floor
200 Insulation
1200 gauge DPM/radon barrier

100 leaf

40 Blinding

150 Hardcore

18 External render
100 External leaf
Cavity
100 Insulation
100 Internal leaf
12 Internal plaster
Wall tie
Stepped DPC
100 x 65 Reinforced concrete lintel
65 Vent

150 Concrete infill

1050 x 350 Reinforced concrete foundation

Fig. 9.20 Different methods of linking floors.

UPPER FLOORS

Upper floors must meet the same requirements as ground floors: they must be durable, level and hard wearing. As well as this, they must limit sound transmission from upper rooms to lower ones. Traditionally, upper floors are constructed with timber. It is becoming increasingly popular to install concrete or steel upper floors, though this can only be done when the load-bearing capacity of the foundation is able to support the additional weight.

TIMBER UPPER FLOORS

Where upper floors are laid using timber, joists are used to spread the weight of the floor. The joists measure 200 x 50mm and are spaced at 400mm centres. Both ends of the joist are supported on load-bearing walls. The ends of the joist are treated with preservative in order to prevent decay. The joists are laid so that they span the shortest distance between the walls or supports. Joists can either be built into the blockwork or supported using metal hangers, as shown in Fig. 9.21.

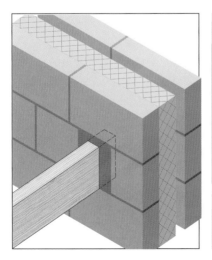 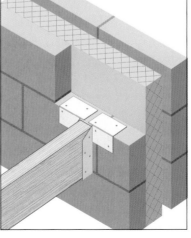

Fig. 9.21 LEFT: Joist built into the inner leaf of the external load-bearing wall.
RIGHT: Joist is secured to the wall using a joist hanger made of galvanised steel.

Due to their span, timber joists have a tendency to move and/or twist. Bridging is used to prevent this. There are two bridging techniques used in timber upper floors: solid bridging and herringbone strutting.

Solid Bridging

Solid bridging consists of vertically fixed short boards (struts), which are fixed either in line or staggered. The method used will depend on the carpenter carrying out the work. Where the struts are in line, they must be skew nailed to stay in place. Where the struts are staggered, the worker is more easily able to nail them in place. Both methods are shown in Fig. 9.22.

Strutting of the joists occurs halfway along the span, or more frequently if the span is wider. Packing is used between the joists and the walls to prevent movement between the wall and the floor.

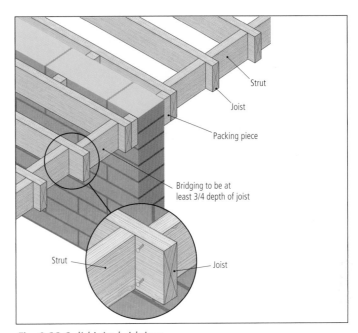

Fig. 9.22 Solid joist bridging:
LEFT staggered bridging, RIGHT in line bridging.

Herringbone Strutting

Herringbone strutting can be constructed using timber or steel struts. The struts measure at least 36 x 36mm. Two struts are used in the space between joists, each one fixed to the bottom of one joist and the top of the other. As with solid bridging, it is necessary to pack the area between the joists and the wall. The technique is shown graphically in Fig. 9.23.

There are a number of advantages to using herringbone strutting rather than solid bridging. If the joists shrink, the herringbone strutting will remain pressed against them, whereas gaps will appear between the struts and the joists in solid bridging. Less wood is used in

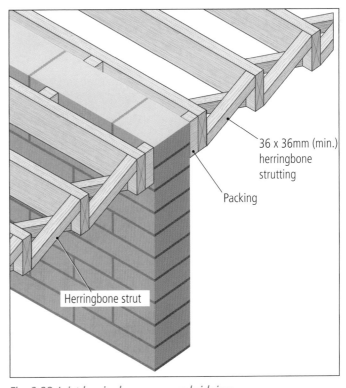

Fig. 9.23 Joist herringbone or cross bridging.

CHAPTER 9

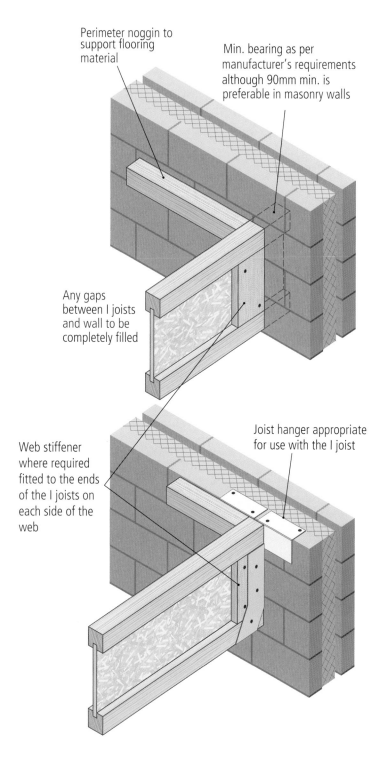

Perimeter noggin to support flooring material

Min. bearing as per manufacturer's requirements although 90mm min. is preferable in masonry walls

Any gaps between I joists and wall to be completely filled

Web stiffener where required fitted to the ends of the I joists on each side of the web

Joist hanger appropriate for use with the I joist

Fig. 9.24 Beam end-bearing details of the I joist. The notching and accommodation of services through these beams should follow manufacturers' specifications.

herringbone strutting, and it is easy to pass electrical cables and plumbing between the joists. The main drawback with this method is that it demands a great deal of time and labour.

I Joists

I joists are engineered joists that can be used as an alternative to traditional timber jointing. They are constructed using two solid timber or laminated veneered lumber (LVL) members on the top and bottom of the beam. The I joists act as a flange or groove for a panel of orientated strand board (OSB), which is placed in the groove of the top and bottom members. Like solid timber joists, they can be housed internally within the wall or suspended from wall hangers, as seen in Fig. 9.24.

CONCRETE AND STEEL UPPER FLOORS

Concrete and steel upper floors can both reduce noise transmission and make it easier to install services between floors. There are a number of methods used in each of these floor constructions. Figs 9.25 and 9.26 show different methods of creating upper floors using concrete and steel. The materials can be used individually or in combination.

Concrete and steel floors have become more popular due to their sound insulation properties, and because they make it much easier to install underfloor heating in upstairs rooms.

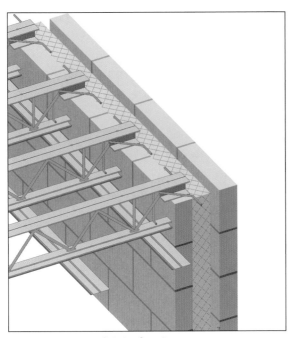

Fig. 9.25 Open web joist framing.

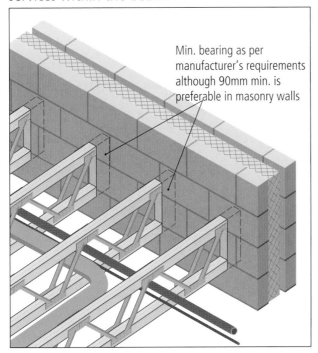

Timber and Steel Open Web Joist

A different type of engineered joist is an open web joist. This joist is a lightweight alternative to a pure steel truss. It consists typically of two members of timber, similar to the flanges in the I joists, with a triangular web between them, which is convenient for the accommodation of services within the beam.

Span of precast slab

Fig. 9.26 Precast floor sections.

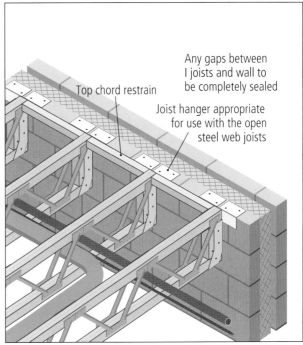

Min. bearing as per manufacturer's requirements although 90mm min. is preferable in masonry walls

Any gaps between I joists and wall to be completely sealed

Top chord restrain

Joist hanger appropriate for use with the open steel web joists

Fig. 9.27 End-bearing details for timber and steel open web joist. Services can be easily accommodated through the open web.

CHAPTER 9

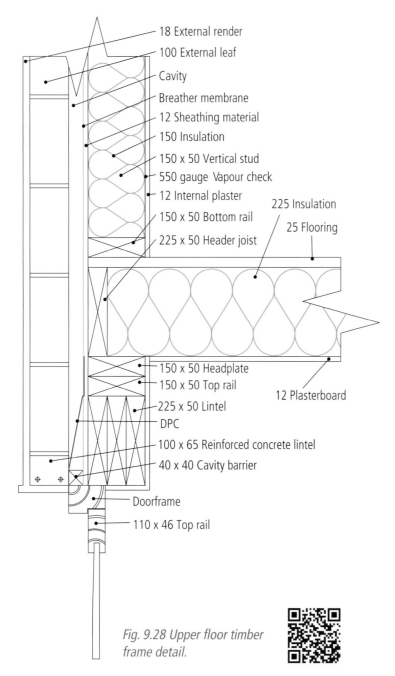

18 External render
100 External leaf
Cavity
Breather membrane
12 Sheathing material
150 Insulation
150 x 50 Vertical stud
550 gauge Vapour check
12 Internal plaster
150 x 50 Bottom rail
225 x 50 Header joist
225 Insulation
25 Flooring
150 x 50 Headplate
150 x 50 Top rail
12 Plasterboard
225 x 50 Lintel
DPC
100 x 65 Reinforced concrete lintel
40 x 40 Cavity barrier
Doorframe
110 x 46 Top rail

Fig. 9.28 Upper floor timber frame detail.

TIMBER FRAME UPPER FLOORS

In timber frame construction, the upper floors are constructed differently. With timber frame builds, the upper joists are built into the interior leaf of the cavity wall. The details, along with typical dimensions and specifications, are shown in Fig. 9.28.

FLOOR COVERING

There are many types of floor finish or covering, and it is important to use the materials that are most appropriate for different parts of the building. Floors may need to be:

- **Hard wearing:** Areas with high traffic will need hard-wearing and durable covering.

- **Moisture resistant:** Some areas may need surfaces to be sealed and moisture resistant, for example the bathroom and kitchen.

- **Low maintenance:** Coverings should not require constant upkeep.

- **Hygienic:** Some areas in the home may need surfaces that are easy to keep clean.

There are many different types of floor covering, among them:

- **Natural stone:** Including marble, granite, slate
- **Tiles:** Quarry, baked clay, cork, ceramic, thermoplastic
- **Wood:** Solid or laminated
- **Sheet flooring:** Linoleums, vinyl, carpet
- **Seamless chemical flooring:** Usually latex, polyester, urethane or epoxy compounds
- **Polished concrete:** Concrete can be ground and polished to give a high-quality finish.

PRACTICE QUESTIONS

1. What is radon?

2. Why must buildings be protected from radon?

3. Describe using notes and neat freehand sketches the difference between the active and passive systems used to deal with radon.

4. What are the functions of a ground floor?

5. To a scale of 1:10 draw a section through a solid concrete ground floor. Indicate on your drawing all typical dimensions and specifications.

6. To a scale of 1:10 draw a section through a timber suspended ground floor. Indicate on your drawing all typical dimensions and specifications.

7. To a scale of 1:10 draw a vertical section through a timber suspended floor linked to a solid concrete floor. Indicate in your drawing how the timber suspended floor is ventilated. Include all typical dimensions and specifications.

8. Describe how timber upper floors are constructed.

9. Describe using notes and neat freehand sketches the differences between solid bridging and herringbone strutting.

10. List the advantages of using herringbone strutting over solid bridging.

11. Suggest flooring materials for use in sitting room, hallway and bathroom, giving two reasons for your answer.

SAMPLE EXAMINATION QUESTIONS

2010 Ordinary Level Question 1

A living room has a solid concrete ground floor with a 20 mm quarry tile finish as shown. The external wall of the living room is a 350 mm concrete block wall with an insulated cavity. The wall is plastered on both sides. The foundation is a traditional strip foundation.

(a) To a scale of 1:5, draw a vertical section through the external wall and ground floor. The section should show all the construction details from the bottom of the foundation to 400 mm above finished floor level. Indicate the typical sizes of **four** main components.

(b) Show on your drawing the typical design detailing to prevent a thermal/cold bridge at the junction of the concrete floor and the external wall.

2009 Higher Level Question 1

An insulated suspended timber ground floor abuts the external wall of a dwelling house, as shown in the accompanying sketch. The external wall is a 350 mm concrete block wall with a 150 mm cavity. Rigid insulation board is fixed in the cavity. The suspended timber floor has a 25 mm tongued and grooved hardwood finish.

(a) To a scale of 1:5, draw a vertical section through the external wall and the suspended timber ground floor. The section should show all the construction details from the bottom of the foundation to 400 mm above finished floor level. Include **four** typical dimensions on your drawing.

(b) Indicate clearly the position of a barrier that would prevent radon gas entering the dwelling.

2007 Higher Level Question 4

A suspended timber ground floor abuts a 300 mm concrete block external wall of a dwelling house.

(a) Using *notes and freehand sketches* show the construction details of the wall and the suspended timber ground floor from foundation to finished floor level. Indicate clearly the position of a radon barrier and give typical sizes and materials of the floor components.

(b) Discuss in detail **two** functional requirements of a suspended timber ground floor for a domestic dwelling.

SAMPLE EXAMINATION QUESTIONS

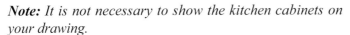

2007 Ordinary Level Question 1

A kitchen has a solid concrete ground floor with a 20 mm quarry tile finish as shown. The external wall of the kitchen is a 300mm concrete block wall with an insulated cavity. The wall is plastered on both sides. The foundation is a traditional strip foundation.

(a) To a scale of 1:5, draw a vertical section through the external wall and ground floor. The section should show all the construction details from the bottom of the foundation to 300 mm above finished floor level.

Note: It is not necessary to show the kitchen cabinets on your drawing.

(b) Recommend a suitable floor covering, other than tiles, for the kitchen floor and give **two** reasons for your choice.

2007 Ordinary Level Question 9

The accompanying sketch shows the first floor of a dwelling house which consists of wooden joists, tongued and grooved flooring boards with a plasterboard ceiling beneath.

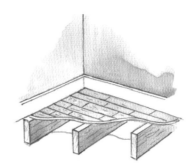

(a) Show by means of a *neat freehand sketch*, herringbone bridging for the floor structure.

(b) Discuss **two** advantages of using herringbone bridging instead of solid bridging.

(c) Using a *large freehand sketch*, show the tongued and grooved joint between two flooring boards and list **one** advantage of this method of jointing.

SUPERSTRUCTURE

WALLS AND PLASTERING

INTRODUCTION

Walls are a fundamental part of a building. A wall is a solid structure that rises vertically and distributes loads from the roof to the foundations. With regard to the structure of the building, walls can be classified into two types (as shown in Fig. 10.1):

• **Load bearing:** These walls rest on foundations in order to spread the loads from the top of a wall, through the wall, to the ground.

• **Non-load-bearing:** These walls, which may or may not rest on foundations, are generally used to divide internal spaces between rooms.

Walls are built up from the foundations. Walls that are built up to ground level are called rising walls. Rising walls are filled to ground level with concrete. This is done for two reasons:

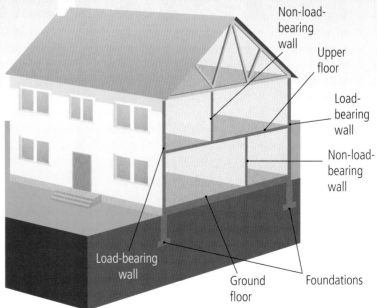

Fig. 10.1 Load-bearing walls transmit the weight of the building down to the foundations. Non-load-bearing walls have no structural weight on them.

1. It gives additional strength to the walls.
2. It directs moisture build-up out through the external leaf of the cavity wall.

The construction of a wall is important. It must be in line, strong and stable. Block and brick walls are staggered to improve stability and to transfer loads evenly. Fig. 10.2 shows a bricklayer building a brick wall.

Walls serve a number of functions, including:

Protection: Walls form a protective enclosure around a building. They protect from weather, pollution, fire, noise, etc.

Fig. 10.2 A bricklayer lays bricks in rows. Each brick overlaps the brick in the previous row by half its length.

Support/stability: Walls are used as support for both roofs and ceilings, and transfer their loads to the foundations.

Space separation: Walls are used as partitions to divide large spaces into smaller rooms or spaces.

Privacy: Walls provide privacy, blocking one space off from another.

There are many types of wall, and they are constructed with a variety of materials.

LOAD-BEARING WALLS

Load-bearing walls are generally made of block, brick or timber. They are extremely important as they give structural integrity to a building. Locations of load-bearing walls include the inner leaf of exterior walls and interior walls that support the rafters.

EXTERNAL LOAD-BEARING WALLS

External load-bearing walls need to sit on a foundation. These walls take the weight of the roof and must therefore distribute loads to the foundations.

One of the main functions of an external wall is to prevent moisture penetrating through to the inner surface. The old approach was to construct very thick external walls, so that, while moisture was able to penetrate through the pores, it would not reach the inner surface due to the thickness of the wall, as shown in Fig. 10.3.

Fig. 10.3 Older building methods used thick walls for stability and to protect against wind and rain.

Newer methods involve using an external fabric that is impervious to water. This is most commonly seen in commercial buildings in the form of plastic/aluminium cladding, as shown in Fig. 10.4, but due to the cost involved it is not often seen in residential buildings. The impervious layer is placed on the exterior side of the masonry work, and allows no moisture to penetrate. In the past, slate was used for this kind of exterior cladding.

Fig. 10.4 External cladding using a waterproof material.

CAVITY WALLS

The most modern and widely used method is to use two walls (an inner leaf and outer leaf) with a cavity between them. Moisture is absorbed by the outer leaf but the cavity prevents this moisture from reaching the inner leaf.

A cavity wall, as shown in Fig. 10.5, is really two walls that run parallel and rest on the same foundation. The inner leaf is the load-bearing wall. The outer leaf was developed as a way of preventing moisture entering a dwelling. The cavity between the two walls stops moisture seeping through to the inside wall. Later, the cavity began to be filled with insulation, improving the thermal comfort of

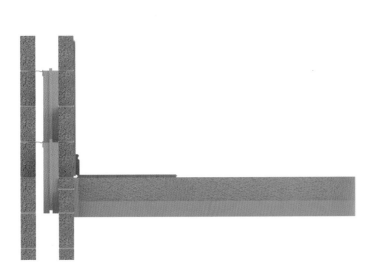

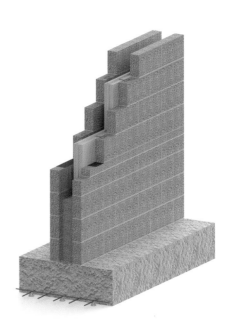

Fig. 10.5 Cavity wall construction. The outer leaf protects the inner leaf from the weather. The inner leaf is the structural element of the wall.

dwellings as a result. In traditional solid block cavity walls, the insulation is placed against the inner leaf and held in place with wall ties (Fig. 10.6).

The outer leaf of a timber frame cavity wall resembles that of a solid block-built one. The major difference between the block-built cavity wall and the timber frame cavity wall is that the insulation is placed within the wall itself rather than butted up against it (see Chapter 11).

The inner leaf of a cavity wall is the load-bearing one, while the outer leaf protects it from damage and weathering. Wall ties help to bind the inner and outer leaves so that they act as one. The wall ties are built into both walls, and improve the building's structural stability by unifying the two walls and reducing shear stress. The wall tie has a built-in 'drip' to prevent moisture travelling along its length and seeping from the outer leaf to the inner leaf. It is also used to tie the insulation to the wall, as shown in Fig. 10.6. In Ireland, the two most popular building methods, concrete cavity and timber frame construction, use two different types of wall tie. The concrete cavity wall tie reduces shear stress, as well as preventing movement of the walls. The timber frame wall tie anchors the timber frame panels to the rising walls.

A damp proof course (DPC) is installed in all ground level external walls. Moisture does not only come from rain, it also rises as damp from below ground. This

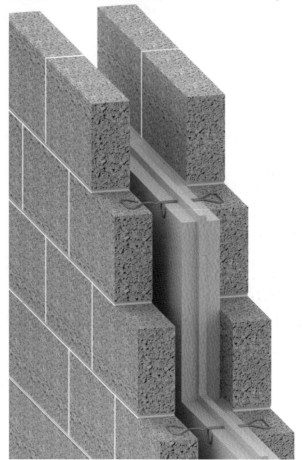

Fig. 10.6 Concrete cavity wall ties, used to brace both leaves of a cavity wall and hold insulation in position.

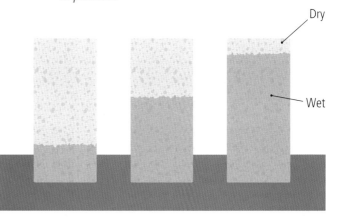

Fig. 10.7 Capillary action in blockwork.

moisture can seep upwards through small air pockets, against the force of gravity, in a process known as capillary action. In construction, these pockets are the pores in the building material itself; in blocks and bricks, for example. The thinner the pores, the higher the moisture will rise. Fig. 10.7 demonstrates how capillary action affects blocks. The DPC protects a wall from this 'rising damp'.

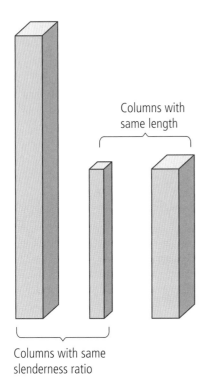

Columns with same length

Columns with same slenderness ratio

Fig. 10.8 The slenderness ratio.

INTERNAL LOAD-BEARING WALLS

Foundations are also required for all internal load-bearing walls. The walls must be strong and stable in order to support the upper floors and roof of the dwelling.

Strength and stability are vitally important for load-bearing walls. The strength of the wall is not just related to the blocks or bricks used to build it, but also to the type of mortar used. It is also important that loads are centred on walls to prevent them buckling. Short, thick walls are stronger and more stable than tall, thin walls; the ratio between height or length and width or thickness is known as the slenderness ratio.

A DPC is also laid for all ground level internal walls.

Wall Bonding

One of the most important factors in giving a wall strength and stability is the way the wall is bonded. Bonding is the practice of overlapping blocks or bricks to ensure that loads are transmitted evenly through the wall. Bonding is also used for aesthetic reasons – to improve the appearance of the finished wall. Sometimes different types of brick are used in the bond to create a pleasing design. Fig. 10.9 shows some different brick bonds.

Running bond

Stacked bond

Flemish garden bond

English garden bond

English bond

Flemish bond

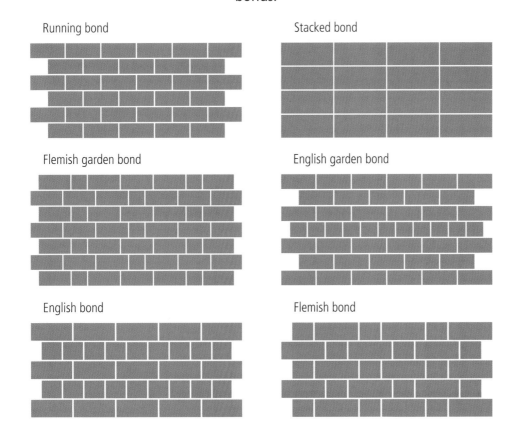

Fig. 10.9 Various types of brick bonds.

Fire Integrity

A load-bearing wall must be fire resistant. In the event of a fire in a domestic dwelling, all walls must remain structurally stable for a minimum of thirty minutes. This is more easily achieved in a concrete block construction because concrete has a high resistance to fire.

When load-bearing walls are made of timber, it is crucial that these structural timbers are treated and fireproofed. Layers of non-combustible materials (insulation) are used to provide extra protection against fire. This is discussed in Chapter 11.

Sound Transmission

Sound can be an irritant in a dwelling, an issue we will deal with in detail in Chapter 21. Walls also insulate against noise coming from outside. In this respect, cavity walls have higher sound insulation than a single leaf wall, because of the cavity. Sound is first absorbed by the outer leaf. The cavity reduces sound transmission between the two walls and the plaster. The inner leaf then prevents sound from penetrating through gaps in the blockwork.

Concrete cavity walls are a lot more dense than timber frame walls, which allows sound to travel more freely through them. In timber frame buildings, quilted insulation is installed between the studs, where it acts as an absorber of sound and heat. Fig. 10.10 shows the differing noise paths through concrete and timber walls.

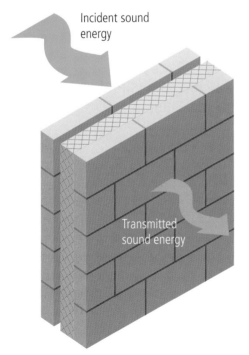
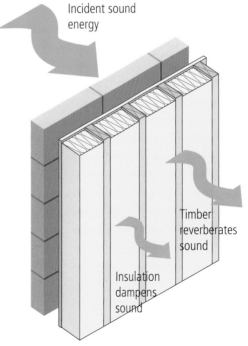

Fig. 10.10 LEFT: Incident sound is reduced by the density of the wall. RIGHT: Method of sound insulation in a timber frame construction.

Fig. 10.11 Reinforced concrete lintels.

Support for Openings

Lintels are used to support the loads, or loadings, above the openings in walls for windows and doors. A lintel is a horizontal element that spans the top of an opening and transmits the loads to either side of it. They can be made from reinforced concrete, steel or timber.

In a cavity wall construction, it is necessary to have a lintel at each leaf. The lintel used in the inner leaf is usually made of reinforced concrete (a precast lintel with steel reinforcement) or steel. The reinforcement is needed because the inner leaf is the structural one, which carries the building load.

If the outer leaf is brick, a steel lintel (Fig. 10.12) is generally used, because it allows the aesthetic appearance of the brick to continue over the front façade of the opening in the wall. The choice of lintel on the inner leaf is more a structural decision than an aesthetic one, as it is not visible externally.

In the case of a timber frame building, lintels on the inner leaf are constructed of timber. The lintels are supported by trimmer studs. Trimmer studs are vertical members of the frame which are the same height as the opening. The lintel to be used in the outer leaf will either be reinforced concrete or steel, depending on whether blocks or bricks are being used. Fig. 10.13 shows a timber lintel in a frame with the trimmer studs supporting it.

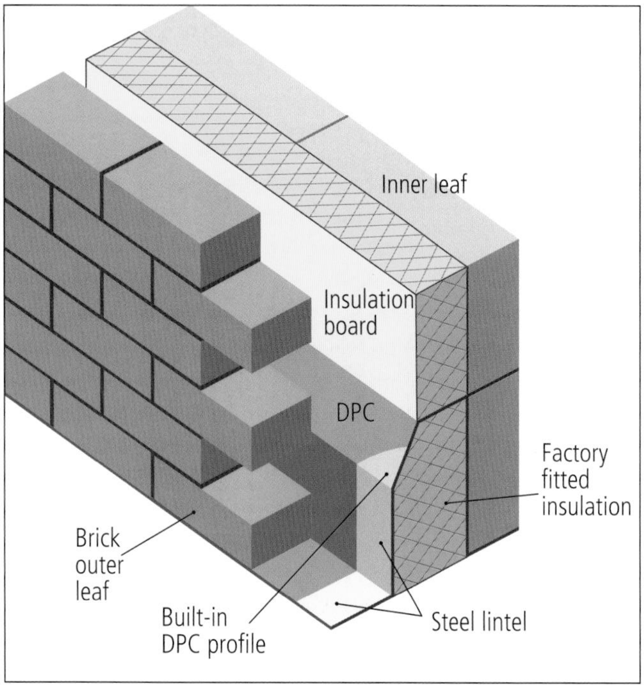

Inner leaf

Insulation board

DPC

Factory fitted insulation

Brick outer leaf

Built-in DPC profile

Steel lintel

Fig. 10.12 Steel lintel used to distribute loading at an opening.

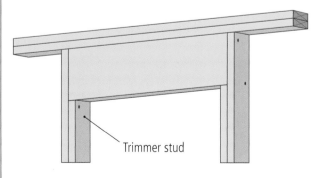

Trimmer stud

Fig. 10.13 Load-bearing lintel over a door in a timber frame construction.

INTERNAL WALLS

The internal walls of a dwelling are generally made of block or timber. In concrete builds it is traditional to use blocks for ground floor internal walls, and to use timber in the upper levels. As we have seen, there are two types of internal wall: load-bearing and non-load-bearing. Non-load-bearing walls are more commonly known as partitions. The functions that partitions serve are to:

- Divide space into smaller rooms/areas
- Resist the spread of fire for a minimum of 30 minutes
- Accommodate services – plumbing and electrics
- Provide acoustic insulation so that sound from one room to another is reduced.

INTERNAL BLOCK WALLS

Solid block internal walls are constructed in much the same way as external walls. They are usually built up at the same time, so that the internal wall can be built into the inner leaf of the external wall, which increases the stability of the internal wall. Some methods used to bond the two walls together are shown in Fig. 10.14.

When solid block internal walls are used to support an upper floor, a timber wall plate is attached to the top of the wall, so that the floor joists can be fixed to it. (See Chapter 9, where wall plates are discussed in detail.)

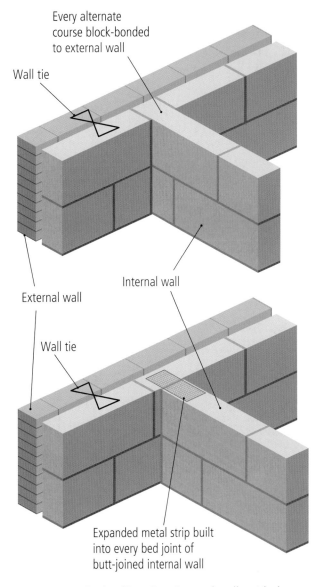

Fig. 10.14 Methods of bonding internal walls with the inner leaf of an external wall.

Fig. 10.15 Cable chased into the wall using plastic conduit protection.

The wall plate also helps to spread the upper floor's load. Lintels are used over door openings, as with external walls. These reinforced concrete members allow the load above to be transmitted safely to the ground. To accommodate services in a solid block wall, a groove is cut – or 'chased' – in the wall. Then a conduit, usually made of plastic, is placed in the groove and the wiring is fed through. The conduit protects the electric cables, and once the wall is plastered it will no longer be visible. Fig. 10.15 shows a conduit chased into a wall.

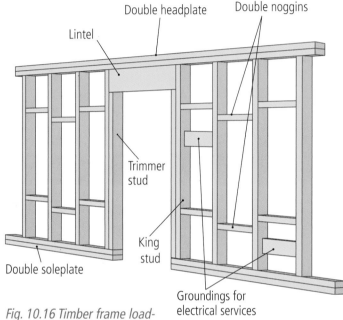

Fig. 10.16 Timber frame load-bearing wall. Note the double headplate and soleplate to give greater support.

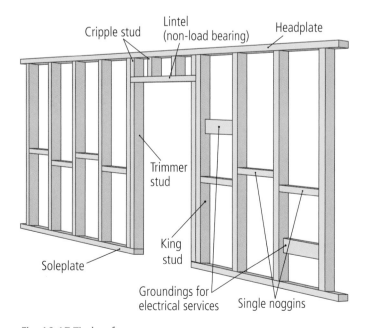

Fig. 10.17 Timber frame non-load-bearing wall.

INTERNAL TIMBER WALLS

Timber can be used for load-bearing and non-load-bearing internal walls. A timber load-bearing wall must have a foundation underneath it. A timber soleplate, and a DPC, are secured to the rising wall, and the framework of the wall is then either built on top or fitted as a panel. This framework is made up of a number of parts, including headplate, studs, noggins, groundings and soleplate.

Timber non-load-bearing walls do not need foundations: they are built on the floor. They do not require a DPC as moisture cannot get to the base of these walls. A soleplate is fixed to the floor and a headplate to the ceiling, and vertical studs are fixed to both at 400mm centres. Noggins are fixed between the studs to ensure rigidity.

Elements of the Internal Timber Wall

The soleplate and headplates are horizontal members that sandwich the studs, which are vertical members spaced at 400mm centres. If the wall is load bearing, both the headplate and the soleplate are doubled. Noggins are the horizontal brace pieces; they give rigidity to the wall. For load-bearing walls two rows are used. Lintels are made from solid timber, and trimmer studs are used to give them extra support. Groundings are horizontal members placed between studs and are used to hold sockets in place. Figs 10.16 and 10.17 show a timber load-bearing wall and a non-load-bearing wall.

The headplate of a stud partition is nailed to the joists above it. Where the partition runs parallel to the joists, noggins are used to fix the headplate to the joists. In upper floors, the joists where stud partitions are to be placed are doubled to provide extra support. When the partition is at right angles to the joists, a double soleplate is used instead of doubled joists.

Accommodating services in timber load-bearing walls is not the same as for solid block walls. It is important that any holes drilled to allow passage for cables or piping are drilled only along the centre line of the stud, known as the neutral axis, and even then only within certain parameters. If holes or notches are taken from the stud or joist outside these parameters, it will have a detrimental affect on its structural integrity. The parameters are shown in Fig. 10.18.

Timber walls, whether they are load-bearing or partitions, are finished in the same way. Plasterboard is fixed to each side of the frame with nails or screws. To allow for any movement in the wall, a gap is left where two sheets of plasterboard meet.

Plasterboard is made of gypsum plaster, a chalky material, which is backed with paper on each side. Sheets intended for use on ceilings are backed on one side with foil to prevent moisture ingress. Plasterboard

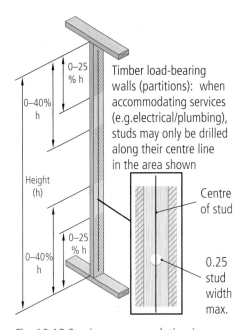

Fig. 10.18 Service accommodation in vertical members of the timber stud frame.

is a fire-resistant material, which makes it suitable for use on internal walls. It has a smooth, clean surface and only needs one coat of plaster to create a finished inside wall. Plaster finishing will be looked at in greater detail later on in this chapter.

PARTY WALLS

A party wall is a shared wall which separates one building from its neighbour. When these two buildings are homes, each residence has half of the wall (Fig. 10.19) on its property.

The two main functions of a party wall are to prevent the spread of fire and to prevent the transmission of sound. A number of measures are employed to prevent these two things happening.

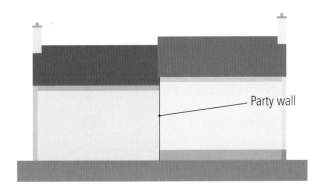

Fig. 10.19 A party wall is the wall that divides neighbouring buildings.

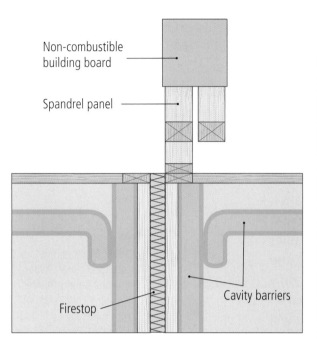

Non-combustible building board

Spandrel panel

Firestop

Cavity barriers

Fig. 10.20 Firestop in place.

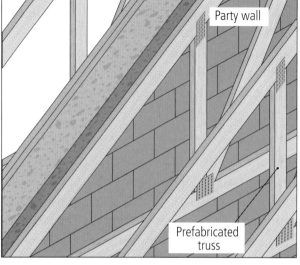

Party wall

Prefabricated truss

Fig. 10.21 The wall rises to the top of the slope of the roof, ensuring that each residence has its own attic space.

Party walls are two completely separate walls, with no bridging except for non-combustible insulation, which is packed in at the top. After it is filled with this non-combustible material (mineral wool), the wall is capped with mortar (Fig. 10.21). Allowing this cavity to run from the foundation to the top of the party wall ensures that fire will not spread, and that the transmission of noise from one building to its neighbour is reduced. Fig. 10.20 shows a firestop in place.

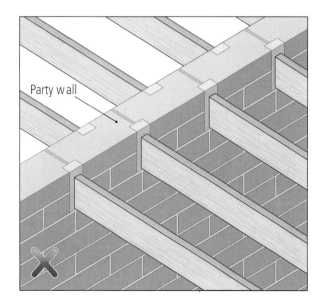

Party wall

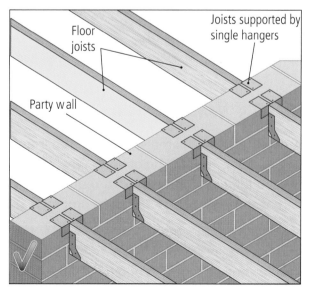

Floor joists

Joists supported by single hangers

Party wall

Fig. 10.22 LEFT: Joists **must not** be built into party walls. RIGHT: Correct method, using single hangers as support.

Party walls can be constructed of either concrete or timber. It is also common to see concrete party walls in timber frame developments. Concrete party walls are a simpler construction, and they permit masonry chimneys to be attached, which timber party walls do not. We will look at this further in Chapter 13.

When joists are set at right angles to a concrete party wall, they must not be built into it: hangers are used instead (Fig. 10.22). When the joists run parallel to the wall, they must not come into contact with it, as this can lead to joist movement – which results in springy floors. Instead, small timbers are packed between the joists and the wall, and these work to keep the joists completely rigid.

Extra fire protection is needed when a party wall is made of timber. Wire-reinforced mineral wool is packed into the cavity at floor level. Details of other fire protection measures in timber frame houses can be found in Chapter 11.

BOUNDARY WALLS

A boundary wall is built to set out the boundaries of a property. It encloses the space and provides a degree of privacy. In order to remain consistent with the dwelling, the boundary wall should be finished in a material that links to the building. Common materials used in boundary walls include brick, stone, steel and timber. Materials can often be used in combination to good effect, e.g. brick pillars with timber fencing.

Boundary walls need to be built on a foundation. The type of foundation will depend on the soil type in the area (see Chapter 8). The height of the wall becomes an issue if the wall is to span a long distance, in which case the wall can buckle. Increasing the thickness or reducing the height are two ways of combating this. A more common method to counteract the slenderness ratio is to construct piers at intervals along the wall, which allows a thin, high wall to be built.

Fig. 10.23 Typical stone boundary wall surrounding a home.

Gravity wall

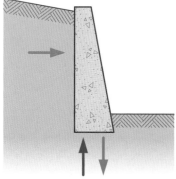

Piling wall

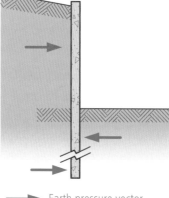

Cantilever wall

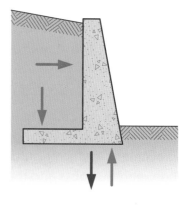

Anchored wall

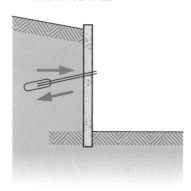

→ Earth pressure vector

→ Gravity vector of wall

→ Reactive force vector
(not all shown)

Fig. 10.24 Common types of retaining wall, with various types of pressure exerted on the wall.

RETAINING WALLS

Retaining walls are often seen in gardens with large slopes or alongside roadways. They restrain soil and generally help to secure separate levels on a site. Fig. 10.24 shows different types of retaining wall.

PLASTERING/RENDERING

The finish applied to a wall is extremely important because it affects a building's overall appearance. The finish on an external wall is called rendering. Plastering is the application of a surface finish to an internal wall. The main difference between the two materials is that there is more cement in render than in plaster.

It is important to note that, while external renders can be used indoors, internal plasters cannot be used outdoors. The function of render is to provide a weather-resistant finish for an external wall, which plaster will not do. The function of plaster is to provide a smooth, clean surface on internal walls.

Render and plaster also:

- Improve thermal insulation
- Improve acoustic insulation
- Improve the durability of the wall.

Fig. 10.25 Rendering a house.

EXTERNAL WALLS

External walls are rendered. The render is in effect a skin on the outside of the wall that resists damage from rain and weather. It also improves the look of the building. Render is applied in three coats:

1. Scud coat
2. Scratch coat
3. Finish coat.

Fig. 10.26 shows these three coats.

The scud coat provides a link between the wall and the render, acting as a key to hold the render in place. The scud coat mix has the appearance of thick slurry. It is mixed using 1:2 (cement:sharp sand), with enough water to achieve the desired consistency. The scud coat is applied by throwing the mixture at the wall using a hand scoop. The surface of the wall is dampened periodically to allow better adhesion for the scud coat, which reaches a thickness of 3–5mm.

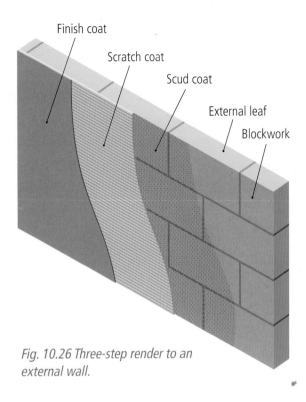

Fig. 10.26 Three-step render to an external wall.

The scratch coat is applied once the scud coat has cured. This coat provides a key for the final coat. It is made from a mix of 1:½:4 (cement:lime:sand), and when lime is not used a plasticiser is added to the mix. This coat is applied with a trowel to a thickness of 10–16mm. The surface is allowed to become firm but not to harden before it is scratched; this provides the grooves which the final coat will grip to.

The finish coat will be the finished surface of the render. The mix is the same as for the scratch coat, or slightly weaker, but never stronger. If the outer coat is stronger than the one it is applied to it leads to defects such as cracking and crazing due to shrinkage (Fig. 10.27). The scratch coat is allowed to cure fully before work on the final coat begins. When it has completely dried out, it is moistened to prevent excessive suction, and then the final coat is applied using a plasterer's float. This presses the wet plaster to the wall and closes off the pores to create a smooth finish. To create a soft, irregular texture rather than a smooth one, a plasterer's sponge is used.

Although the scratch coat and the final coat are made with the same mix, and are

Fig. 10.27 An example of crazing caused by the rapid drying of the finish coat.

Fig. 10.28 Wet-dash finish.

Fig. 10.29 Dry-dash finish.

therefore the same strength, their thicknesses differ. The final coat is around 6mm thick. It is thinner than the scratch coat, which prevents cracking from the movement caused by changes in temperature and moisture. If the final coat is allowed to dry out too quickly, i.e. in warm weather, or has dirty sand in it, crazing can occur. The overall thickness of the combined coats must not be more than 20mm.

Thrown finishes are often preferred in regions where weather conditions are extreme, for example in coastal regions. A thrown finish has greater resistance to weather, greater durability and is more resistant to cracking and crazing. There are two types: wet finishes, more commonly referred to as roughcast or wet dash; and dry dash.

A roughcast finish is achieved by throwing the final coat of render at the wall while it is wet, and leaving it un-trowelled. The shape and size of the coarse aggregate used in the mix determines how 'rough' the finished surface will be Fig. 10.28.

A dry-dash finish is produced by throwing loose chippings on to a fresh layer of render. The chippings are thrown onto the wall while the final coat is still soft. The work must be done in one sitting to ensure that the finish is uniform Fig. 10.29.

INTERNAL WALLS

The finish used on internal walls depends on whether they are block walls, which are finished using wet plaster, or stud partitions, which are finished using plasterboard.

Internal Block Wall

There are two ways of completing a plaster finish to concrete block internal walls: plastering or dry-lining. They suit different situations.

Plastering an internal block wall can be done using a two- or three-stage method. The three-stage method is the more popular, and it follows the same progression as that of external rendering, though the mix is not the same.

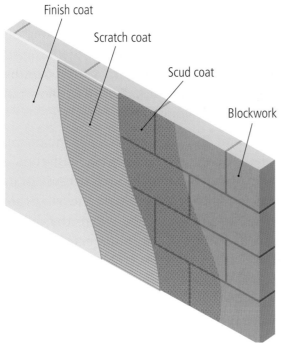

Finish coat
Scratch coat
Scud coat
Blockwork

Fig. 10.30 The three-stage method plaster finish.

Finish coat
Undercoat

Fig. 10.31 The two-stage method plaster finish.

Three-Stage Coat Method of Finish

1. *Scud coat:* applied to the bare blockwork; provides a base for the scratch coat. (Mix – 1:2 sand:cement.)

2. *Scratch coat:* applied with a trowel on to the scud coat; provides a base for the final plaster. (Mix – 1:1:6 cement:lime:sand.)

3. *Finish coat:* the final layer, which will be painted. (Gypsum plaster.)

Two-Stage Coat Method of Finish

1. *Undercoat:* a 9mm gypsum undercoat is applied to the wall. This coat is scratched deeply to provide a key for the finish coat.

2. *Finish coat:* a 2–3mm gypsum finish coat is applied and finished smoothly.

Dry Lining

Dry lining was first introduced as a means of keeping the plaster finish of internal walls away from the moisture that penetrated through thick walls. Due to the development of cavity walls, it is not used as much as it once was, but it is still a viable method of finishing blockwork, because with dry lining electrics and plumbing do not need to be chased into the wall.

Dry lining panels can be made with timber, plywood and fibreboard, but by far the most common material used is plasterboard. Plasterboard is a rigid 2.4 x 1.2m sheet with a gypsum core, lined on either side with durable paper. It is also available with a foil backing to prevent moisture ingress. It comes in thicknesses of 9.5mm and 12.7mm.

To install the dry lining, timber battens are fixed to the wall and insulation is placed between them. Room is made for services like electricity and plumbing.

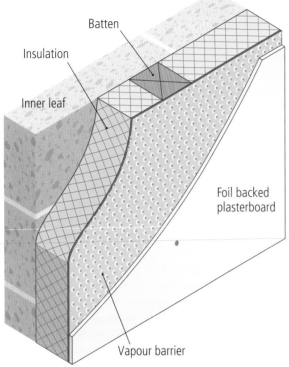

Batten

Insulation

Inner leaf

Foil backed plasterboard

Vapour barrier

Fig. 10.32 Dry lining battened to a concrete block wall.

It is important that the battens are spaced to suit the size of the plasterboard, which is nailed or screwed onto them. This plasterboard is then finished with a gypsum plaster up to 5mm thick. Fig. 10.32 shows an example of dry lining.

Ceilings are also finished with a combination of plasterboard and wet plaster. Plasterboard lined with foil is generally used because of its ability to combat condensation. The boards are screwed to the joists, and where the ceiling meets the wall a canvas fibre material called 'scrim' is used to reinforce the join and prevent it cracking. The plasterboard ceiling is finished in the same way as the walls, with a 5mm gypsum plaster finish.

PAINTING

Painting gives the wall a decorative finish. It is extremely important that the plaster is completely dry before it is painted. This can take up to six weeks in the case of external render. Failure to allow the plaster to dry can lead to mould growth, which is a result of moisture remaining trapped within the plaster.

When the plaster is dry the surface is brushed to remove dust, and sealed using a mix of one part water to four parts paint. The seal wets the plaster so that it will not suck the moisture out of the paint, which would make it dry out and flake.

The wall is then primed and finished using sprays, rollers or brushes. The paint must be applied evenly to create a smooth finish.

PRACTICE QUESTIONS

1. Name the functions that walls serve.
2. Where are load-bearing walls located in dwellings and what are their functions?
3. Describe a cavity wall in detail, and explain in your answer why a cavity wall is necessary.
4. Discuss fire resistance in relation to wall construction.
5. Describe using notes and neat freehand sketches how internal solid block walls are constructed.

PRACTICE QUESTIONS

6. Sketch neatly the framework required for an internal timber load-bearing wall. Label your sketch to indicate the main components.

7. Discuss party walls in the context of their construction.

8. Describe in detail how an external block wall is plastered.

9. Explain what dry lining is and where it is used.

10. Describe in detail how plastered walls are painted.

SAMPLE EXAMINATION QUESTIONS

2010 Ordinary Level Question 5(a)

A non-load bearing timber stud partition separates two bedrooms on the first floor of a two storey dwelling house, as shown in the accompanying sketch. The first floor joists are 225 mm × 50 mm, the floor is a tongued and grooved floor and there is a plasterboard ceiling beneath. A flush panel door is fitted in the partition.

(a) To a scale of 1:5, draw a vertical section through the floor and stud partition. Show all the construction details from the bottom of the plasterboard ceiling, through the floor joists, the door and saddle to a point 1.5 metres above finished floor level. Label the components and give their typical sizes.

2009 Ordinary Level Question 1

The sketch shows an internal load bearing wall built of solid concrete blocks. The wall is 225 mm thick and is plastered on both sides. The ground floor is an insulated solid concrete floor. The floor is finished with 25 mm thick hardwood flooring fixed to battens.

(a) To a scale of 1:5, draw a vertical section through the foundation, the 225 mm wall and the ground floor. Show all the construction details from the bottom of the foundation to 500 mm above finished floor level. Include four typical dimensions on your drawing.

(b) Indicate on your drawing the insulation to the floor slab and show clearly the position of the radon barrier.

Note: Show a floor width of 500 mm at either side of the internal wall.

CHAPTER 11
TIMBER FRAME BUILDING

INTRODUCTION

Timber has been used to build houses for thousands of years, though it is only in the last twenty years that Ireland has seen a real increase in the number of timber frame constructions built here.

The term timber frame refers to the internal structure and how it is supported. The outer leaf of the building may be built of materials like block or brick, so it may not be easy to distinguish between timber frame and more traditional builds.

The frame is the element that provides the structural support, and, much like the human skeleton, it is stronger than it looks.

Timber frame homes are constructed in prebuilt sections or panels, which are brought on site and fastened in situ. It is also possible to construct sections on site, but this is time consuming and the sections may not be as accurate as the prebuilt model.

Fig. 11.1 A timber frame dwelling under construction.

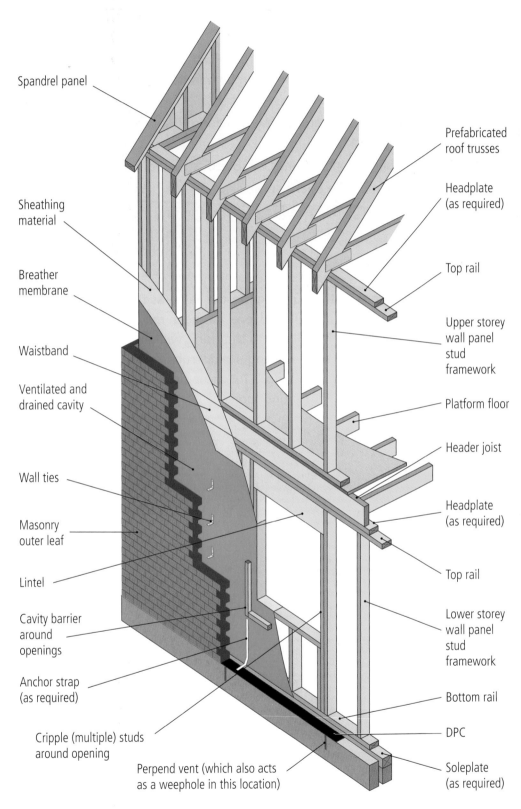

Spandrel panel

Sheathing material

Breather membrane

Waistband

Ventilated and drained cavity

Wall ties

Masonry outer leaf

Lintel

Cavity barrier around openings

Anchor strap (as required)

Cripple (multiple) studs around opening

Perpend vent (which also acts as a weephole in this location)

Prefabricated roof trusses

Headplate (as required)

Top rail

Upper storey wall panel stud framework

Platform floor

Header joist

Headplate (as required)

Top rail

Lower storey wall panel stud framework

Bottom rail

DPC

Soleplate (as required)

Fig. 11.2 Elements of a timber frame construction. Note that plasterboard, insulation and vapour control layer have been omitted for clarity.

Timber frame buildings have a number of advantages over concrete buildings. These include, but are not limited to:

- Timber is a relatively easy material to process. The material is lighter than block or brick, so it can be handled with more ease and worked with lighter tools.
- Due to the material being less dense than concrete or brick, it heats up more quickly.
- Timber frame buildings can be constructed more quickly.
- They are more energy efficient.
- Less energy is needed to produce the raw materials.

FOUNDATIONS

The foundations of the building are the same as those for a traditional cavity wall dwelling. When the ground level has been reached, the panels are brought to the site. They are fixed both to the rising wall and then to each other, using steel straps, which makes a strong, rigid structure. The straps are galvanised to prevent rust. Figs 11.3 and Fig. 11.4 show both the details and specifications involved in timber frame foundations.

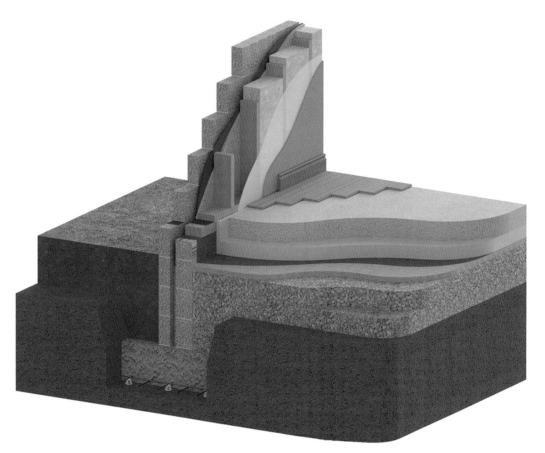

Fig. 11.3 Timber frame foundation detail.

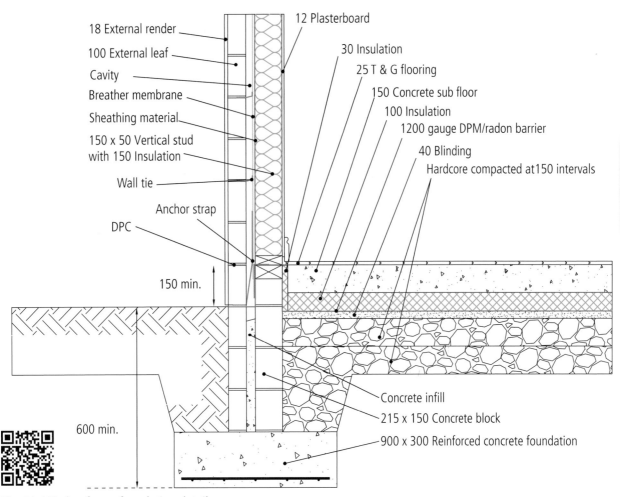

18 External render
100 External leaf
Cavity
Breather membrane
Sheathing material
150 x 50 Vertical stud with 150 Insulation
Wall tie
Anchor strap
DPC
150 min.
600 min.

12 Plasterboard
30 Insulation
25 T & G flooring
150 Concrete sub floor
100 Insulation
1200 gauge DPM/radon barrier
40 Blinding
Hardcore compacted at 150 intervals
Concrete infill
215 x 150 Concrete block
900 x 300 Reinforced concrete foundation

Fig. 11.4 Timber frame foundation detail.

PANELS

The panels themselves consist of many layers, each of which has a different function.

1. **Plasterboard:** The finished internal surface of the panel. Gives the panel a surface to paint, etc.

2. **Vapour membrane:** Prevents condensation occurring between the wall and the insulation.

3. **Timber stud:** This is the load-bearing part of the panel. It is also the framework for sheathings, fixings, etc.

4. **Insulation:** Prevents heat from being lost through the panel.

5. **Plywood:** Ties the frame together and prevents movement.

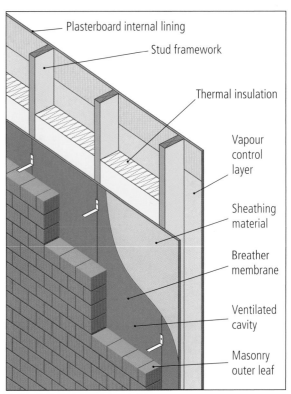

Plasterboard internal lining
Stud framework
Thermal insulation
Vapour control layer
Sheathing material
Breather membrane
Ventilated cavity
Masonry outer leaf

Fig. 11.5 Timber frame panel with external brick leaf.

6. **Breather membrane:** Allows moisture to breathe out through the membrane, but stops moisture coming in. As a result, rain cannot permeate through the membrane, and any moisture within the panel can make its way to the outside. This is necessary during the construction phase when the building is exposed to the elements.

The panels are fitted to a soleplate on the inner leaf of the cavity wall. The external wall is built up in the same way as if the inner leaf were blocks. The timber frame wall is anchored to the outer leaf using galvanised steel straps. The sheets of ply fixed to the frames give the structure its strength and stability.

Ventilation is very important in timber frame construction. A build-up of moisture in a wooden environment is not desirable as it can lead to rot (see Chapter 7). Moisture is ventilated at two points in the cavity: at eaves level and below the level of the DPC.

Fig. 11.6 Timber lintels are grouped above the ope.

Once the walls have been erected, including internal walls, the upstairs floors are constructed. The details of building timber upstairs floors were discussed in Chapter 9. The floors and walls are fixed to each other to create a rigid frame that prevents movement. The upper walls are fixed in place, and the roof is constructed on top of them.

Lintels, which are a load-bearing element, are required over every opening in a wall, whether the wall is load bearing or not. Timber frame dwellings use timber lintels to transmit the loadings to the trimmer studs. The lintels measure 225 x 50mm and are placed above the ope in groups of three. Fig. 11.6 shows a timber lintel in place.

Wall ties are needed in timber frame builds to keep the external and internal cavity wall leafs apart. Wall ties in timber frame builds differ from those in block builds. They resemble straps; one end is stapled/nailed to the studs while the other end is built into the masonry external leaf. Fig. 11.7 shows an example of a wall tie used in timber frame construction.

A cavity barrier is used to seal around openings (windows, doors, etc). It is pressure treated to prevent fungal and insect

Fig. 11.7 A timber frame wall tie.

attack. It fills the cavity, and thus prevents moisture from seeping into the area. A DPC is placed over the cavity barrier and tucked under the breather membrane. Fig. 11.8 shows details of how the cavity is closed.

Shrinkage, which can happen as a result of changes in the moisture content of timber, can pose problems in timber frame builds. To combat any detrimental effects that may occur, gaps are left to allow the timber to move downwards. As the timber is constrained in every other direction, shrinkage affects movement in a downward direction. Areas in which these shrinkage gaps are left are at eaves level and underneath openings.

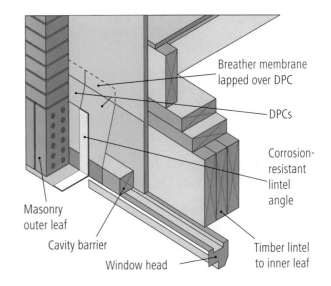

Fig. 11.8 The cavity is closed by the DPC, draped under inner breather membrane and out under the top of the ope.

A timber frame house heats up a lot more quickly than a traditional concrete one. This is due in part to the method of insulation. Traditional concrete constructions fix the insulation to the opposite side of the wall, which means that the whole wall must heat up if the heat is to be retained. However, the

insulation is contained in the timber frame panel, which means that heat is not lost in the panel before it is returned to the room. Timber frame houses cool down very quickly, though, as the materials in the panel do not retain the heat. Concrete block walls, by comparison, take longer to cool down as the blocks themselves absorb some of the heat energy and release it slowly.

Fire is of course a hazard, as it is with any wooden product. To combat this danger, plasterboard is fixed to the inside leaf. Plasterboard is non-combustible and protects the timber for thirty minutes in the event of a fire. Fire barriers are situated at other important locations to prevent fire spreading, including:

- Between party walls and roof
- On external walls
- Around eaves and opes.

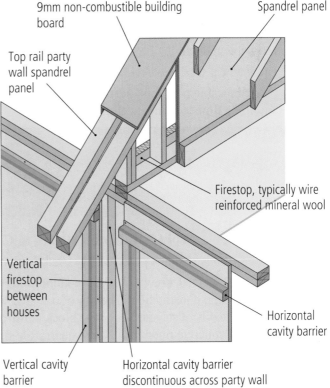

Fig. 11.9 Party wall, under construction, at eaves level.

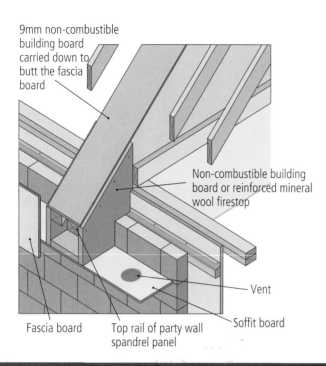

9mm non-combustible building board carried down to butt the fascia board

Non-combustible building board or reinforced mineral wool firestop

Vent

Soffit board

Fascia board

Top rail of party wall spandrel panel

The fire barriers themselves are made of non-combustible material. Fig. 11.9 and Fig. 11.10 show a partly built and completed firestop between party walls.

Fireplaces and chimneys require special attention when building with timber. This will be explained in greater detail in Chapter 13.

Fig. 11.10 Completed party wall at eaves level. Note how the party wall is enveloped in a fireproof layer.

PRACTICE QUESTIONS

1. Name some of the advantages of timber frame over block built dwellings.
2. To a scale of 1:10 draw a vertical section through a typical strip foundation with timber frame walls.
3. Neatly sketch and label a typical timber frame panel.
4. Describe in detail the function of each part of a timber frame panel.
5. Draw a neat freehand sketch to illustrate how openings in timber frame builds are sealed.
6. Describe using notes and neat freehand sketches how fire is prevented from spreading between adjoining timber frame dwellings.

SAMPLE EXAMINATION QUESTIONS

2005 Higher Level Question 9 (Refer to Chapter 15 for cill measurements)

Timber frame construction is now widely used for domestic dwellings in Ireland.

(a) To a scale of 1:10, draw a vertical section through the external wall and ground floor of a house of timber frame construction. The top of a window cill is positioned 900mm above floor level, the external leaf is of standard concrete block construction with a rendered finish and the ground floor is a solid concrete floor with 20mm quarry tile finish. Show all the constructional details from the bottom of the foundation to the top of the concrete cill.

(b) Discuss in detail **two** advantages of timber frame construction and two advantages of standard concrete block wall construction and recommend a preferred wall type for a new house.

CHAPTER 12
ROOFS

LEARNING OUTCOMES:

After studying this chapter students will:

- Know the main functions of a roof.
- Be able to name various roof types.
- Understand how pitched roofs are constructed.
- Be able to draw to scale various aspects of a roof.

KEYWORDS:

- ROOF • PITCHED ROOF • TRUSS ROOF • CUT ROOF • LEAN-TO ROOF • FLAT ROOF • PURLIN
- RAFTER • COLLAR • STRUTS • HIP • VALLEY • RIDGE BOARD • SARKING • BATTENS • TILES
- SLATES • GUTTER • TILTING FILLET • SOFFIT • FASCIA • EAVES • FLASHING • GABLE
- WARM DECK • COLD DECK

INTRODUCTION

A roof is the upper covering of a building. It prevents moisture entering the building from above, and it is designed to transfer its loads to the load-bearing walls of the building.

When designing a roof the following functional requirements are taken into account:

- Insulation
- Strength
- Durability
- Weather resistance
- Fire resistance.

Insulation: Because heat rises, a building can lose a lot of heat through the roof. Preventing this heat loss is critical. This is achieved by using layers of insulation, which must be a combined depth of 270mm to meet the current building regulations.

Strength: The structure of the roof must be strong enough to support its own weight as well as any loads that may be imposed on it, i.e. wind, rain, snow.

Durability: The roof must last for the lifetime of the building. The materials used will affect its durability.

Weather resistance: The roof must not allow the elements (wind, rain, snow) to penetrate it.

Fire resistance: The roof must meet all current fire regulations.

The aesthetics of the roof should also be considered because the look of the roof can affect the look of the building as a whole. The slope, style, the use of tiles or slates all contribute to the aesthetic qualities of a roof.

TYPES OF ROOF

There is a wide range of roof types. Some of the most common in Ireland and around Europe are shown in Fig. 12.1.

The type of roof chosen does not affect the functionality of that roof. The choice of roof style is aesthetic, practical and functional, rather than a structural issue.

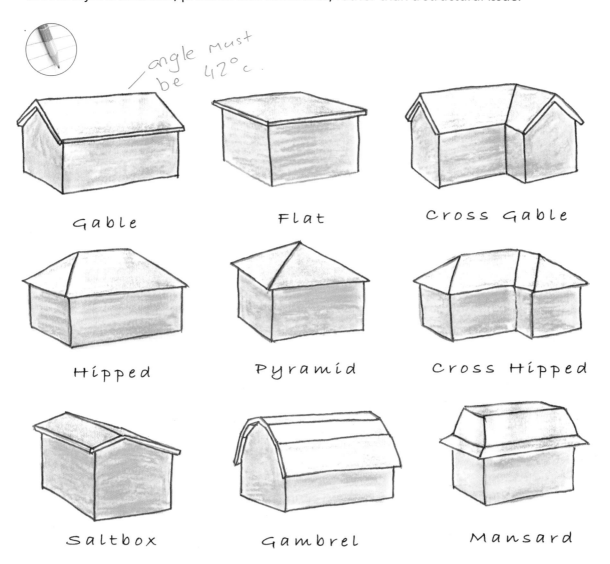

Fig. 12.1 Common roof styles.

ROOF TERMINOLOGY

There are a number of terms specifically associated with roofing. Some of these are shown in Fig. 12.2.

Apron: Aprons are strips of felt that are attached between vertical walls and a sloped roof. They prevent moisture gaining access through the junction between the wall and the roof.

Barge boards: Decorative boards that are attached under the gable end. These boards were traditionally made of timber but are now more commonly made from uPVC.

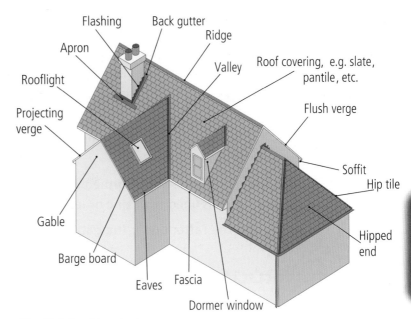

Fig. 12.2 Roof terminology.

Battens: Used to hold down the felt of the roof and to support the tiles or slates. They are fixed horizontally to the rafters and are evenly spaced.

Dormer: A window that is built vertically into the slope of a pitched roof.

Eaves: The area that includes the fascia, soffit and guttering.

Fascia: A vertical board, attached to the rafters, to which the guttering is fixed. It was traditionally made of timber, but now is more commonly made of uPVC.

Flashing: Usually made of zinc or lead, the flashing is a weatherproof seal. It is placed where a part of the roof adjoins a structural part of the house (e.g. the chimney, a vertical wall). One side of the flashing is built into the structural element and the other is fitted to the roof surface, preventing water from getting underneath the tiles or slates.

Gable: The section of wall between the sloping edges of the roof.

Guttering: Collects and redirects water from the roof to soakaway pits.

Hip: A sloping ridge formed where a pitched roof and hipped end meet.

Hipped end: The sloping area of the roof at the end of the pitch that is covered with tiles or slates.

Rafter: A timber used to form the shape of the roof.

Ridge: The line formed by the meeting of the two sloping surfaces of a pitched roof.

Ridge board: The horizontal board that the rafters are fixed to, and which forms the line of the ridge.

CHAPTER 12

Ridge tiles: Angled or rounded tiles that are used along the ridge to seal the top of a pitched roof.

Sarking: Waterproof, breathable felt that is used to line the roof before the battens and tiles are fixed.

Rooflight: A window built into the roof. Its glazing is parallel to the rafters.

Soffit: A board that seals the space between the fascia and the wall. Air vents are placed along the soffit to allow air into the attic space. Traditionally the soffit was a timber or cement board product, but it is now more commonly made with uPVC.

Valley: This is the angle formed when two pitches meet and incline downwards. The valley is lined with zinc or lead to channel water downwards.

Verge: The rafter under the gable end of a roof.

ROOF CONSTRUCTION

There are a number of different roof constructions used for different purposes in the building trade. The most common types are pitched (either cut or truss), lean-to and flat.

TRADITIONAL CUT ROOF

This type of roof is a pitched roof built up on site with rafters and joists. The joists are the horizontal members that both support the ceiling below them and prevent the wall/rafters from spreading outwards. The distance between the wall plate and the ridge of the roof determines the size of the rafters to be used, as well as whether purlins will be necessary. Technical specifications for the ridge of a cut roof are shown in Fig. 12.3.

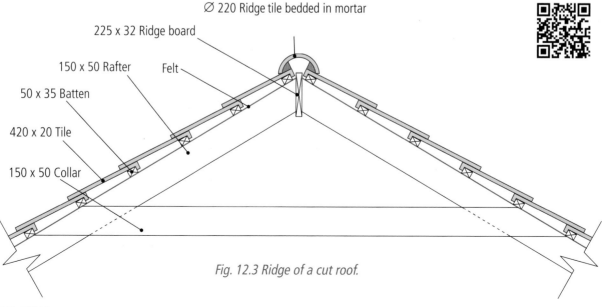

Fig. 12.3 Ridge of a cut roof.

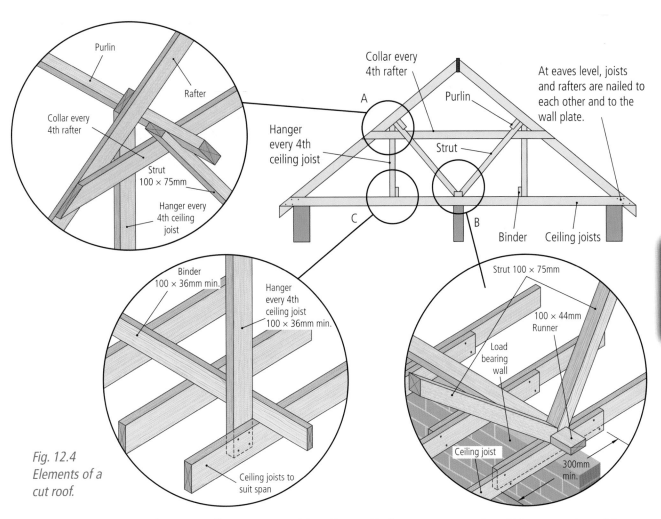

Fig. 12.4
Elements of a
cut roof.

Rafters usually measure 150 x 50mm. Rafters are spaced at 400mm centres. They are nailed to a wall plate at the top of each supporting wall. The wall plate is a 100 x 75mm timber that is strapped to the top of the inner leaf of the cavity wall. In order for the rafter to fit over the wall plate, a small triangular section referred to as a birdsmouth is cut out of the rafter. To fit them to the ridge board, the rafters are cut at an angle and fixed using 100mm wire nails.

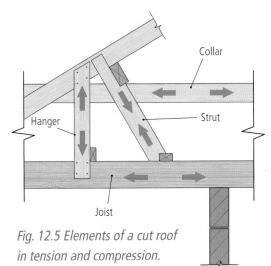

Fig. 12.5 Elements of a cut roof
in tension and compression.

Purlins – long horizontal beams – give additional support to the rafters. The purlins are supported by struts (125 x 50mm), which must bear onto a load-bearing wall below.

Hangers and binders work together to hold up the ceiling joists. Where large joists are used, hangers may not be necessary. Collars provide additional binding between the rafters on opposite sides of the ridge board. Fig. 12.4 shows the typical elements of a cut roof. The stresses acting on the various elements of the cut roof are shown in Fig. 12.5.

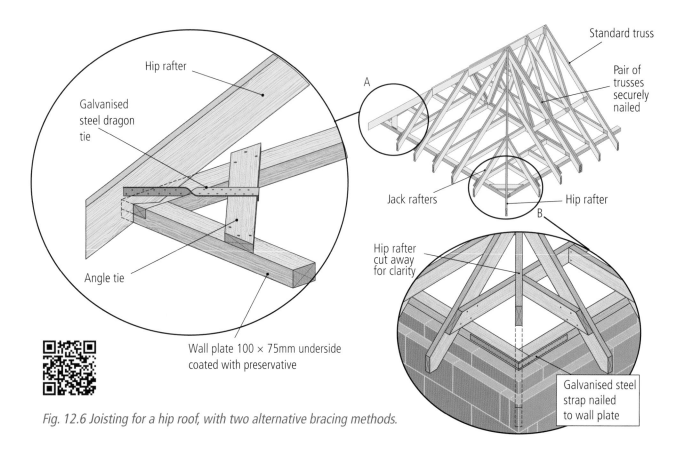

Fig. 12.6 Joisting for a hip roof, with two alternative bracing methods.

Labels in figure:
- Hip rafter
- Galvanised steel dragon tie
- Angle tie
- Wall plate 100 × 75mm underside coated with preservative
- Standard truss
- Pair of trusses securely nailed
- A
- Jack rafters
- Hip rafter
- B
- Hip rafter cut away for clarity
- Galvanised steel strap nailed to wall plate

Where a hipped section is incorporated into a cut roof, the rafters are cut to fit. The line that defines the hip is created with a hip rafter that spans from the ridge to the eaves. The hip rafter is stronger than normal rafters and has jack rafters nailed to it. A jack rafter is not as long as a normal rafter and is used as added support. The jack rafters span from the wall plate to the hip rafter and are nailed in place. An angle tie is used to provide extra strength at the corner.

Fig. 12.6 shows details of hip construction.

There are a number of advantages associated with constructing a cut roof. Living spaces can be built into the roof space; the roof can be constructed by local tradespeople and without specialist equipment; and there is a spacious attic area.

TRUSS ROOF

A truss roof is a pitched roof prefabricated in a factory and delivered to the site, where it is erected by a crane. Each separate frame is known as a truss. Each truss consists of joists, rafters and struts. Where timbers meet they are nailed together using a nail plate. Various designs of truss are available. Fig. 12.7 shows the elements of a truss roof. The stresses imposed on a truss roof are shown in Fig. 12.8.

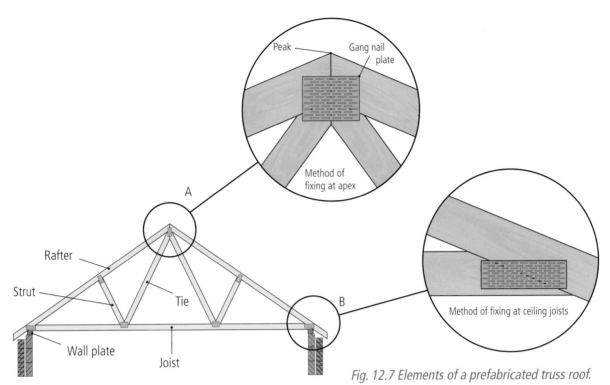

Fig. 12.7 Elements of a prefabricated truss roof.

Trusses are not built into the structure of the roof, so they must be held down firmly. Truss clips are used to hold the truss to the wall plate.

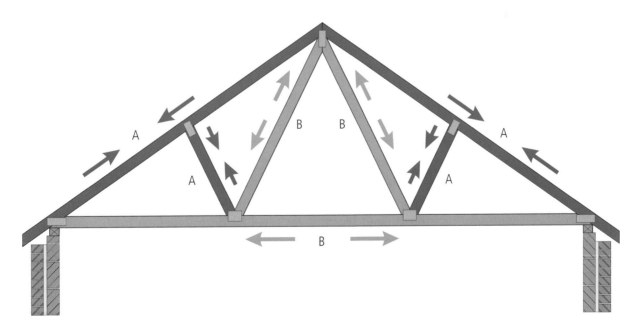

Fig. 12.8 Members of a prefabricated truss: members A are in compression; members B are in tension.

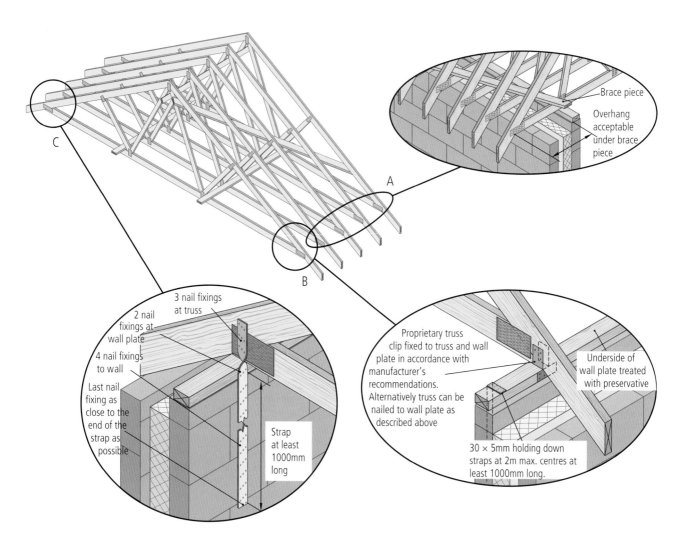

Brace piece

Overhang acceptable under brace piece

C

A

B

3 nail fixings at truss

2 nail fixings at wall plate

4 nail fixings to wall

Last nail fixing as close to the end of the strap as possible

Strap at least 1000mm long

Proprietary truss clip fixed to truss and wall plate in accordance with manufacturer's recommendations. Alternatively truss can be nailed to wall plate as described above

Underside of wall plate treated with preservative

30 × 5mm holding down straps at 2m max. centres at least 1000mm long.

Fig. 12.9 The trusses are held together by a longitudinal binder and diagonal rafter bracing. Both of these brace the roof structure against wind loads.

In order for the roof to act as one unit, the trusses must be tied together. Longitudinal binders are used at ceiling level along the joists and at ridge level. Diagonal bracing is used from eaves level to ridge level on both sides of the roof. Where the span is longer than normal, additional longitudinal bracing is incorporated into the structure. Fig. 12.9 shows how the binders and braces hold the roof together.

Gable walls need to be stabilised due to their expanse. Fig. 12.10 demonstrates the added pressure that a gable wall is under as it takes the force of the wind.

The gables are secured by tying them to the roof timbers. Galvanised steel straps are nailed to the wall and then to the rafters. The strap extends out to the second rafter in order to provide support. A packing piece is used to keep the truss from making contact with the wall. This ensures that all elements are tied together, as shown in Fig. 12.11.

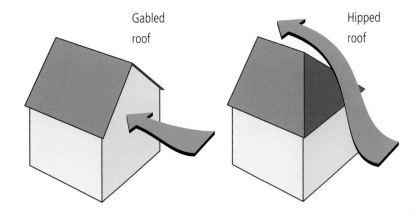

Fig. 12.10 Gable walls take huge pressure from the wind due to their expanse.

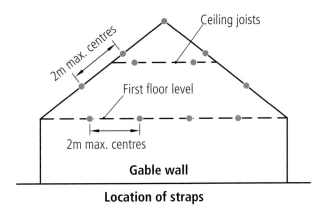

Gable wall

Location of straps

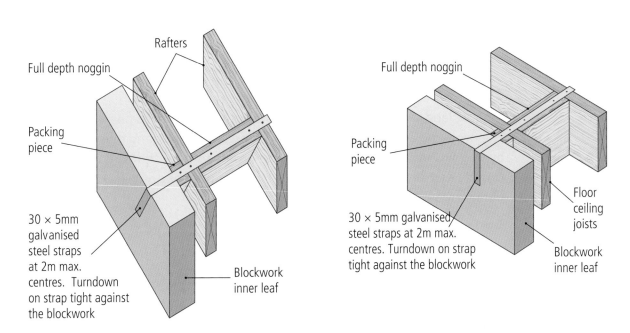

Fig. 12.11 Typical lateral strapping restraints at the gable wall.

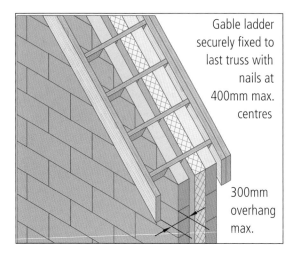

Gable ladder securely fixed to last truss with nails at 400mm max. centres

300mm overhang max.

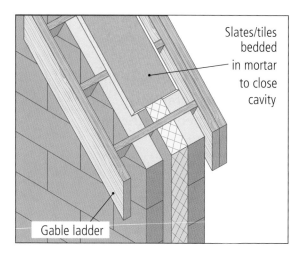

Slates/tiles bedded in mortar to close cavity

Gable ladder

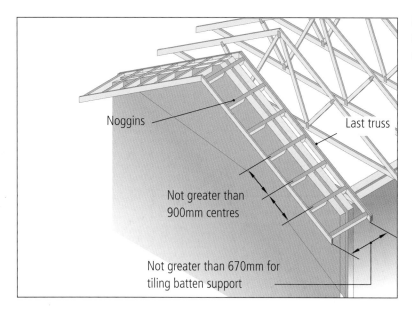

Noggins

Last truss

Not greater than 900mm centres

Not greater than 670mm for tiling batten support

Fig. 12.12 A gable ladder is used where the truss roof extends past the gable wall.

A gable ladder is constructed where the truss roof extends past the gable wall. The overhang of the gable ladder cannot exceed 300mm and must be supported by noggins at 900mm centres. It is important to note that the cavity must be closed regardless of whether a gable ladder is used or not. Fig. 12.12 shows the details of a gable ladder attached to a truss roof.

Truss roofs have the following advantages:

- They can be erected quickly
- Trusses are made to accurate measurements in the factory
- They are economic as they use less timber than other types of roof
- No load-bearing internal walls are necessary for support.

EAVES

Regardless of whether the pitched roof constructed is cut or trussed, there will be eaves where the roof meets the exterior wall. Eaves comprise a number of elements, including fascia, soffit and guttering. Fig. 12.13 shows a detailed illustration of the eaves detail of a pitched roof, and the technical specifications for the sizes of the individual elements are shown in Fig. 12.14.

Fig. 12.13 Timber frame wall with eaves detail.

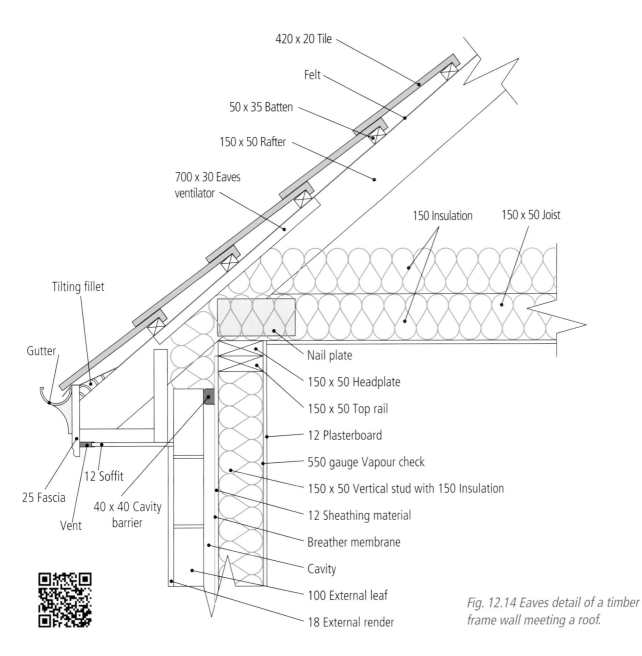

420 x 20 Tile
Felt
50 x 35 Batten
150 x 50 Rafter
700 x 30 Eaves ventilator
150 Insulation
150 x 50 Joist
Tilting fillet
Nail plate
150 x 50 Headplate
150 x 50 Top rail
Gutter
12 Plasterboard
550 gauge Vapour check
150 x 50 Vertical stud with 150 Insulation
12 Soffit
12 Sheathing material
25 Fascia
40 x 40 Cavity barrier
Breather membrane
Vent
Cavity
100 External leaf
18 External render

Fig. 12.14 Eaves detail of a timber frame wall meeting a roof.

LEAN-TO ROOF

A roof with a single slope is referred to as a lean-to roof. These are most commonly used in extensions and porches and not usually planned at the initial stage of the build as they tend to be added when the main work is complete. Where the roof abuts the wall, flashings are built into the wall to prevent moisture penetrating through the abutting joint. The details of the lean-to roof as well as the technical specifications are shown in Figs 12.15 and 12.16.

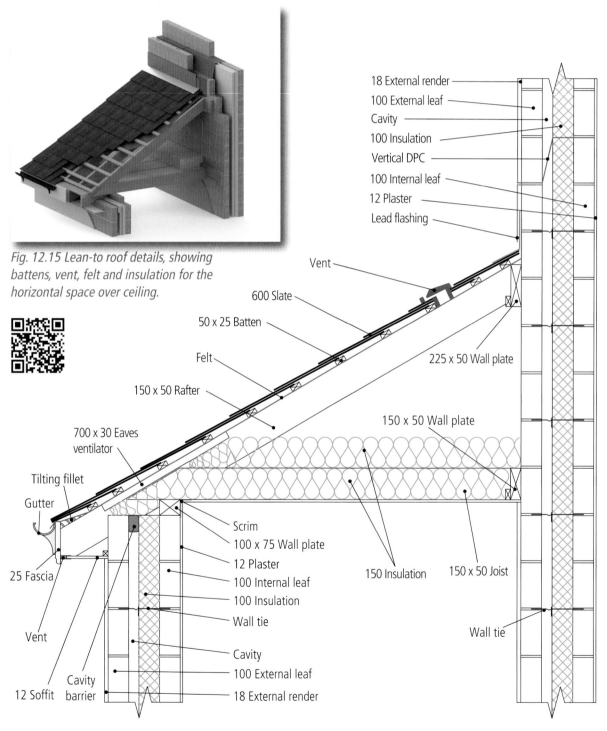

Fig. 12.15 Lean-to roof details, showing battens, vent, felt and insulation for the horizontal space over ceiling.

18 External render
100 External leaf
Cavity
100 Insulation
Vertical DPC
100 Internal leaf
12 Plaster
Lead flashing

Vent
600 Slate
50 x 25 Batten
Felt
150 x 50 Rafter
700 x 30 Eaves ventilator
Tilting fillet
Gutter
25 Fascia
Vent
12 Soffit
Cavity barrier

Scrim
100 x 75 Wall plate
12 Plaster
100 Internal leaf
100 Insulation
Wall tie
Cavity
100 External leaf
18 External render

225 x 50 Wall plate
150 x 50 Wall plate
150 Insulation
150 x 50 Joist
Wall tie

Fig. 12.16 Lean-to sectional detailed drawing.

FLAT ROOF

A flat roof does in fact have a small slope – this allows for water run-off. This type of roof is commonly used for garages, extensions and commercial buildings.

There are two methods of constructing a flat roof: cold deck construction and warm deck construction.

Cold deck roof construction is the traditional method, used before insulation became a necessity in meeting building regulations. The cold deck roof starts with the joists, which are covered with tongue-

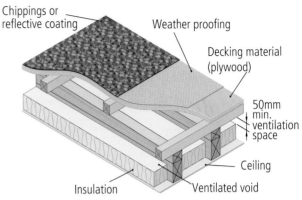

Fig. 12.17 Pictorial view of a cold deck roof construction.

and-groove sheets of exterior grade plywood or chipboard. Mineral wool insulation is laid between the joists. A minimum of 50mm ventilation space must be provided between the roof deck and the insulation. This space allows warm, moist air to flow out of the roof and prevents condensation. The underside of the joists are covered with a vapour barrier and foil-backed plasterboard. The structure is then covered with three layers of roofing felt to make it weatherproof, and a final layer of chips is added to prevent the roof surface overheating.

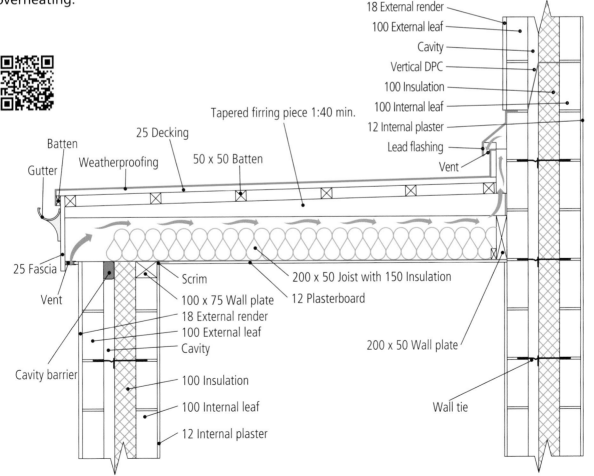

Fig .12.18 Flat roof abutment: cold deck.

In general, however, this type of flat roof construction is not recommended because there is a high risk of damp developing due to inadequate ventilation and heat loss.

Figs 12.17 and 12.18 show both a pictorial view of a cold deck roof construction and the technical specifications associated with this roof type.

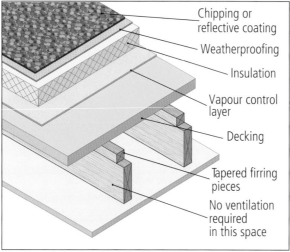

Fig. 12.19 Pictorial view of a warm deck roof construction.

Warm deck construction is so named because the insulation is placed outside the deck, thereby 'warming' the deck. As with a cold deck, the construction starts with the joists, which are covered with tongue-and-groove sheets of exterior grade plywood or chipboard. A vapour barrier is placed over the plywood/chipboard and rigid insulation is laid over the vapour barrier. Three layers

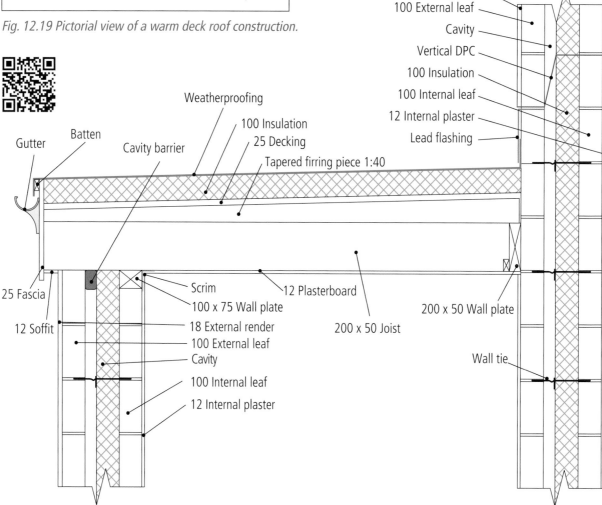

Fig. 12.20 Flat roof abutment: warm deck.

of felt are fitted and chippings spread to prevent the roof overheating. No ventilation is required in warm deck construction as there is no opportunity for moisture to build up through condensation. Figs 12.19 and 12.20 show a pictorial view of a warm deck roof construction and the technical specifications associated with this roof type.

Whether the construction of the deck is cold or warm, the roof is finished in the same way. The edge of the roof that is not attached to the house needs to be sealed. This is done with aprons. Aprons are strips of felt that are sealed and taken over the fascia board. Along the edge of the fascia board a batten is fixed to allow any moisture to travel from the apron into the gutter. Flashing is used at the join between the wall and the roof to prevent moisture transfer. Chippings are spread along the top surface of the roof where the roof will be exposed to direct sunlight. The chippings prevent the felt overheating.

LIVING SPACES IN ROOFS

The 'one-and-a-half-storey' house is one of the most common in this country. Rooms in roof spaces, often with rooflights and dormer windows, are very popular in this type of house. Where living space is required within the roof, enough clear height and width is needed to accommodate the rooms.

There are a number of functional requirements that must be met in order to successfully house living space in the roof:

- Adequate floor area and height
- Light
- Ventilation
- Fire resistance
- Sound insulation
- Thermal insulation
- Access.

The method of constructing the roof differs in that windows are built into it. This is discussed in detail in Chapter 15. Typical constructions for accommodating living space within a roof are shown in Fig. 12.21.

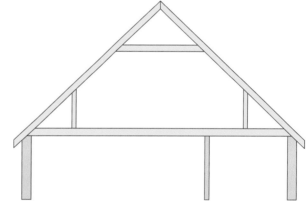

Typical dormer roof configuration

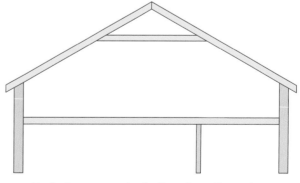

Typical storey-and-a-half roof configuration

Fig. 12.21 Dormer roof configuration and storey-and-a-half roof configuration (some structural details are omitted for clarity).

COVERING A ROOF

It is vital that the covering of the roof prevents moisture from penetrating and withstands any loads that are imposed upon it. There are a number of different ways of covering the structural elements of the roof. Pitched and lean-to roof types are generally tiled or slated. The type of material used to cover a roof will depend on a number of factors, including aesthetics, price, durability and location.

Aesthetic qualities of the roof include the slope of the roof, the tiles or slates used, etc.

Price is dependent on the materials to be used as well as the labour costs involved. Significant savings can be made by choosing less expensive types of slate or tile. Both synthetic and natural products are available, and synthetic materials are cheaper.

Durability depends on the quality of materials used: some materials are more durable than others. The durability of the roof covering, as well as the most appropriate materials for the location of the build, are considered when designing the roof.

Location can play a huge role in deciding which roof covering to use. Where local slates or tiles are available, using these can help a builder integrate the roof with its surroundings. This also ties the building with the traditional building style of the area.

The roof must be prepared before any cover is fixed to it. The first layer to be put over the rafters is sarking felt. Sarking felt is a breathable, waterproof covering that prevents moisture penetrating through to the rafters. The felt is layered in horizontal strips, starting from the eaves level, with an overlap of not less than 150mm, and is lapped over the ridge for water to run on. This is included as an additional protection in cases where moisture permeates through the tiles/slate due to damage. If the felt is torn or punctured during installation it must be repaired to ensure that the roof is watertight.

A tilting fillet is a piece of timber that allows a more gradual slope from the roof slope to the fascia board (i.e. the lower end of the roof). Its purpose is to lift the bottom row of slates/tiles as well as to prevent a build-up of moisture between the rafters and the fascia board. Additional felt is left at the very bottom of the roof and positioned over the tilting fillet in such a way that any water will run into the gutters. Tilting fillets are also used if there are valleys in the roof. In this case, the tilting fillet is raised to the same height as the battens and directs water from under the slates/tiles into the valley.

Battens are the next layer fixed to the roof surface. The dimensions of the battens depend on the slate/tile manufacturer's specifications. Generally tiles require a batten of 50 x 35mm, and slates require 50 x 25mm battens. The battens are evenly spaced and nailed through the sarking felt onto the rafters;

each batten must be nailed to a minimum of three rafters in order to be fully secure.

Tiles or slates are the final layer of the roof. Tiles are individually nailed down, using clout nails, in layers from the eaves to the ridge. The sides of the tiles interlock together to provide additional strength to the roof.

Slates are laid in the same sequence, from eaves to ridge. Each slate is nailed individually with copper slate nails and stainless steel hooks; they are spaced to overlap each other by a half of their full width and length in order to provide sufficient seal and strength for the roof surface. Fig. 12.22 shows the layers of a roof.

Fig. 12.22 Slate layers are started at the eaves and continued up towards the ridge.

VENTILATION

Ventilating the roof space is very important. Air flow is needed to remove moisture and prevent condensation. Inadequate ventilation can lead to condensation, which can cause problems such as rot, rust and mould growth.

In order to ventilate the space sufficiently, there must be an unobstructed air flow from one side of the eaves to the other, or from eaves level to ridge level. Ventilation is provided through the soffit, and a vent is used to prevent insects, birds and other small creatures entering. Eaves ventilators are built into the structure at eaves level to prevent the roof insulation from blocking the flow of air from the vents in the soffit. Fig. 12.23 shows the eaves ventilator in position.

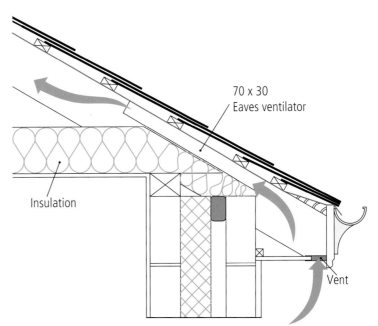

70 x 30
Eaves ventilator

Insulation

Vent

Fig. 12.23 Vents are built into the eaves of the building. This allows air to circulate under the roof covering.

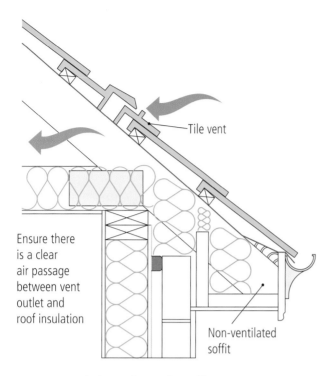

Ensure there is a clear air passage between vent outlet and roof insulation

Tile vent

Non-ventilated soffit

Fig. 12.24 Vent tile located near the soffit.

Ventilation can also be provided using a vent tile. This tile must be located as close to the eaves as possible, as in Fig. 12.24. This means that the insulation can be packed right into the soffit area, filling the space within the fascia, soffit and rafter.

GUTTERING

Guttering is used to direct water away from the roof surface without it splashing straight down onto the ground. Water runs from the roof into the guttering, which is fixed along the eaves. This water is then directed to a downpipe which channels it into a drain. Guttering is explained in greater detail in Chapter 23.

PRACTICE QUESTIONS

1. What are the functional requirements of a roof?

2. Using notes and neat freehand sketches, describe the differences between cut and truss pitched roofs.

3. To a scale of 1:10 draw a vertical section through the eaves of a traditionally cut timber roof finished with tiles. Indicate on your drawing the typical dimensions for building elements.

4. To a scale of 1:10 draw a vertical section through the ridge detail of a traditionally cut timber roof finished with tiles. Indicate on your drawing the typical dimensions for building elements.

5. To a scale of 1:10 draw a vertical section through a lean-to roof finished with slates. Indicate on your drawing typical dimensions for building elements.

6. To a scale of 1:10 draw a vertical section through a flat roof. Indicate on your drawing typical dimensions for the building elements.

7. Explain using notes and neat freehand sketches how a living space is created in a roof.

SAMPLE EXAMINATION QUESTIONS

2012 Ordinary Level Question 1

The sketch shows a tiled roof of a dwelling house, which is supported on a 350 mm external concrete block wall with an insulated cavity. The roof is a traditional cut roof and has a pitch of 45°.

(a) To a scale of 1:5, draw a vertical section through the eaves of the tiled roof and the external wall. Show the typical construction details from a level 400 mm below the wall plate, through the eaves and include **three** courses of tiles at eaves.

Include the roof insulation and show clearly the ventilation path to the roof structure at the eaves. Include **three** typical dimensions.

(b) On your drawing, show **one** method of closing the cavity at eaves level.

2011 Higher Level Question 2

(a) Discuss in detail, using notes and freehand sketches, **three** functional requirements of a roof suitable for a dwelling house.

(b) Using notes and freehand sketches, show **two** different types of pitched roof structure suitable for a dwelling house having an internal span of 6.0 metres and one internal load-bearing wall. For **each** roof type, indicate the design detailing that ensures the structural stability of the roof and include the typical dimensions of **three** structural members.

(c) Recommend a preferred roof structure for a dwelling house and give **two** reasons in support of your recommendation.

2009 Higher Level Question 7

A new house with an internal width of 7.0 metres, has a traditional cut roof which is slated and has a pitch of 45 degrees, as shown in the accompanying sketch. The roof is designed to incorporate bedroom accommodation in the attic space. The external wall supporting the floor joists of the attic is of timber frame construction with a concrete block outer leaf. The floor joists are supported internally on a centrally located load-bearing wall.

(a) To a scale of 1:10 draw a vertical section through one half of the roof structure from eaves to ridge, showing one external wall and one rafter length. Show all the construction details from 400 mm below the floor joists to the ridge and include three courses of slate at eaves. Include **four** typical dimensions of the roof structure.

(b) Indicate clearly on the drawing the design detailing to show the continuity of insulation from the wall to the roof structure.

2009 Ordinary Level Question 5

A dwelling house has a traditional cut roof with a pitch of 45 degrees, as shown in the sketch. The roof, which is insulated, is covered with concrete roof tiles which are supported on 200 mm × 50 mm rafters. To a scale of 1:5, draw a vertical section through the portion of the roof at the ridge, as shown within the circle in the sketch. Show all the construction details from the top of the ridge to 150 mm below the collar tie and include three courses of tiles at the ridge. Label the roof components and give their typical sizes.

CHAPTER **13**
FIREPLACE AND CHIMNEY

LEARNING OUTCOMES:

After studying this chapter students will:

• Understand the functions of a fireplace.
• Be able to explain how a chimney is constructed.
• Be able to draw to scale both the fireplace and the chimney.
• Be able to explain how water is kept out of the chimney at roof level.
• Understand the maximum and minimum guidelines for chimney placement.

KEYWORDS:

• FIREPLACE • CHIMNEY • DRAUGHT • FIREBACK • FLUE-GATHERING LINTEL • STACK
• FLUE LINERS • FLASHING • DPC TRAY • APRON FLASHING • SOAKERS • BACK GUTTER
• COVER FLASHING

INTRODUCTION

Fireplaces have been an important focus in the home for as long as houses have been built. Since there is a long tradition of including fireplaces in dwellings, their design has changed over the years, but whether traditional or modern in style, the fireplace continues to be a central part of the home.

A fireplace in a house requires a chimney, as do stoves, which are an aesthetically pleasing alternative to an open fire. The chimney stack, which surrounds and supports the flue, can be located either internally or externally. A chimney stack that is located internally can be built in any of the positions shown in Fig. 13.3.

For all its aesthetic qualities, the fireplace is also a functional addition to a house. It provides a safe source of direct heat, and it removes smoke and gases through the flue, including carbon dioxide and carbon monoxide given off by burning solid fuels.

Fig. 13.1 A line of rooftops with traditional chimneys.

Fig. 13.2 A modern and traditional fireplace.

(a) External walls   (b) Partition walls   (c) Party walls

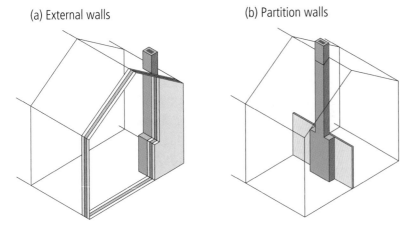
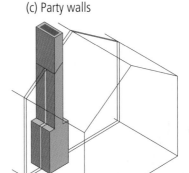

Fig. 13.3 Different locations for a chimney in the home.

(d) Freestanding

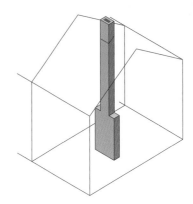

Heat is lost directly up the chimney through the same path as the smoke and gases. Only around 25 per cent of the heat generated in a fireplace makes it into the room, and a portion of this escapes too, depending on how well insulated the building is.

The fireplace fulfils a number of functions:

Safely generate heat: The fireplace must be constructed using non-combustible materials so that it contains the heat safely. Materials used to construct the fireplace include ceramics and concrete – these materials are able to withstand high temperatures. The fireplace must also be very well insulated at the back so that the heat is reflected into the room rather than absorbed by the wall.

(e) External flue

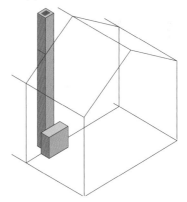

Extract smoke and gases produced in the fireplace: Smoke and gases do not just rise up through the chimney of their own accord. A draught is created by the height of the flue and the air pressure at the top of the flue. This pulls the smoke and gases up the length of the flue. In order for this draught to function correctly, the flue must not be too wide, because the pressure at the top may not be strong enough to extract the smoke and gases.

Burn fuel efficiently: If the grate is well designed and allows air to flow through from underneath, solid fuel can reach high temperatures and burn completely. Unfortunately, because it has an open top, an open fire has a heat loss of as much as 80 per cent.

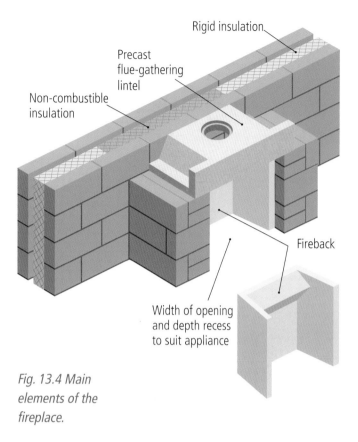

Rigid insulation

Precast
flue-gathering
lintel

Non-combustible
insulation

Fireback

Width of opening
and depth recess
to suit appliance

*Fig. 13.4 Main
elements of the
fireplace.*

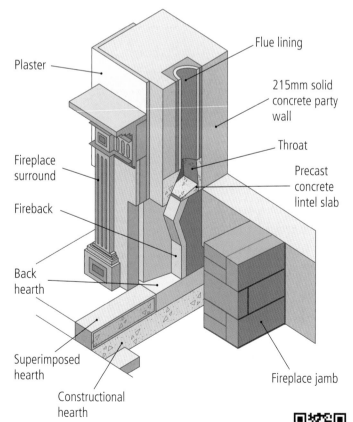

Plaster

Flue lining

215mm solid
concrete party
wall

Throat

Fireplace
surround

Precast
concrete
lintel slab

Fireback

Back
hearth

Superimposed
hearth

Fireplace jamb

Constructional
hearth

Fig. 13.5 Fireplace and surrounds.

CONSTRUCTION OF A FIREPLACE

Blockwork jambs or piers are built to create the opening for an internal fireplace. A fireback (a solid, cast concrete sheet at the back of the fireplace) is set into this recess, so the dimensions of the recess depend on the size of the fireback being used.

A precast, flue-gathering lintel is placed on top of the jambs/piers as shown in Fig. 13.4. This is a support for the top opening of the fire which has a hole in it to allow the gases from the fire to escape.

The shape of the flue-gathering lintel affects the performance of the fireplace. To prevent smoke entering the room (rather than going up the flue), the distance between the fireback and the inner circular surface of the precast flue-gathering lintel must be 100mm to create an upward draught. The smoke shelf (the area just above the fireback) prevents downdraughts. The cavity wall behind the fireplace and chimney stack is filled with non-combustible insulation.

The chimney stack is then built up. This is done in stages. The internal part of the chimney is made up of flue liners of 200mm diameter and the chimney stack is built around them. The flue liners are fixed with fire-resistant mortar. The flue liners do not come into contact with the chimney stack – the cavity between the two is filled with a dry mix of cement, lime and sand in the ratio 1:1:12, or with insulating concrete. Fig. 13.5 shows a fireplace in its surrounds, while the details and technical specifications of the fireplace are illustrated in Fig. 13.6.

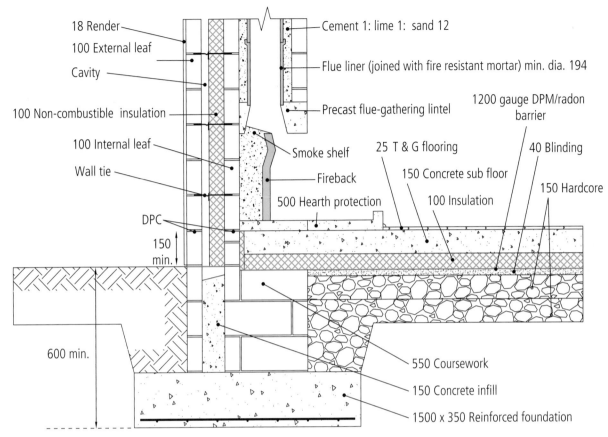

18 Render
100 External leaf
Cavity
100 Non-combustible insulation
100 Internal leaf
Wall tie
DPC
150 min.
600 min.

Cement 1: lime 1: sand 12
Flue liner (joined with fire resistant mortar) min. dia. 194
Precast flue-gathering lintel
1200 gauge DPM/radon barrier
Smoke shelf
Fireback
25 T & G flooring
150 Concrete sub floor
40 Blinding
500 Hearth protection
100 Insulation
150 Hardcore
550 Coursework
150 Concrete infill
1500 x 350 Reinforced foundation

Fig. 13.6 Fireplace specification.

When a chimney stack is built in a timber frame construction, it is important to ensure that heat cannot travel from the fire source to the timbers. There are a number of ways of doing this:

- Make the back of the chimney stack wider
- Position the chimney stack away from the timber frame wall
- Make the back of the chimney stack deeper.

Each of these methods is shown graphically in Fig 13.7.

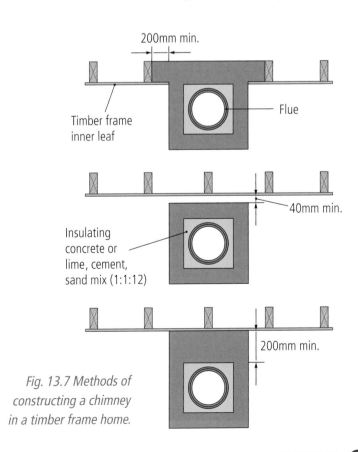

200mm min.
Flue
Timber frame inner leaf
40mm min.
Insulating concrete or lime, cement, sand mix (1:1:12)
200mm min.

Fig. 13.7 Methods of constructing a chimney in a timber frame home.

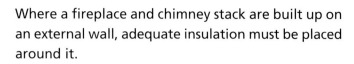

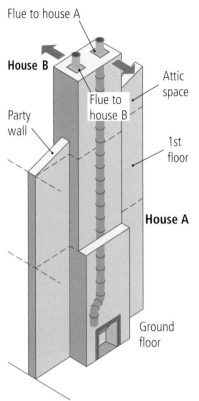

Flue to house A

House B

Party wall

Flue to house B

Attic space

1st floor

House A

Ground floor

Fig. 13.8 Double-flue chimney stack in the party wall of two semi-detached homes.

Where a fireplace and chimney stack are built up on an external wall, adequate insulation must be placed around it.

Fireplaces in semi-detached houses can be built back to back on the party wall between the dwellings, with the flues for each chimney contained in the same stack. Fig. 13.8 shows how this is achieved.

WEATHERPROOFING

The top of the stack protrudes from the roof, so the junction between the chimney stack and the roof must be watertight. Not only can water leach in through the junction, it can also soak through the masonry. A number of elements are used to prevent water travelling down the brickwork. These are referred to as flashings and consist of:

DPC tray: The DPC tray is built into the chimney during construction. The right-angled bend prevents dampness penetrating into the stack. The front of the tray has drainage channels, which allow water to run off through weepholes in the masonry. The front surface of the tray incorporates a flashing, which is lapped over the apron to prevent moisture penetration. Fig. 13.9 shows the DPC tray.

Apron flashing: This is situated at the front of the chimney. It sits on top of the slates and its top is covered by the DPC tray. This flashing prevents moisture entering between the slates and the front of the chimney. It covers the two corners at the front and extends down by 100mm over the slates. Fig. 13.10 shows a diagram of apron flashing.

Drainage channel to be kept free of mortar to allow water to discharge over flashing via weepholes in brickwork

Apron cover flashing attached to tray

Fig. 13.9 Lead tray DPC, the base on which the external stack sits.

Apron flashing

Fig. 13.10 Apron flashing for the lower side of the chimney stack.

Soakers: Used at the sides of the chimney stack to prevent water entering between the chimney stack and the slates. Each slate that runs alongside the chimney stack has a soaker on top. Fig. 13.11 shows a soaker.

Back gutter: This is placed on the upper part of the sloping roof at the back of the chimney stack, and its purpose is to direct water from the back to the sides of the chimney. It covers the back corners of the chimney and is raised at the back to prevent water seeping under the slates. Fig. 13.12 shows the back gutter.

Cover flashing: This is installed on all four sides of the chimney. It guides the water from the face of the chimney down onto the other components of the flashings. The top of the cover flashing is chased into the masonry to ensure that no water penetrates into the brick/blockwork. Fig. 13.13 shows cover flashing in place.

The elements described above combine to prevent water from penetrating through the chimney. Figs 13.14 and 13.15 (next page) show a pictorial view of the combined elements and a detailed technical drawing of the chimney at roof level.

Chimney capping: A chimney cap is placed at the very top of the chimney. A chimney cap can be made from a number of materials, including stainless steel, galvanised steel and copper. It is a protective covering that not only protects against the entry of rain and snow, but also stops birds getting into the chimney, and prevents downdraughts. Fig. 13.16 shows some of the different kinds of chimney capping or cowls.

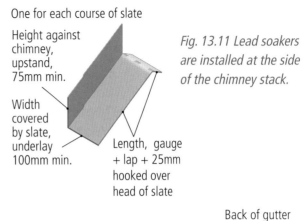

One for each course of slate

Height against chimney, upstand, 75mm min.

Width covered by slate, underlay 100mm min.

Length, gauge + lap + 25mm hooked over head of slate

Fig. 13.11 Lead soakers are installed at the side of the chimney stack.

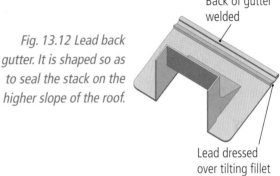

Back of gutter welded

Fig. 13.12 Lead back gutter. It is shaped so as to seal the stack on the higher slope of the roof.

Lead dressed over tilting fillet

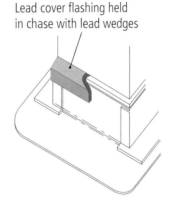

Lead cover flashing held in chase with lead wedges

Fig. 13.13 Cover flashing chased into the masonry of the chimney stack.

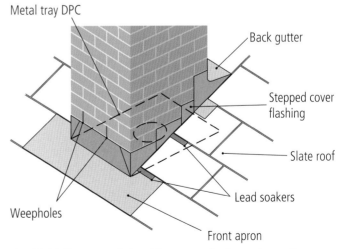

Metal tray DPC

Back gutter

Stepped cover flashing

Slate roof

Lead soakers

Front apron

Weepholes

Fig. 13.14 Elements of the chimney stack above the roof.

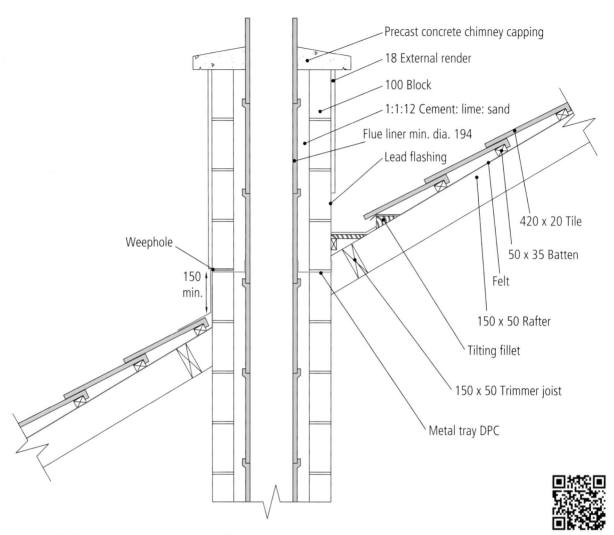

Precast concrete chimney capping
18 External render
100 Block
1:1:12 Cement: lime: sand
Flue liner min. dia. 194
Lead flashing
420 x 20 Tile
50 x 35 Batten
Felt
150 x 50 Rafter
Tilting fillet
150 x 50 Trimmer joist
Metal tray DPC
Weephole
150 min.

Fig. 13.15 Sectional view of chimney stack through a roof.

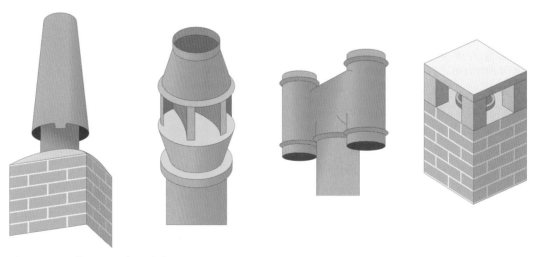

Fig. 13.16 Different styles of chimney capping or cowls.

HEIGHT REQUIREMENTS

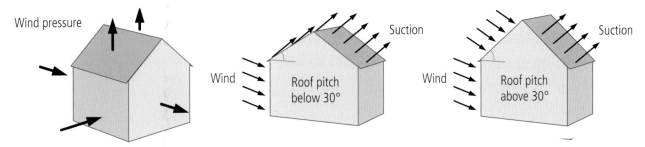

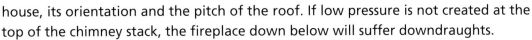

Fig. 13.17 The movement of air around a building can create push and pull factors (as we saw in Chapter 6). Here we can see areas of pressure and suction.

A chimney functions by using differences in air pressure, as shown in Fig. 13.17. The low pressure at the top of the stack draws the air up from below. Where the areas of high and low pressure are located depends on the position of the house, its orientation and the pitch of the roof. If low pressure is not created at the top of the chimney stack, the fireplace down below will suffer downdraughts.

The height of the chimney helps to create this area of low pressure (Fig. 13.18). The top of the chimney stack must be a minimum of one metre from the highest point of contact between the chimney stack and the roof slope. As well as that, the top of the stack must be at least 4.5m above the top of the fireplace to ensure adequate draw.

Because of its height, and because it protrudes above the top of the building, wind can be problematic for a chimney stack. To compensate for this the width of the chimney is increased in relation to its height to make it more stable. The distance between the top of the chimney stack and the ridge of the roof can also affect the pressure zones. The dimensional guidelines shown in Fig. 13.18 aim to prevent any problems in that regard.

The top of the stack must be finished to prevent rain penetrating into it. A precast concrete chimney cap with a layer of DPC underneath it is used to achieve this.

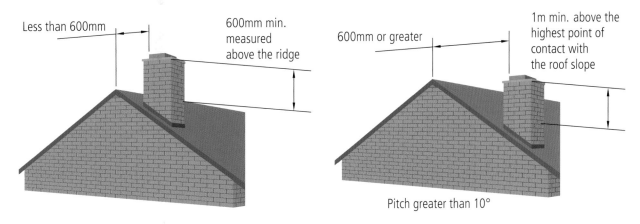

Fig. 13.18 Chimney height requirements.

PRACTICE QUESTIONS

1. Name the functional requirements of a fireplace.

2. Neatly sketch three places suitable for the location of a fireplace and chimney stack.

3. To a scale of 1:5 draw a vertical section through a fireplace. Include the foundations as well as all the necessary technical specifications.

4. Explain using notes and neat freehand sketches how the chimney is weatherproofed at roof level.

6. To a scale of 1:10 draw a vertical section through a chimney at roof level.

7. Explain using notes and neat freehand sketches the requirements regarding the height of a chimney in relation to the roof.

SAMPLE EXAMINATION QUESTIONS

2011 Higher Level Question 7

A concrete block chimney stack with a sand/cement render passes through a cut roof which is slated and is pitched at 45°, as shown in the sketch.

(a) To a scale of 1:5, draw a vertical section through the chimney stack and roof, showing the typical details of the chimney stack, flue, chimney capping and portion of the roof structure. Show clearly the design details necessary to prevent the penetration of water between the chimney stack and the adjoining roof surface.

(b) On your drawing, show **two** design details that will help prevent the occurrence of a downdraught in a chimney as shown. Include dimensions as appropriate.

2008 Higher Level Question 1

An open fireplace is located on the party wall between two semi-detached houses, as shown in the accompanying sketch. The party wall is a 300 mm solid block wall and the ground floor is a concrete floor with a 25 mm woodblock finish.

(a) To a scale of 1:5, draw a vertical section through the ground floor, hearth and fireplace. The section should show all the construction details from the bottom of the foundation to the top of the second flue liner. Include **four** typical dimensions on your drawing.

(b) Indicate clearly on the drawing how the flue liners are joined to ensure the safe removal of smoke and gasses from the fireplace.

CHAPTER 14
STAIRS

INTRODUCTION

The main function of a set of stairs is to provide a safe, comfortable and easy way to walk between floors. In order to be safe and comfortable to use, internal stairs are designed so that their dimensions are always the same, wherever they are located. There are strict guidelines governing the measurements and tolerances for each element of the stairs. These guidelines ensure that stairs are:

- Ergonomically sound
- Structurally strong and stable enough to withstand loads placed on them
- Durable
- Easily navigable
- Aesthetically pleasing.

STAIRS TERMINOLOGY

A number of terms are associated with stairs:

Flight: A series of steps with a landing. For safety reasons each flight must have no more than 16 steps.

Step: A component that divides the large vertical distance between floors into smaller vertical distances. The step itself comprises the tread and the riser.

Tread: This is the part of the stair that you tread on. Tread depth is the measurement from the front edge of the step to the riser. The width is the measurement from side to side.

Riser: This is the vertical component at the back of each tread. Sometimes the riser is omitted to create an open stair effect.

Nosing: This is the small protrusion above each riser. It is part of the tread. It is designed to make you lift your foot around it so you don't stub your toe when climbing the stairs. It also makes the tread deeper, so the stairs are more comfortable to climb.

Strings: These are the long diagonal members of the stairs that support the steps. There are two types: closed string and cut string. In a closed string the steps are housed within the string. In a cut string a portion of the string is cut away and the tread is placed on top.

Newel post: The post that the string is joined to. These posts support the handrail and can be found at the top and bottom of the stairs.

Handrail: The rail that you hold on to when going up or down stairs. The handrail is fixed to the newel posts and runs parallel to the string.

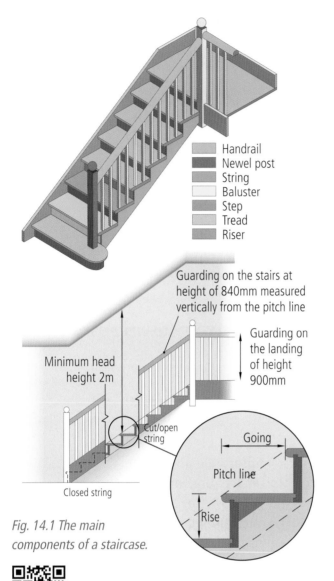

Key:
Handrail
Newel post
String
Baluster
Step
Tread
Riser

Guarding on the stairs at height of 840mm measured vertically from the pitch line

Guarding on the landing of height 900mm

Minimum head height 2m

Cut/open string

Going

Pitch line

Rise

Closed string

Fig. 14.1 The main components of a staircase.

Baluster: Vertical member that is placed between the string and the handrail.

Balustrade: The framework comprising the handrail and the balusters.

All these elements are joined together to make a complete staircase (Fig. 14.1).

Other important terms are:

Going: The horizontal distance between the front face of one riser and the front face of the next riser.

Rise: The vertical distance between the top surface of one tread and the top surface of the next tread.

Pitch: The angle of the staircase. The pitch is measured between a line connecting the nosings of all treads in any one flight and the ground.

Winder: Used where there is limited space, a winder is a tapered tread that allows a staircase to change direction.

Glue blocks: Triangular wooden blocks that are attached to the underside of the stairs between the tread and the riser in order to reinforce the staircase, making it sturdier. They also prevent the steps creaking.

Wedges: Used in stair construction where the tread and riser are housed in the string. They are inserted between any gaps in the housing to wedge the riser and tread in place. Like the glue blocks, they support and reinforce the structure of the stairs, and prevent creaking.

TYPES OF STAIRCASE

The layout of the house can affect the type of staircase used. Some of the most common types of staircase are shown and described below.

Straight flight: A straight flight, as shown in Fig. 14.2, has no twists or turns. It rises from one floor to another in a straight line. There are a maximum of 16 steps in a flight.

Fig. 14.2 Straight flight of stairs.

Fig. 14.3 Half turn stairs.

Fig. 14.4 Quarter turn stairs.

Fig. 14.5 Spiral stairs.

Half turn stairs: Has a landing with two flights. Each flight has a maximum of 16 steps. When you walk up the stairs you do a U-turn on the landing between flights.

Quarter turn stairs: The flights are at 90 degrees to each other with a landing between flights. The maximum number of steps in any flight is 16.

Spiral: A spiral staircase is used where space is extremely limited, and sometimes for aesthetic affect. The steps wind around a central axis.

CHAPTER 14

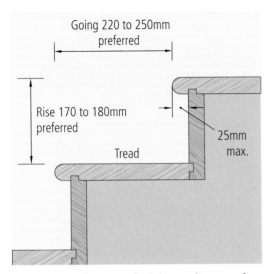

Fig. 14.6 Maximum and minimum distances for rise and going.

STAIR SAFETY

Stairs can be dangerous if not designed or used properly. To reduce risk, stairs are governed by a number of regulations and requirements. Some of these are outlined below.

- Twice the rise plus the going should equal between 550mm and 700mm.

$$2R + G = 550–700mm$$

This is a person's average stride length. If stairs are constructed to this calculation, a person will be able to climb them without breaking stride or feeling uncomfortable. Fig. 14.6 shows how the calculation works.

- **Maximum rise** = 220mm, with an optimal height of 175mm. A bigger rise can make the stairs difficult for younger or older people to climb.

- **Minimum going** = 220mm, with an optimal depth of 250mm. This is to ensure that there is enough space to put your foot on each step.

- **Headroom** between pitch line and ceiling level = at least 2m. This allows enough headroom for even the tallest person.

- **Maximum pitch** = 42°, with an optimal pitch of 35°. Any more than this and the stairs would be too steep to climb comfortably.

- **Nosing** = 16–25mm. This teaches a person to move their leg in such a way that they do not stub a toe or trip on the way up the stairs, as well as providing an increased depth to the tread.

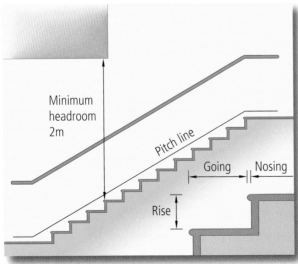

Fig. 14.7 Headroom and pitch line.

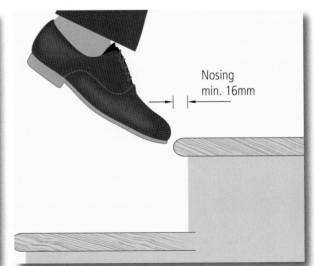

Fig. 14.8 Nosing.

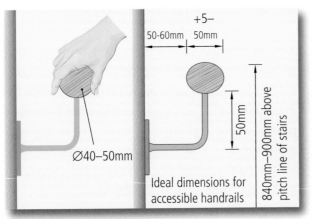

Fig. 14.9 Handrail design.

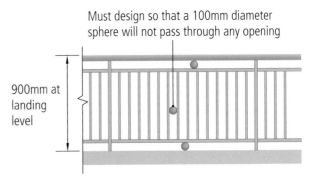

Must design so that a 100mm diameter sphere will not pass through any opening

900mm at landing level

Fig. 14.10 Baluster design.

- **Handrail = 840–900mm** above the pitch line. At this height the average person will be able to hold the handrail without difficulty or discomfort. (Fig. 14.9)

- **Balusters** must be close together; the test is that a 100mm diameter sphere will not pass between them. This measurement is based on the size of an infant's head and is aimed at reducing the risk of a small child getting its head stuck between the balusters. (Fig. 14.10)

Fig. 14.11 Open stairs without riser.

- **Maximum 16 steps** between floors/landings. This is a safety measure designed to reduce the distance a person would fall if they tripped. It also reduces the distance between landings for those who find it difficult to walk up or down stairs. There must be a landing at the top of each flight.

- **Guarding** of the stairs (all members used to protect against falls through openings) should not be climbable by children and should be a minimum height of 900mm.

- **Minimum width** = 800mm. If the width exceeds 1000mm a handrail must be provided on both sides.

In some staircases, the risers may be omitted. This is for aesthetic reasons – it does not affect the functionality of the staircase. An example is shown in the photograph (Fig. 14.11). If risers are omitted the stairs must comply with additional safety guidelines: a lip must be provided at the back of the tread to prevent feet or objects slipping through; and the spacing between treads must not allow a sphere of 100mm diameter to pass through.

CHAPTER 14

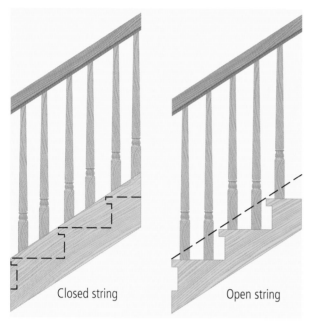

Fig. 14.12 Stair string types. Should be constructed so that a 100mm sphere cannot go through the opening of adjacent treads.

STAIR CONSTRUCTION

Timber stairs are usually made from pine, ash or oak. The stairs are erected in a space known as a stairwell. This area is usually against an external wall. The stairs consist of three main parts: two strings and the steps. There are two main types of stair, one which houses the riser and tread within the string (closed string) and one where the string itself is cut to accommodate the steps (cut or open string). Fig. 14.12 shows the two string types.

Housing a tread and riser into a closed string is achieved using wedges, and glue blocks (triangular cross-section pieces of wood) on the underside of the tread and riser, which stop the tread and riser from moving. To increase the strength and stability of the stairs, the tread and riser are joined to each other. This is done using a housing joint, which prevents the individual movement of each member, as shown in Fig. 4.13.

In a cut or open string stairs, the string board itself is cut to accommodate the steps. As with the closed string stairs, glue blocks secure the tread and riser from underneath. Occasionally a return nosing is attached to the exposed end of the

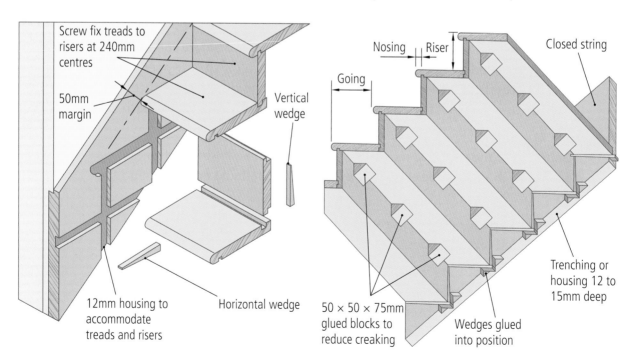

Fig. 14.13 Closed string stairs construction. The second image shows the wedges and blocks glued to the underside of the stairs.

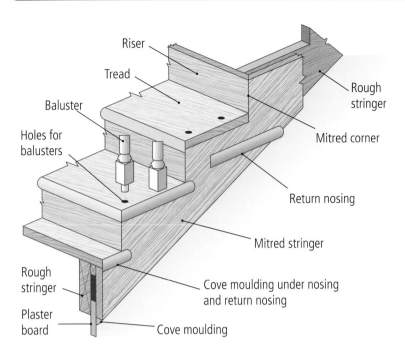

Riser
Tread
Baluster
Holes for balusters
Rough stringer
Plaster board
Cove moulding
Rough stringer
Mitred corner
Return nosing
Mitred stringer
Cove moulding under nosing and return nosing

Fig. 14.14 Cut/Open string step configuration.

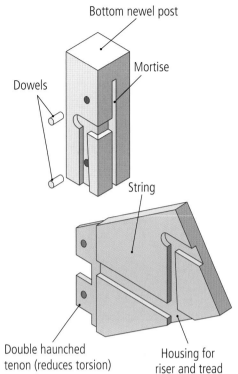

Bottom newel post
Dowels
Mortise
String
Double haunched tenon (reduces torsion)
Housing for riser and tread

Fig. 14.15 Newel post joint.

riser on the string side. This allows for a decorative finish, as seen in Fig 14.14.

The strings are fixed at the top and bottom of the staircase. Where a string is positioned against the wall, it is hooked over the trimmer, which is the joist at the top of the stairs. An outer string is joined to the newel post using a mortise and tenon joint. Dowels are used to hold the joint together. Fig. 14.16 shows the technical specifications associated with the bottom four steps of a closed string stairs.

To join the stairs to the landing above, the trimmer joist is housed into the newel and they are bolted together. The newel post is joined to the string as at the bottom of the stairs. A detailed view of this joint is shown in Fig. 14.15.

Fig 14.16 Bottom of stairs showing newel post in position.

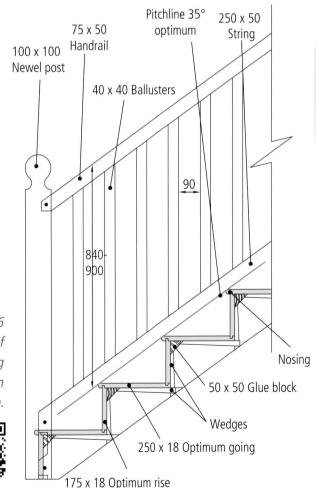

100 x 100 Newel post
75 x 50 Handrail
40 x 40 Ballusters
Pitchline 35° optimum
250 x 50 String
90
840–900
Nosing
50 x 50 Glue block
Wedges
250 x 18 Optimum going
175 x 18 Optimum rise

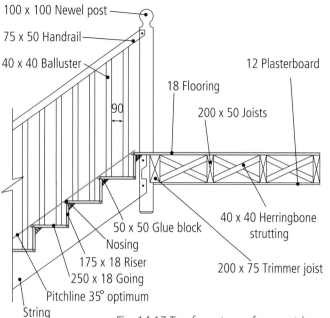

100 x 100 Newel post
75 x 50 Handrail
40 x 40 Balluster
90
18 Flooring
12 Plasterboard
200 x 50 Joists
50 x 50 Glue block
40 x 40 Herringbone strutting
Nosing
175 x 18 Riser
200 x 75 Trimmer joist
250 x 18 Going
Pitchline 35° optimum
String

Fig. 14.17 Top four steps of open string stairs, including landing.

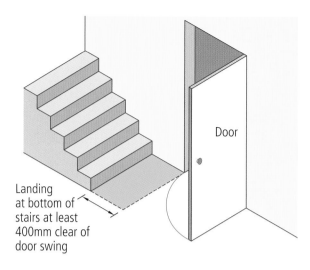

Door

Landing at bottom of stairs at least 400mm clear of door swing

Fig. 14.18 Door clearance for stair landings.

Mortise and tenon joints are also used to fix the handrail to the newel posts. The balusters can be either housed or mortised into the handrail.

If there is a door at the top or bottom of the stairs, sufficient clearance must be allowed for it to be opened. The maximum swing of the door must be at least 400mm from the bottom or top of the stairs.

CALCULATIONS

Stairs are designed for the specific space in which they are to fit. Because of the safety requirements and specifications outlined above, a lot of calculations must be made when designing the staircase. The rise and going of every step must be equal to prevent risk of injury to the user. The size of the rise and going depend on the number of steps and the total rise between floors.

First the overall rise is measured. This measurement is the overall height that the stairs will climb, that is from floor to floor. As outlined earlier, the maximum number of steps the flight can contain is 16 and the rise must be 220mm or less. The tread must be a minimum of 220mm. The relationship between the rise and going must also be satisfied:

$$2R + G = 550–700mm$$

An example of the calculation to be made is shown opposite.

Sample Calculation 1

Two floors are 2700mm apart. Calculate the rise and going of a staircase that meets all building regulations.

STEP 1

First we must find the number of steps that divides into the total rise. We start by dividing the total rise by the maximum number of steps (16):

$$\frac{2700}{16} = 168.75\text{mm}$$

Although 168.75mm meets the building regulations, it is too difficult to adhere to a measurement this precise in the construction of the stairs. So we will divide by 15 steps, as this is the next logical number.

$$\frac{2700}{15} = 180\text{mm}$$

Fifteen steps meets the requirements, and 180mm is a straightforward measurement to work with.

STEP 2

Now that we have a rise we must calculate a going. The formula we will use for this part of the calculation is:

$$2R + G = 550\text{–}700\text{mm}$$

We use the optimum rise and see if our equation is satisfied.

$$2(180) + (\text{optimal going}) = 550\text{–}700\text{mm}$$
$$360 + 250 = 610\text{mm}$$

As 610mm falls within the average stride length (550–700mm) this is an acceptable set of dimensions:

Maximum rise = 220 (our rise = 180mm)
Minimum going = 220 (our going = 250mm)

Both of our calculations fall within the requirements and therefore 15 steps with a rise of 180mm and a going of 250mm are the recommended dimensions for this staircase.

Sample Calculation 2

Two floors are 2035mm apart. A stairs is to be constructed between the floors with a maximum overall going of 3300mm. Calculate a rise and going that will satisfy all building regulations and allow safe passage between the floors.

STEP 1

Divide the total rise by the maximum number of steps to establish whether it will work.

Total rise/16 = 2035/16 = 127.1875mm. Not a round number, so try 15 steps.

Total rise/15 = 2035/15 = 135.6mm. Again not a round number, try 14 steps.

Total rise/14 = 2035/14 = 145.357mm. Try 13 steps.

Total rise/13 = 2035/13 = 156.538mm. Try 12 steps.

Total rise/12 = 2035/12 = 169.583mm. Try 11 steps.

Total rise/11 = 2035/11 = 185mm. This is a round number that fits the regulations (max. rise = 220mm).

STEP 2

Check if this number of steps allows for the going to fit building regulations.

Total going = 3300mm, number of steps = 11. Going = 300mm.

2R + G = 550–700mm

2(185) + 300 = 670mm. These measurements fit the building regulations. Therefore a rise of 185mm and a going of 300mm will produce a stairs of 11 steps that spans an overall going of 3300mm and rises 2035mm between floors.

PRACTICE QUESTIONS

1. What is the function of a staircase?

2. Why are there such strict regulations in relation to the construction of stairs?

3. Explain with the aid of notes and neat freehand sketches each of the following terms:
   (a) Tread and riser
   (b) Handrail
   (c) Newel post
   (d) String
   (e) Balustrade

4. Explain the design detail incorporated into the stairs to prevent creaking.

5. There are many types of staircase. Using notes and neat freehand sketches describe four of the most common.

6. What is the maximum number of steps that can be contained in any one flight?

7. Using notes and neat freehand sketches outline two specific safety features of an open riser stairs.

8. Using notes and neat freehand sketches outline five design features that make the stairs safe for all users.

9. Use notes and neat freehand sketches to describe the difference between a cut string and closed string stairs.

10. Use a neat freehand sketch to show the detail of the joint used to attach the string to the newel post.

11. What is the formula used to calculate the rise and going of a staircase given the distance between floors?

12. Two floors are 2660mm apart. Calculate the rise and going of a staircase that meets current building regulations.

13. Draw to a scale of 1:5 a vertical section of the bottom three steps of a closed string stairs. Include the newel post, handrail and balusters.

14. Draw to a suitable scale a vertical section through the top three steps of a cut string stairs. The stairs lead to a landing with a suspended timber floor with tongued-and-grooved flooring boards on timber joists and a plasterboard ceiling.

CHAPTER 14

SAMPLE EXAMINATION QUESTIONS

2011 Ordinary Level Question 5

The sketch shows a portion of a closed string timber stairs suitable for a dwelling house.

(a) To a scale of 1:5, draw a vertical section through the bottom three steps of the stairs. Show the string, treads and risers and give their typical sizes.

(b) Show on your drawing **one** design detail which will ensure that the stairs does not creak when in use.

2010 Higher Level Question 7

The top portion of an open riser timber stairs is shown in the accompanying sketch. The first floor landing has a suspended timber floor with 25 mm hardwood flooring on timber joists and a plasterboard ceiling beneath.
The newel post is 100 mm × 100 mm.

(a) To a scale of 1:5 draw a vertical section through the top three steps of the stairs and landing. Show the newel post, balusters and handrail of the stairs. Indicate on the drawing the:

- handrail height to stairs
- handrail height to landing
- spacing between balusters.

(b) Using notes and *freehand sketches*, show **two** safety features in the design of an open riser stairs to ensure that the stairs is safe for all users.

2008 Higher Level Question 7

A cut-string timber stairs suitable for a domestic dwelling is shown in the accompanying sketch.

(a) To a scale of 1:5, draw a vertical section through the bottom four steps of the stairs. Include the newel post and balustrade and show the typical dimensions of **four** main structural members of the stairs.

(b) Using notes and *freehand sketches* show **two** design features that ensure that the stairs is safe for all users.

CHAPTER 15
WINDOWS AND DOORS

LEARNING OUTCOMES:

After studying this chapter students will:

- Understand the importance of windows and doors in dwellings.
- Be able to explain the main functions of both windows and doors.
- Draw to scale vertical sections through windows and doors.
- Explain how both windows and doors are installed.

KEYWORDS:

- WINDOW • DOOR • FENESTRATION • SLIDING SASH • CASEMENT • PIVOT • GLAZING • CILL
- LINTEL • TRANSOM • MULLION • RAIL • THERMAL BREAK • PANELLED DOOR • FLUSH DOOR
- SOLID CORE • HOLLOW CORE • STAMPED HARDBOARD DOOR • THRESHOLD • JAMB • HEAD
- STILE • INTUMESCENT STRIP • HINGE • LOCK

INTRODUCTION

Windows and doors are essential elements of a living space. They let in air and light and provide a means of access, security and protection for the people living in a building.

WINDOWS

Windows allow light and air into a dwelling, which is both essential for people's well-being and enhances the atmosphere in a room. They 'open up' the space in a room and make it feel less claustrophobic. They not only allow for rapid ventilation (now known as purge ventilation), they also protect the inside of the dwelling from the weather, as well as maximising solar gain (see Chapter 16).

The placement of windows has a major impact on the overall appearance of the building. The windows must be in proportion to the building's wall area. The function of the building also affects the position, size and shape of the windows.

The arrangement of the windows on a building's

Fig. 15.1 Fenestration add enormously to the appearance of buildings. A vertical emphasis should be placed on these details for both aesthetic and functional reasons.

façade is known as fenestration. Fenestration also includes the way the window is divided up into subsections, the proportion of the panes in relation to the wall, and how the window sits into the wall. Fig. 15.1 shows an example of traditional fenestration, while Fig. 15.2 shows some of the many different window types available.

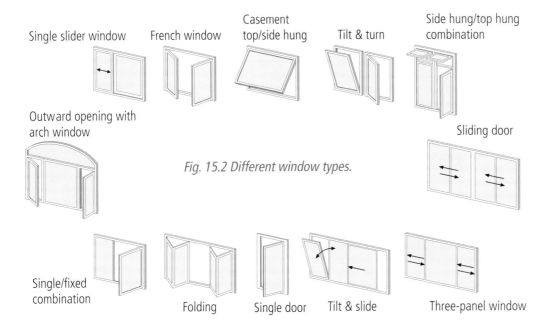

Fig. 15.2 Different window types.

A number of general rules help to make the windows aesthetically pleasing. These include:

- Keep the size of all windows the same, as far as possible.
- Avoid elaborate shapes.
- Position windows at the same height.
- Use fenestration to ensure that wall to window ratio is balanced.

FUNCTIONS OF WINDOWS

The main functional requirements of windows are outlined below.

Fig. 15.3 Illuminating a room with natural light.

Let in Light

The amount of light needed in a room depends on how the room is used. The window area of a room must be at least 10 per cent of the floor area of that room to ensure adequate light and ventilation. As long as this requirement is met the windows can be placed at the client's discretion. Larger windows are installed in high-use rooms, such as the kitchen, so that adequate light is available for tasks such as preparing food. In contrast, bedroom windows can be made smaller.

Ventilation

Water vapours and accumulated gases such as carbon dioxide and carbon monoxide need to be removed from a building, and ventilation is needed to do this.

Fresh air is let into a room simply by opening the windows. Ventilation requirements apply to 'habitable' rooms. A habitable room is used for living or sleeping and has a minimum floor area of 6.5m². Two types of ventilation are required: purge ventilation and background ventilation.

- **Purge ventilation** (formerly called rapid ventilation) is provided by window openings in the room. For habitable rooms the opening area of the window must equal at least 5 per cent of the floor area. This figure allows sufficient ventilation regardless of room size. Depending on the number of windows, various ventilation patterns can occur. These are shown in Fig. 15.4.

- **Background ventilation** is a more permanent state of ventilation. To achieve this, a vent is built into an external wall. This vent allows a constant flow of air and must never be blocked or filled in.

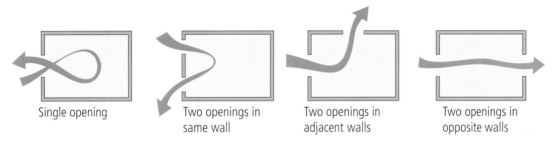

| Single opening | Two openings in same wall | Two openings in adjacent walls | Two openings in opposite walls |

Fig. 15.4 Different configurations of windows provide different patterns of ventilation.

Preventing Excessive Heat Loss

Heat follows the path of least resistance. As it is easier for heat to pass through glass than concrete, heat will first flow through the glazed area of a window – in fact, 20 per cent of the total heat lost from a building is lost through the windows. For this reason, windows must be designed to reduce heat loss as much as possible. This is achieved by adding glazing panels or weather strips. Fig. 15.5 shows how heat passes through the window.

Thermal bridging (or cold bridging) is the term used to describe the transfer of heat through solid surfaces. This happens when there is inadequate insulation. The head and cill of the window are designed to combat cold bridging and will be discussed further in Chapter 17.

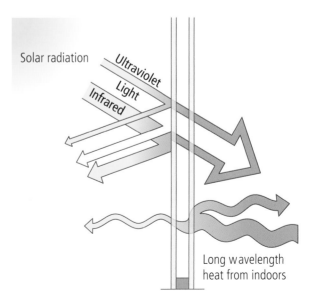

Solar radiation
Ultraviolet
Light
Infrared

Long wavelength heat from indoors

Fig. 15.5 Solar heat transfer through a double-glazed window unit.

CHAPTER 15

Glazing is used to increase the thermal properties of windows. Adding extra glazing panes increases the distance that the heat has to travel through. As well as that, gases filled into the space between the panes (including argon, krypton and xenon, which have lower thermal conductivity than air) further increase the thermal efficiency of the window.

Where the glass pane meets the frame, weather strips – strips made of a flexible material – are added to prevent or reduce draughts.

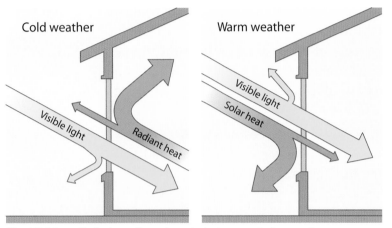

Fig. 15.6 Low E glazing allows heat in but prevents it escaping.

To create a double-glazed unit, two panes are heat sealed to a spacer which ensures the panes are kept separate from each other. The space between the panes is either filled with gas or left empty (which is to say, it is filled with air). The space within the unit improves the window's thermal and acoustic insulation.

Low E (low emissivity) glazing, which has become quite popular in recent times, has a special metal coating on the inner pane of glass. The glazing allows solar energy into the dwelling and prevents it escaping (Fig. 15.6). This type of glazing is quite expensive initially; however, over time it pays for itself by saving on heating costs.

There are many glazing options to make windows more efficient. Some of these are shown in Fig. 15.7. Having a thermal break in a window frame helps to prevent excessive heat loss.

Fig. 15.7 Various window types with approximate U-values for each. U-values are discussed in detail in Chapter 16.

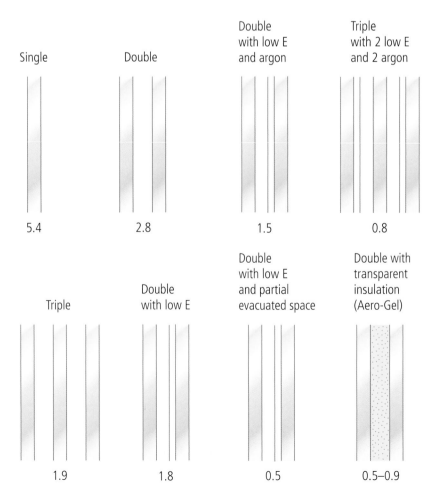

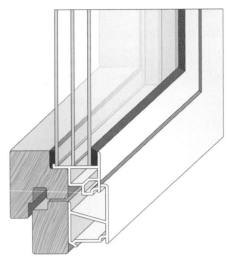

Fig. 15.8 Two different materials combined in a window unit to reduce heat loss.

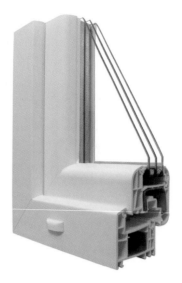

Fig. 15.9 uPVC window frame section.

Incorporating both wood and aluminium or uPVC in the window frame can also save a significant amount of heat because the density of the wood combines with the thermal resistance of the uPVC. Fig. 15.8 shows how these two materials are used in a window. Fig. 15.9 shows a section of a uPVC frame.

Acoustic Insulation

Sound can be an unwelcome irritant. The thermal qualities of the window (i.e. double glazing) also help prevent excessive noise coming into the building. Sealing around the window unit and the wall strengthens the sound insulation further.

Preventing Glare and Solar Heat Gain

Solar heat gain is the heat generated by the sun shining through the windows. One disadvantage of large windows is that they produce a lot of solar heat gain, which can raise the temperature of the room to an uncomfortable level. At the design stage of the build, orientation, window size, etc. should be taken into account so that the solar gain can be kept to a comfortable level.

Glare, which comes from bright light, can cause visual discomfort. Glare can be prevented by installing blinds, while indirect glare, which is caused by the reflection of sunlight on a surface, can be reduced by minimising the number of glossy surfaces in a dwelling.

Security

Although windows are designed to open, locking systems are put in to prevent access from outside. The uPVC locking system has multipoints around the frame to make it secure. Most uPVC windows now have a locked ventilation option, which allows the window to be opened slightly, but not enough to allow access.

CHAPTER 15

Fig. 15.10 Multipoint locking system on a uPVC window.

Fig. 15.10 shows part of the multipoint locking system of a uPVC window.

The locking mechanism on traditional timber framed windows includes a locking handle and a restrictor. In combination, these mechanisms allow the window to be opened to a specific distance and provide the window with secure locking across the bottom and side of the frame.

Emergency Escape

Under current building regulations, every inner room (a room whose only access is through another room) and bedroom in a newly constructed house must have windows suitable for escape or rescue. To satisfy the regulations, both the width and height of the window must be a minimum of 450mm and the area of the window cannot be less than 0.33m². The bottom of the window opening must be between 800mm and 1100mm above the floor, and in dormer windows the bottom of the window can be no more than 1700mm from the eaves. These dimensional regulations are shown in Fig. 15.11.

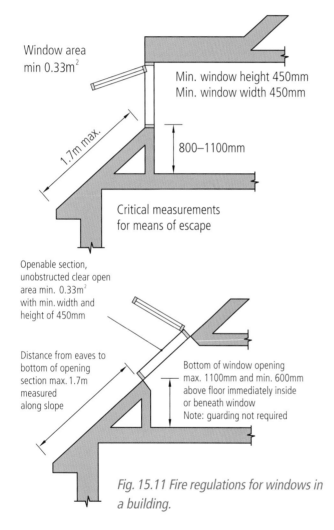

Window area min 0.33m²

Min. window height 450mm
Min. window width 450mm

1.7m max.

800–1100mm

Critical measurements for means of escape

Openable section, unobstructed clear open area min. 0.33m² with min. width and height of 450mm

Distance from eaves to bottom of opening section max. 1.7m measured along slope

Bottom of window opening max. 1100mm and min. 600mm above floor immediately inside or beneath window
Note: guarding not required

Fig. 15.11 Fire regulations for windows in a building.

Durability

The windows installed at the time of the build are expected to last upwards of 50 years. Wooden window frames, which are usually made of hardwoods such as teak and mahogany because of their weather-resistant properties and durability (they can last more than 100 years), need regular maintenance, such as painting and varnishing. In contrast, uPVC windows need no maintenance, but producing uPVC windows is more harmful to the environment.

Fig. 15.12 A poorly maintained wooden window frame.

TYPES OF WINDOW

Three main types of window are used in Ireland: casement windows; pivot windows; and sliding sash windows (Fig. 15.13).

Traditionally the sliding sash window was very popular in Ireland. Wider openings became more popular in the 1950s and 1960s, and this led to an increase in the popularity of casement windows because sash windows are not suitable for such spans. Casement windows also require less maintenance. However, because of their traditional and aesthetic appeal, as well as their improved thermal properties, sliding sash windows are once again becoming a popular choice for house builders in this country.

Timber was for long the only material used to make window frames. Aluminium became popular for a time until uPVC entered the market, and timber lost favour due to its susceptibility to rot. Nowadays, with the use of pressure treatments for timber that reduce the occurrence of rot, and with the heightened public awareness of the importance of sustainability, timber windows have increased in popularity again.

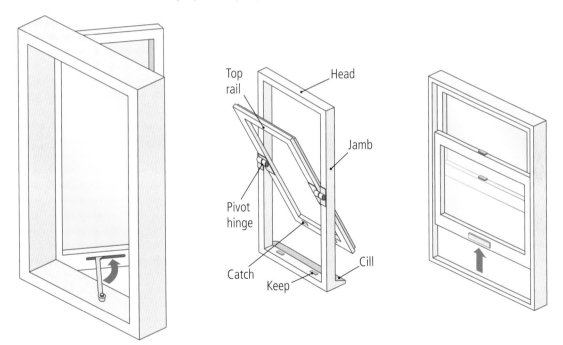

Fig. 15.13 LEFT: Casement window. MIDDLE: Pivot window. RIGHT: Sliding sash window.

Casement Windows

The casement is the part of the window that opens within the frame. The non-opening parts are known as fixed lights. The casement can be hung from either the side or the top of the frame. The extent to which the casement opens is determined by the reach of an average human arm. The direction of opening can be made to either side of the frame, allowing the client to determine the direction of opening. Fig. 15.14 shows the main features of a casement window.

CHAPTER 15

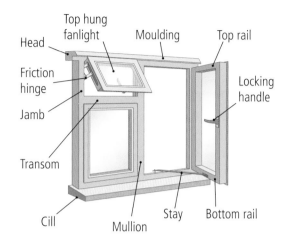

Fig. 15.14 Casement window with fixed element and top hung fanlight.

The casement window can be made from timber or uPVC, or a combination of both. Timber frames are machine made and fixed with weatherproof adhesive. uPVC windows are made with bulky hollow frame sections. These uPVC window frames are not as rigid as timber ones owing to the need to make them bulkier.

Stripping is used to reduce draughts and the penetration of wind-driven rain. The stripping, which is usually either rubber or PVC, is applied to the frame with a self-adhesive strip or by tacking it in place. The strip is fixed so that it acts as the first point of contact for the wind and rain. It can be replaced when it is damaged or worn. Some of the different styles of strip are shown in Fig. 15.15.

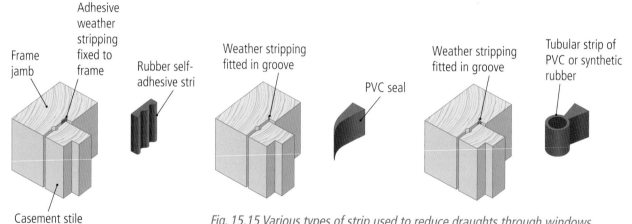

Fig. 15.15 Various types of strip used to reduce draughts through windows.

Pivot Windows

Pivot windows are very popular in Ireland. The centre pivot window is the most common type. When used in a ceiling, the centre pivot window is more commonly known as a rooflight. It allows light into living spaces in the roof. Blinds can be built into these windows and their ability to turn about a centre axis makes for easier cleaning. Fig. 15.16 shows a cross-section through a rooflight showing the weatherproofing detail.

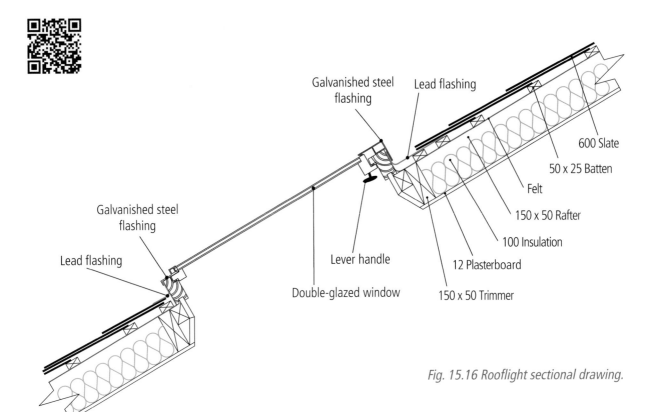

Galvanished steel flashing

Lead flashing

600 Slate

50 x 25 Batten

Felt

150 x 50 Rafter

100 Insulation

12 Plasterboard

150 x 50 Trimmer

Galvanished steel flashing

Lead flashing

Lever handle

Double-glazed window

Fig. 15.16 Rooflight sectional drawing.

Sliding Sash Windows

A sliding sash window is made up of two sashes and a frame. Both sashes slide up and down in a recess, aided by the use of rods or weights. It is important that when both sashes are closed they seal firmly to prevent water from penetrating. Traditionally, sliding sash windows used weights to balance the window in its open position, but this often resulted in the cords wearing out and eventually snapping, leading to costly repairs. It is still common practice to make sliding sash windows with cords and weights, but some windows now incorporate spring balances. The springs are fully extended when the window is closed, and help take the weight of the bottom sash as it is lifted to open the window. Fig. 15.17 shows the details of a sash window.

Note that, in order to let in the maximum amount of light, the bars on the window were traditionally tapered. Modern sliding sash windows are now double- or even triple-glazed and can also be constructed in uPVC.

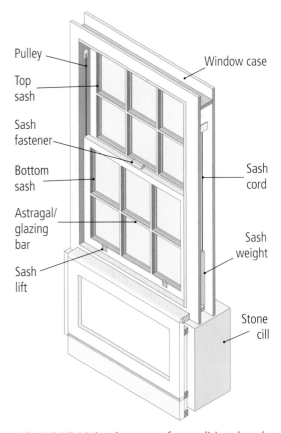

Pulley

Top sash

Sash fastener

Bottom sash

Astragal/ glazing bar

Sash lift

Window case

Sash cord

Sash weight

Stone cill

Fig. 15.17 Main elements of a traditional sash window.

CHAPTER 15

INSTALLING WINDOWS

Windows are built into opes in the walls of the building. A cill is placed at the bottom of the ope and bedded in mortar. The cill is a precast, reinforced concrete element. It must be wrapped with a DPC to prevent moisture coming through from outside. To prevent cold bridging and heat loss from within, thermal insulation is also used. Figs 15.18, 15.19, 15.20 and 15.21 show the cill in place in the ope with the DPC and thermal insulation required in block and timber frame builds.

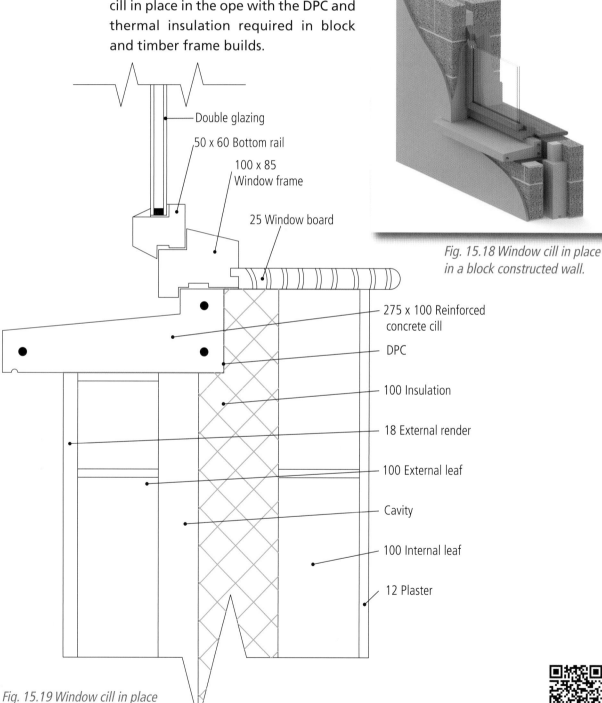

Double glazing

50 x 60 Bottom rail

100 x 85
Window frame

25 Window board

*Fig. 15.18 Window cill in place
in a block constructed wall.*

275 x 100 Reinforced
concrete cill

DPC

100 Insulation

18 External render

100 External leaf

Cavity

100 Internal leaf

12 Plaster

*Fig. 15.19 Window cill in place
in a block constructed wall.*

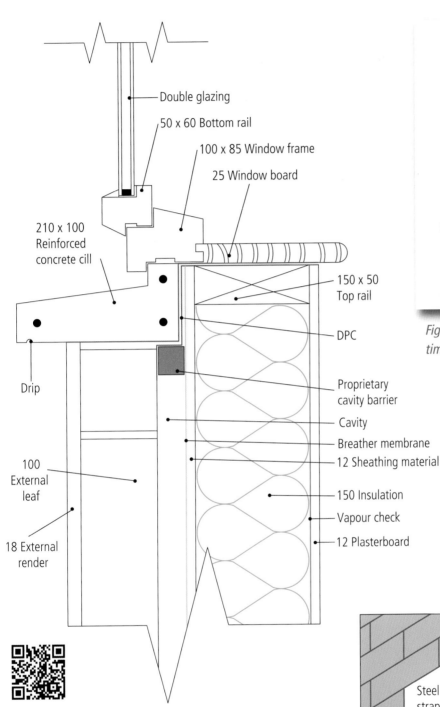

Double glazing

50 x 60 Bottom rail

100 x 85 Window frame

25 Window board

210 x 100 Reinforced concrete cill

Drip

100 External leaf

18 External render

150 x 50 Top rail

DPC

Proprietary cavity barrier

Cavity

Breather membrane

12 Sheathing material

150 Insulation

Vapour check

12 Plasterboard

Fig. 15.20 Window cill in place in a timber frame build.

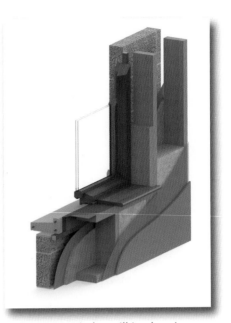

Fig. 15.21 Window cill in place in a timber frame build.

Windows are secured in place using steel straps. The straps are nailed to the wall and are later hidden by plaster. The outer render creates a seal around the window frame when it is finished. Fig. 15.22 illustrates the steel straps.

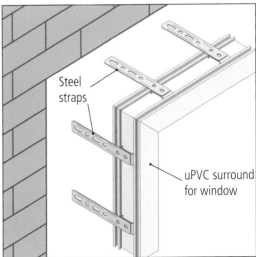

Steel straps

uPVC surround for window

Fig. 15.22 Steel strap used to secure the window in place.

CHAPTER 15

Fig. 15.23 Reinforced concrete lintel.

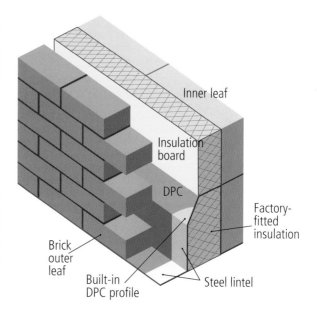

Fig. 15.24 Galvanised steel lintel.

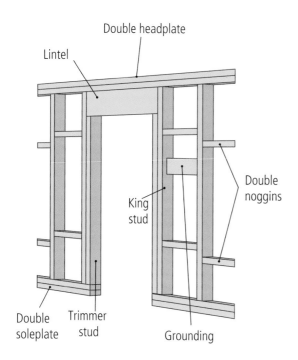

Fig. 15.25 Timber lintel in timber frame construction.

A lintel is installed at the top of the ope. The lintel is a structural member that spreads the weight of the load to either side of the ope. We saw in Chapter 10 that there are three common types of lintel in use in Ireland: reinforced concrete lintels; galvanised steel lintels; and timber lintels. As with cills, lintels must be installed in a manner that prevents moisture penetration and heat loss. A reinforced concrete lintel is the one most commonly used in a block-built house, where the outer leaf is constructed using blocks. This is shown in Fig. 15.23.

A galvanised steel lintel (Fig. 15.24) is generally used where the outer leaf of a block-built or timber frame dwelling is built of bricks. DPCs are used, as with block walls, and insulation must be provided.

A timber lintel is used in a timber frame construction. Timber lintels must be supported using trimmer studs. Fig. 15.25 shows a timber lintel.

Figs 15.26 15.27, 15.28 and 15.29 show the technical details associated with the head of both block-built and timber frame window openings.

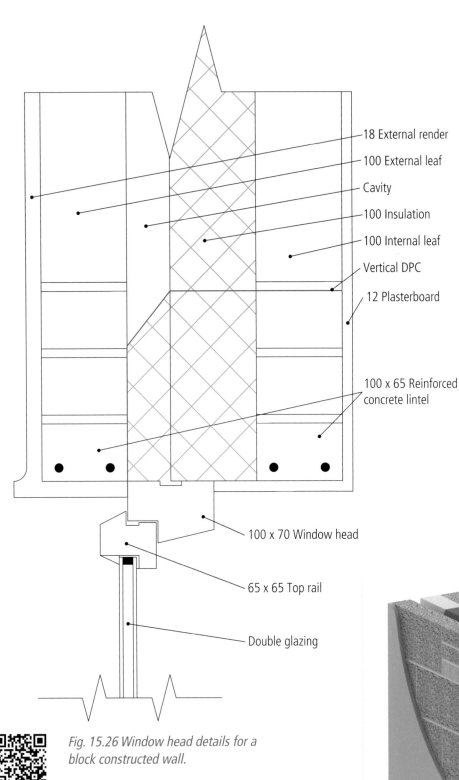

18 External render

100 External leaf

Cavity

100 Insulation

100 Internal leaf

Vertical DPC

12 Plasterboard

100 x 65 Reinforced
concrete lintel

100 x 70 Window head

65 x 65 Top rail

Double glazing

*Fig. 15.26 Window head details for a
block constructed wall.*

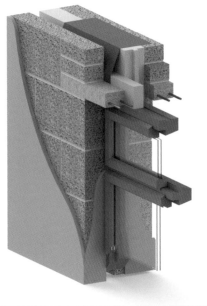

*Fig. 15.27 Window
head for a block
constructed wall.*

CHAPTER 15

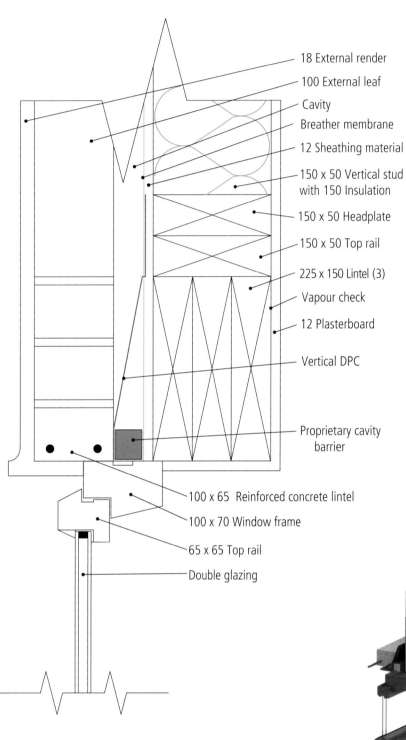

18 External render

100 External leaf

Cavity

Breather membrane

12 Sheathing material

150 x 50 Vertical stud
with 150 Insulation

150 x 50 Headplate

150 x 50 Top rail

225 x 150 Lintel (3)

Vapour check

12 Plasterboard

Vertical DPC

Proprietary cavity
barrier

100 x 65 Reinforced concrete lintel

100 x 70 Window frame

65 x 65 Top rail

Double glazing

Fig. 15.28 Window head details for a timber constructed wall.

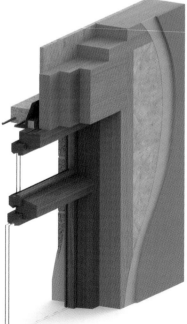

Fig. 15.29 Window head for a timber constructed wall.

Fig. 15.30 is a detailed section view through a storm-proof timber casement window showing head, cill and triple glazing details.

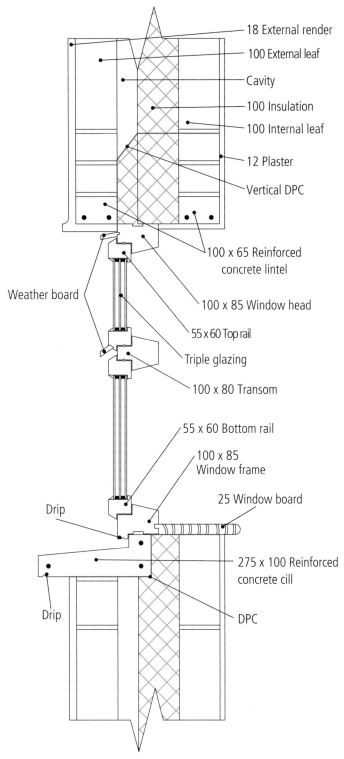

18 External render
100 External leaf
Cavity
100 Insulation
100 Internal leaf
12 Plaster
Vertical DPC
100 x 65 Reinforced concrete lintel
Weather board
100 x 85 Window head
55 x 60 Top rail
Triple glazing
100 x 80 Transom
55 x 60 Bottom rail
100 x 85 Window frame
25 Window board
Drip
275 x 100 Reinforced concrete cill
Drip
DPC

Fig. 15.30 Storm-proof triple-glazed timber casement window

DOORS

Doors allow access to a building and between rooms in the building. External doors affect the fenestration of the building in the same way as windows. This must be taken into consideration when deciding on the external doors for a property. Fig. 15.31 shows how the external door can affect the overall appearance of a building.

A door must prevent wind and rain getting into the building and heat escaping from it. An open door allows ventilation and light into the building; a closed door acts as a noise barrier and helps to slow the spread of fire. Doors must be stable, durable, secure and thermally efficient.

Doors are available in either timber or uPVC. A uPVC door requires little or no maintenance. Timber doors, usually made from hardwood, are more traditional and require regular maintenance.

Door locks are used to prevent unwelcome access. The locks are built into the door during manufacture or attached to the door after production.

Users must be able to gain access to the dwelling with comfort and ease. Areas of the door that have measurement guidelines are the doorbell, doorknocker, letter box and handle. Much like the stairs in Chapter 14, the user must not be conscious of the positioning of the various parts of the door, which should be designed to be ergonomically sound. Fig. 15.32 shows the dimensional requirements for the position of a letter box on a door.

Fig. 15.31 External doors can affect the overall appearance of a building.

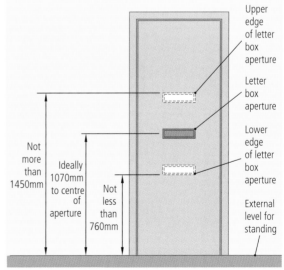

Fig. 15.32 Regulations for positioning a letter box on a front door.

Fig. 15.33 Various types of external door: some are timber and some uPVC.

DOOR TYPES

There are many different types of door in use in dwellings all over the country. The types of door that will be discussed here are external doors, internal doors, sliding doors and fire doors.

External Doors

External doors give access to a building. When these doors are made of timber, hardwood is used because of its durability. They can also be made of uPVC. As they are seen by passers-by, external doors can add to the aesthetic appeal of a building. Some common types of external door are shown in Fig. 15.33.

External timber doors are formed from matchboard or panelling. Panelled doors are made from hardwood; the frame of the door is joined using mortise and tenon joints and the panels sit into grooves created in the frame. Fig. 15.34 gives an exploded view of a panelled door to show how it is constructed.

A matchboard door is made with a series of tongue-and-groove boards that interlock along one another's edges. Matchboard doors are commonly seen on sheds or side gates. They have a number of components. The ledge is the horizontal member that spans the width of the boards. Braces are diagonal members between ledges that create additional support. The frame (where one is used) is fitted opposite the hinges to add strength and stability to the door. Fig. 15.35 shows matchboard doors with these elements.

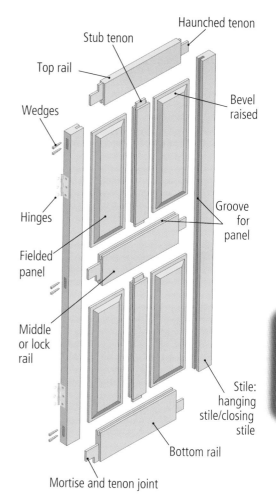

Fig. 15.34 The parts of a panelled door, and its construction.

Ledged and battened (rear elevation)

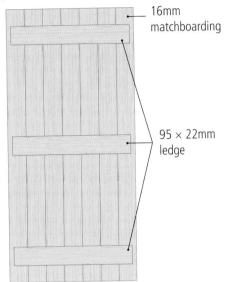

16mm matchboarding

95 × 22mm ledge

Ledged and braced (rear elevation)

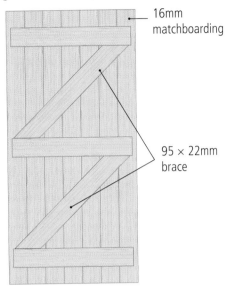

16mm matchboarding

95 × 22mm brace

Alternative brace connection

Framed, ledged and braced (rear elevation)

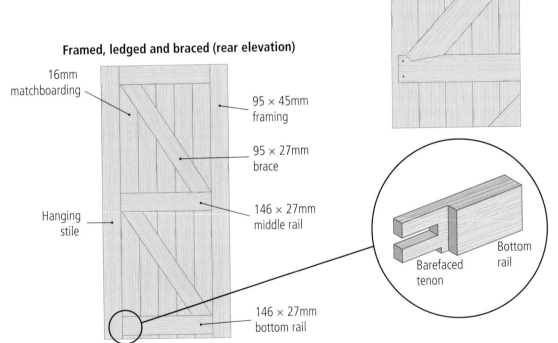

16mm matchboarding

95 × 45mm framing

95 × 27mm brace

146 × 27mm middle rail

Hanging stile

146 × 27mm bottom rail

Barefaced tenon

Bottom rail

Fig. 15.35 Matchboard doors using three different forms of bracing.

For their part, uPVC external doors are either glazed or panelled, or a combination of the two. The panels and/or glazing fit into a frame. The frame itself is hollow, with aluminium reinforcement in the core. The panels are insulated to prevent heat loss. While they are usually white, uPVC doors are available in a wide variety of colours, including a timber grain effect.

Whichever type of external door is chosen, it is essential that rainwater cannot penetrate, either by puddling at the bottom of the door or by being driven under the door by the wind. To prevent this, attention must be paid to the threshold detail. The transition between outside and inside must be as flat as possible to allow comfortable access. A drainage channel is laid in front of the doorway to collect rainwater and direct it away from the building. This channel is covered with a grating that will not trap anything travelling over it (prams, heels, etc.) A detailed view of the threshold detail and the external door is shown in Fig. 15.36.

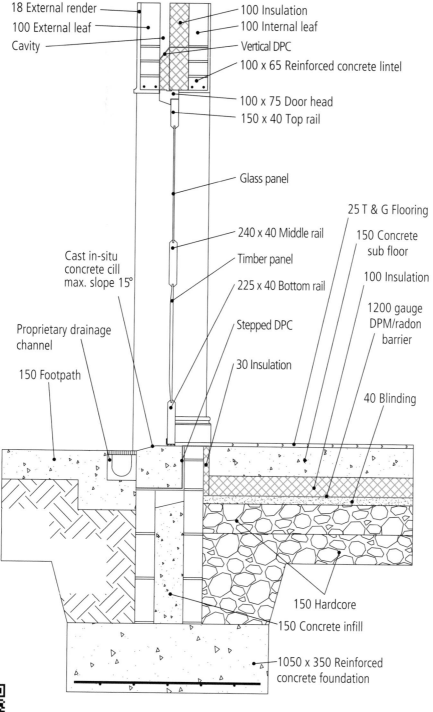

18 External render
100 External leaf
Cavity
100 Insulation
100 Internal leaf
Vertical DPC
100 x 65 Reinforced concrete lintel
100 x 75 Door head
150 x 40 Top rail
Glass panel
25 T & G Flooring
150 Concrete sub floor
240 x 40 Middle rail
100 Insulation
Cast in-situ concrete cill max. slope 15°
Timber panel
225 x 40 Bottom rail
1200 gauge DPM/radon barrier
Proprietary drainage channel
Stepped DPC
150 Footpath
30 Insulation
40 Blinding
150 Hardcore
150 Concrete infill
1050 x 350 Reinforced concrete foundation

Fig. 15.36 Threshold detail of a door.

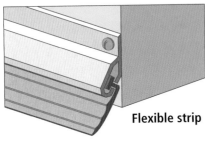

Flexible strip

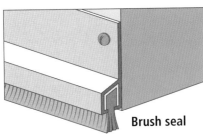

Brush seal

*Fig. 15.37
Threshold seal
sections.*

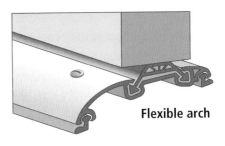

Flexible arch

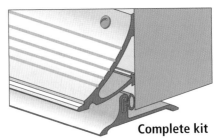

Complete kit

A weatherboard and threshold seal are used to stop wind-driven rain entering at the bottom of a door. These elements are available in a variety of forms. Some of these are shown in Fig. 15.37.

Internal Doors

Internal doors provide access from room to room in a building. They do not need to protect against the weather and can therefore be made from softwood. There are two main types of internal door: flush doors and panelled doors.

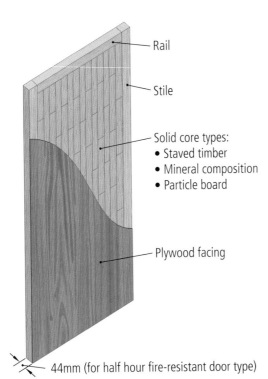

— Rail

— Stile

— Solid core types:
• Staved timber
• Mineral composition
• Particle board

— Plywood facing

— 44mm (for half hour fire-resistant door type)

Fig. 15.38 Solid core internal flush door.

A flush door is a simple door that has a plain face on both sides. Although all flush doors look similar, they can be constructed in different ways.

Solid core flush doors are very strong. They are made solid by joining small timbers or particle board strips edge to edge to fill the core of the frame. Fig. 15.38 shows a solid core flush door.

Hollow core flush doors are a common choice. These doors have a frame made from solid wood. Cardboard webbing is placed within the frame of the door to improve rigidity. This is rather like the honeycomb effect seen in beehives. These doors suffer from dents and puncture easily if they are mistreated. Fig. 15.39 shows a hollow core flush door.

A cheaper option is a stamped hardboard flush door. 'Stamped hardboard' refers to the outer veneer of the door. In the manufacturing process, the hardwood veneer can be made to look like

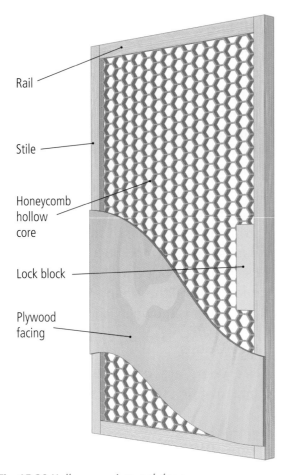

Rail

Stile

Honeycomb
hollow
core

Lock block

Plywood
facing

Fig. 15.39 Hollow core internal door.

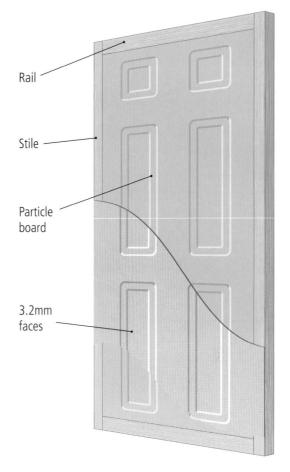

Rail

Stile

Particle
board

3.2mm
faces

Fig. 15.40 Hardboard flush door.

wood grain. These doors can be hollow core or filled with particle board or foam. Like hollow core flush doors they can dent or puncture easily. Fig. 15.40 shows a stamped hardboard flush door.

Panelled internal doors are much like exterior panelled doors. The main difference is that internal doors can be constructed using softwoods rather than hardwoods. Common internal panelled door constructions can be seen in Fig. 15.41.

CHAPTER 15

Fig. 15.41 Internal door designs.

Fig. 15.42 Sliding doors.

Sliding Doors

Sliding doors slide on a track rather than opening on a hinge. One leaf of the door is fixed and the other slides. In domestic dwellings a sliding door is often known as a patio door, because sliding doors often open onto a patio. These doors are reinforced with steel for structural purposes, as well as for security. Wind and rain is eliminated by using weather stripping. Maintenance for sliding doors is minimal; the track must simply be kept clear of debris to ensure smooth operation of the sliding leaf. A sliding patio door is shown in Fig. 15.42.

Fire Doors

Fire doors are designed to delay the spread of fire, smoke and gases produced by a fire. Fire doors are often used for entrances to individual apartments in apartment buildings and in rooms adjoining garages. The classification of a fire door is determined by how long the door will provide protection from fire. The classification is denoted by FD ('fire door') followed by a number. This number is the time in minutes that the door will provide protection.

Materials used in fire door construction include, among others, gypsum, steel, fire-retardant particle board, fibreglass and timber. A strip known as an intumescent strip is built into either the door frame or the door itself. The strip expands under extreme temperatures, creating a seal between the door and the frame. This works to prevent oxygen from entering the room, which would fuel a fire, and to prevent smoke permeating into adjoining rooms. Fig. 15.43 shows the door components and the intumescent strip.

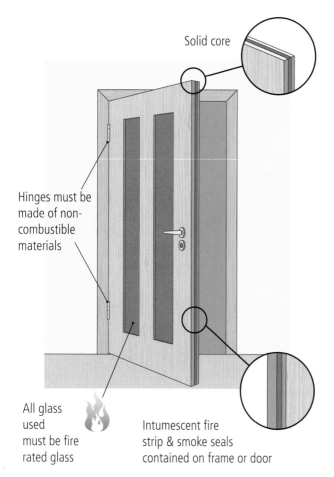

Solid core

Hinges must be made of non-combustible materials

All glass used must be fire rated glass

Intumescent fire strip & smoke seals contained on frame or door

Fig. 15.43 Elements of a fire door.

FITTING A DOOR

A door must be fixed in order to function correctly. The door frame provides this support. The frame is made up of two jambs (side posts) and a head. The head is joined to the two jambs using a rebated butt joint, which is then screwed or nailed for stability. Fig. 15.44 shows a rebated butt joint while Fig. 15.45 shows the frame construction.

A large steel square is used to check for squareness, and the diagonals are also checked, before attaching a brace piece diagonally across the corner of the frame. To keep the correct width, a cross piece is fitted towards the bottom of the jambs. The jambs are secured with screws to the masonry or timber walls. It is common practice to leave a small gap between the door and frame to accommodate any positional changes due to the moisture content of the timber (as discussed in Chapter 7).

Fig. 15.44 Rebated butt joint.

Once the frame and door have been fitted, the architrave can be attached to the frame. The architrave is the decorative element that 'blends' the door frame with the wall. Architraves come in many styles. Fig. 15.46 shows a fitted door with architrave. Fig. 15.47 shows a carpenter fitting a door.

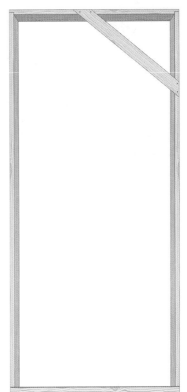

Fig. 15.45 Construction of a door frame.

Fig. 15.46 Door and architrave.

Fig. 15.47 Fitting a door.

CHAPTER 15

FIXINGS: LOCKS AND HINGES

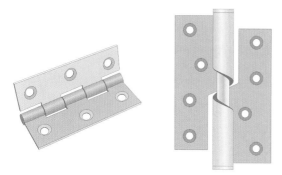

Fig. 15.48 Butt hinge (LEFT) and rising butt hinge (RIGHT).

Fig.15.49 Lift-off butt hinge.

Fig. 15.50 Mortise lock.

A door needs a number of different hardware items in order to open, close and lock. The door is hung from the frame using hinges. A hinge allows the door to rotate on its long axis without other movement. The types of hinge most often used to hang doors are the butt hinge and the rising butt hinge (Fig. 15.48).

While these hinges are simple and easy to install, they are time-consuming to uninstall if the door needs to be removed. To make this easier, a lift-off hinge can be used. A lift-off hinge consists of two separate parts. One part is attached to the frame and the other to the door. This means that the door can be easily lifted up and off the hinge. Fig. 15.49 shows a lift-off butt hinge.

External door locks are essential for security. Locks are often fitted to external and internal doors as standard. The most common type of lock is a mortise lock. A mortise lock is one that requires a mortise to be cut into the door for it to fit in. There are two types of mechanism at work in a mortise lock. The first is the latch, which is operated with the handle. The second is the lock, usually operated with a key. Fig. 15.50 shows a mortise lock being fitted.

Another type of lock, used mainly in external doors, is the night latch. This is a lock that attaches to the surface of the door. It can be opened without a key from the inside but not from the outside.

Fig. 15.51 Multipoint locking system on a door.

One of the most common locks nowadays is the multipoint lock. This lock has more than one locking point. The locking points are spread strategically over the length of the door. This means that, unlike other locking systems, there is no weak point in the door. The door is locked, using a key, from either the inside or the outside. The main disadvantage of this type of locking system is that the door has to be unlocked with the key, which can be a hindrance in the case of a fire or other emergency if the key is not close to hand. Fig. 15.51 shows the multipoint locking system.

PRACTICE QUESTIONS

1. Describe the importance of fenestration in a building.

2. How is the best window size for a room determined?

3. Name and describe using notes and neat freehand sketches the functions of a window.

4. To a scale of 1:10 draw a vertical section through a casement window with a top hung fanlight in a timber frame dwelling. Show details from 300mm above the lintel to 300mm below the cill. Include the typical dimensions on your drawing.

5. Explain how the thermal properties of windows can be improved.

6. Explain using notes and neat freehand sketches how a window is fitted.

7. Name the functions of a door.

8. To a scale of 1:10 draw a vertical section through a solid wood panelled external door in a block built dwelling. Include the threshold detail in your drawing as well as all typical dimensions.

9. Describe using notes and neat freehand sketches the parts of a panelled door and how they fit together.

10. Discuss internal doors, making reference to types and construction methods.

11. Explain in detail how an internal door is fitted.

12. Using notes and neat freehand sketches discuss the different hinge types used in fitting doors.

13. Explain the advantages and disadvantages of different locks in relation to doors.

SAMPLE EXAMINATION QUESTIONS

2012 Higher Level Question 1

A triple-glazed bay window projects 1.5 metres from the external wall of a dwelling house, as shown in the accompanying sketch. The external wall is a 350 mm concrete block wall with an insulated cavity. The lean-to roof is an insulated slated roof and has a pitch of 30°. Insulated plasterboard is fixed to the underside of the rafters to form a sloped ceiling.

(a) To a scale of 1:5, draw a vertical section through the window, roof and front wall of the house. The section should show the typical construction details from 400 mm below the concrete lintels of the bay window, through the fixed frame of the window, wallplate and rafter to a level 400 mm above the abutment of the lean-to roof and the front wall of the house.

(b) Indicate on your drawing the design detailing that ensures moisture does not penetrate at the abutment of the roof and the wall of the house.

SAMPLE EXAMINATION QUESTIONS

2012 Higher Level Question 7(a)

The main entrance door to a two storey dwelling house is a four-panel solid wooden door. The external wall in which the door is fitted is of timber frame construction with a rendered concrete block outer leaf. This wall supports the first floor joists, as shown in the accompanying outline drawing.

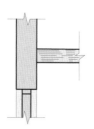

(a) To a scale of 1:5, draw a vertical section through a portion of the external wall, doorframe, door and first floor joists. The section should show the typical construction details from 400 mm below the top of the door to a level 500 mm above the first floor joists. Include typical dimensions.

2012 Ordinary Level Question 5(a)

A triple-glazed timber casement window, as shown in the sketch, is fixed in a 350 mm external concrete block wall with an insulated cavity. The fixed frame of the window is 150 mm × 80 mm. The wall is plastered on both sides.

(a) To a scale of 1:5, draw a vertical section through the bottom portion of the window showing the fixed frame of the window and the concrete cill. Show the typical construction details from 300 mm below to a level 250 mm above the concrete cill. Indicate the typical sizes of **three** main components.

2011 Higher Level Question 1

The main external doorway of a dwelling house is designed to facilitate access for everyone, including a person with reduced mobility, as shown in the sketch. The door is a framed wooden door with 12 mm thick vertical sheeting on both sides. The doorframe is 150 mm × 70 mm and is fixed in a 350 mm external concrete block wall with an insulated cavity. The house has an insulated solid concrete ground floor with a 20 mm quarry tile finish.

(a) To a scale of 1:10, draw a vertical section through the centre of the door. The section should show the typical construction details from 500 mm below finished floor level, through the threshold, the door, the doorframe and the external wall to a level 300 mm above the concrete lintels over the doorframe.

(b) Show on the drawing the design detailing that ensures that rainwater is removed from the threshold area.

2010 Ordinary Level Question 4

A solid pine door and doorframe are shown in the accompanying sketch. The door and frame are fitted in a 100 mm internal concrete block wall which is plastered on both sides.

(a) Show, using notes and *neat freehand sketches*, how to ensure that the doorframe is assembled square prior to fitting the door.

(b) Show, using notes and *neat freehand sketches*, how the doorframe is fitted in the block wall.

(c) Sketch a suitable hinge for this door and show, using notes and n*eat freehand sketches*, the steps involved in fitting one hinge to the door.

CHAPTER 16
U-VALUES

LEARNING OUTCOMES:

After studying this chapter students will:

- Understand U-values and know the maximum U-values for specific elements.
- Be able to calculate U-values having been given material thickness and/or resistivity.
- Further calculate monetary gains and losses based on U-value results.
- Be able to explain the differences between heat loss and heat gain and where they occur.

KEYWORDS:

- U-VALUE • HEAT • KELVIN • CELSIUS • CONDUCTIVITY • RESISTIVITY • RESISTANCE
- ELEMENTAL HEAT LOSS • OVERALL HEAT LOSS • HEAT GAIN • SOLAR HEAT GAIN • BER

INTRODUCTION

Heating is one of the most expensive running costs in a dwelling. Losing heat is costly. When warmth escapes, cold air must be heated again, which drains energy from the building. There are many systems in place to heat air, from both renewable and non-renewable sources. With technology at the forefront of today's society, faster and cheaper methods of heating are continually being explored.

U-value refers to how well building materials conduct heat. A U-value is a measurement of the amount of heat lost through material. The number given is the amount of heat transfer of 1 kelvin through 1m² of building material and is expressed as W/m²K (where W stands for watts, m is metres and K is kelvin).

$$\text{U-value} = \text{W/m}^2\text{K}$$

A watt is a unit of power, defined as one joule (unit of energy) per second.

Kelvin is a temperature scale similar to Celsius. One kelvin unit is equal to one Celsius unit. However, while Celsius uses both positive and negative numbers, kelvin uses positive numbers only. It is measured from zero. While the graduations between kelvin

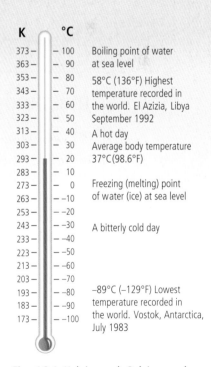

K	°C	
373 –	– 100	Boiling point of water at sea level
363 –	– 90	
353 –	– 80	58°C (136°F) Highest
343 –	– 70	temperature recorded in
333 –	– 60	the world. El Azizia, Libya
323 –	– 50	September 1992
313 –	– 40	A hot day
303 –	– 30	Average body temperature
293 –	– 20	37°C (98.6°F)
283 –	– 10	
273 –	– 0	Freezing (melting) point
263 –	– –10	of water (ice) at sea level
253 –	– –20	
243 –	– –30	A bitterly cold day
233 –	– –40	
223 –	– –50	
213 –	– –60	
203 –	– –70	
193 –	– –80	–89°C (–129°F) Lowest
183 –	– –90	temperature recorded in
173 –	– –100	the world. Vostok, Antarctica, July 1983

Fig. 16.1 Kelvin and Celsius scales use different but comparable figures to measure temperature.

degrees and Celsius degrees are the same, they begin at different levels, so the numbers themselves are not the same. Take, for example, the freezing point of water. It is 0°C but 273.15°K.

The lower the U-value, the less heat is lost from the area in question. It is desirable to have as low a U-value as possible. In fact it is so important that new builds must comply with U-value regulations.

U-values vary according to:

- The material used in a building
- The building's location
- Temperature difference between outside and inside.

Each building element is given a specific U-value, which is set out in current building regulations. This value indicates the maximum amount of heat that can be allowed to escape through the building material. The current building regulations (2011) are shown in Table 16.1.

TABLE 16.1 CURRENT (2011) BUILDING REGULATIONS

Building element	Maximum acceptable U-value (W/m²k)
Roof (pitched with horizontal insulation)	0.16
Roof (pitched with parallel insulation)	0.16
Roof (flat)	0.2
Wall	0.21
Floor	0.21
Window/Door/Rooflight	1.6

BUILDING ENERGY RATING

The Building Energy Rating (BER) gives an assessment of the energy performance of a house. It takes into account energy usage as well as the dwelling's CO_2 output. The characteristics of the major elements of the build, including walls, roof, windows, doors and floors, are taken into account, along with insulation levels, airtightness, etc. The BER is an overall rating for the entire building.

The energy performance of the dwelling is expressed as primary energy use per unit of floor area per year:

$$kWh/m^2/yr$$

(where kWh is kilowatt hours, m is metres and yr is year).

The BER label has a scale from A (most efficient) to G (least efficient) and is similar to the label applied to white household goods, i.e. washing machines,

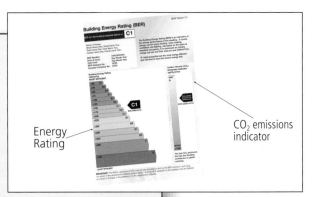

fridges, etc. Every dwelling in Ireland that is sold or rented must have a BER certificate. A BER is valid for ten years from first certification, provided that there have been no changes that affect the energy use of the dwelling. Fig. 16.2 shows the layout of the BER certificate.

Energy Rating

CO_2 emissions indicator

Fig. 16.2 Building Energy Rating certificate.

U-VALUES

Each material has its own U-value. These can be found in tables of thermal conductivity, which are supplied by material manufacturers. If these are unavailable, the material's U-value can be calculated.

The U-value of each building element is calculated individually. The thermal resistance of each material within the element is added to give an overall resistance value of the area being calculated. The overall resistance of each material is added to give a total resistance value, which is then used to find the U-value of the building element.

The terms and formulae required for basic U-value calculation are:

Conductivity (k)	$k = \frac{1}{r}$	(W/mK)
Resistivity (r)	$r = \frac{1}{k}$	(mK/W)
Thickness (T) **measured in metres**		(m)
Resistance (R)	$R = r \times T$ or $R = \frac{T}{k}$	(m²K/W)
U-value	$= \frac{1}{R^T}$	(W/m²K)

CALCULATING U-VALUES

Calculation

Leaving Certificate Higher Level 2010 Question 5 (a)
Calculate the U-value of an uninsulated external solid concrete wall of a dwelling house built in the 1950s given the following data:

External render	thickness	16 mm
Solid concrete wall	thickness	225 mm
Internal plaster	thickness	13 mm

Thermal data of external wall of house:

Resistivity of the solid concrete wall (r)		1.190 m °C/W
Resistivity of external render	(r)	2.170 m °C/W
Resistivity of internal plaster	(r)	6.250 m °C/W
Resistance of external surface	(R)	0.048 m² °C/W
Resistance of internal surface	(R)	0.122 m² °C/W

Section of solid concrete wall to be calculated.

CHAPTER 16

STEP 1

Draw a sectional drawing of the wall using the information from the question. This will help you to visualise the object and make sure that no elements are omitted from the calculation.

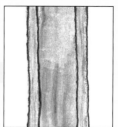

Fig. 16.3 Sectional drawing of the wall.

STEP 2

Draw a table and fill in the known information, as shown in Table 16.2.

TABLE 16.2

Element	Conductivity $k = \frac{1}{r}$	Resistivity $r = \frac{1}{k}$	Thickness (m)	Resistance $R = r \times T$ $R = \frac{T}{k}$
Internal surface	–	–	–	0.122
A Internal plaster		6.250	0.013	
B Solid concrete wall		1.190	0.225	
C External render		2.170	0.016	
External surface	–	–	–	0.048

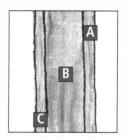

STEP 3

Using the formulae described earlier, fill in the conductivity values, or go to the resistance values as shown (in red) in Table 16.3.

TABLE 16.3

Element	Conductivity $k = \frac{1}{r}$	Resistivity $r = \frac{1}{k}$	Thickness (m)	Resistance $R = r \times T$ $R = \frac{T}{k}$
Internal surface	–	–	–	0.122
A Internal plaster	0.16	6.250	0.013	0.08125
B Solid concrete wall	0.84	1.190	0.225	0.26775
C External render	0.46	2.170	0.016	0.03472
External surface	–	–	–	0.048

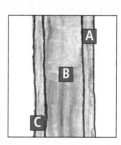

STEP 4

The total resistance (R^T) is found by adding all values in the resistance column.

$$R^T = 0.55372$$

STEP 5

The U-value is then found ($\frac{1}{R^T}$)

U-value = 1.8 W/m²K   (This does not comply with the 2011 regulations when we compare it to the regulation U-value for walls in Table 16.1.)

As can be seen in the worked example, a solid wall built in the 1950s allows heat to pass through it at a rate that would be unacceptable in the construction industry today.

REDUCING U-VALUES

There are a number of ways of reducing a U-value in a building or of a building element. The first method is to create a cavity in the wall. Air is a good insulator, and prevents a certain amount of heat loss. Placing a layer of insulation in the cavity, against the inner leaf, allows even less heat to be lost through the wall. The easiest way to see this difference is with a second example.

Calculation

Calculate the U-value for the external wall of a house using the data in Table 16.4.

TABLE 16.4

External render: thickness 19mm	*Thermal data of external wall:*		
	Conductivity of render	(k)	0.57 W/mK
Aerated block outer leaf: thickness 100mm			
	Conductivity of blockwork	(k)	0.18 W/mK
Cavity width: 150mm			
	Conductivity of insulation	(k)	0.025 W/mK
Extruded polystyrene insulation: thickness 100mm			
	Conductivity of plaster	(k)	0.18 W/mK
Aerated block inner leaf: thickness 100mm	Resistance of external surface	(R)	0.053 m²K/W
	Resistance of cavity	(R)	0.176 m²K/W
Internal plaster: thickness 15mm			
	Resistance of internal surface	(R)	0.123 m²K/W

Section of cavity wall to be calculated.

CHAPTER 16

STEP 1

Draw a diagram using the information in the question.

STEP 2

Draw a table and fill in the given values as shown in Table 16.5.

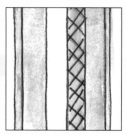

Fig. 16.4 Section of cavity wall to be calculated.

TABLE 16.5

Element	Conductivity $k = \frac{1}{r}$	Resistivity $r = \frac{1}{k}$	Thickness (m)	Resistance $R = r \times T$ $R = \frac{T}{k}$
External surface	–		–	0.053
A External render	0.57		0.019	
B Block outer leaf	0.18		0.1	
C Cavity	–		–	0.176
D Insulation	0.025		0.1	
E Block inner leaf	0.18		0.1	
F Internal plaster	0.18		0.015	
Internal surface	–		–	0.123

STEP 3

Calculate values for resistivity and resistance, as shown (in red) in Table 16.6.

TABLE 16.6

Element	Conductivity $k = \frac{1}{r}$	Resistivity $r = \frac{1}{k}$	Thickness (m)	Resistance $R = r \times T$ $R = \frac{T}{k}$
External surface	–	–	–	0.053
A External render	0.57	1.754	0.019	0.033
B Block outer leaf	0.18	5.555	0.1	0.555
C Cavity	–	–	–	0.176
D Insulation	0.025	40	0.1	4
E Block inner leaf	0.18	5.555	0.1	0.555
F Internal plaster	0.18	5.555	0.015	0.083
Internal surface	–	–	–	0.123

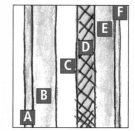

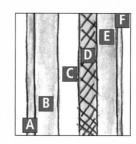

STEP 4

Add all resistance values: $R^T = 5.578$

STEP 5

U-value = $\left(\dfrac{1}{R^T}\right) = 0.18 \text{ W/m}^2\text{K}$

This figure meets the maximum requirements of 0.21 W/m²K.

U-VALUES WITH TWO HEAT PATHS

Apart from introducing a cavity and insulation, other ways of lowering the U-value include using additional layers of a material, and using materials with higher resistance values.

When different materials are used in a wall, a different method of calculation is needed to find the U-value of the wall. Take the example of a timber frame wall, as shown in Fig. 16.5.

Here there is more than one path for heat to travel through. It can escape through the insulation or through the studs. In this case, a more accurate calculation is needed to find the U-value. This calculation works by taking the mean of two values:

- The first value is calculated by treating each heat flow path separately.
- The second is calculated by combining the materials.

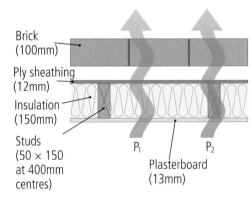

Brick (100mm)
Ply sheathing (12mm)
Insulation (150mm)
Studs (50 × 150 at 400mm centres)
P_1
P_2
Plasterboard (13mm)

Fig. 16.5 Brick exterior with timber frame interior.

Calculation

Calculate the U-value for the timber frame wall using the following data:

Brick: thickness 100mm	***Thermal data of timber frame wall:***		
	Conductivity of brick	(k)	0.77 W/mK
Cavity: thickness 50mm	Conductivity of ply sheathing	(k)	0.13 W/mK
Ply sheathing: thickness 12mm	Conductivity of insulation	(k)	0.024 W/mK
Insulation: thickness 150mm	Conductivity of studs	(k)	0.13 W/mK
Studs: thickness 150mm	Conductivity of plasterboard	(k)	0.25 W/mK
Plasterboard: thickness 13mm	Resistance of external surface	(R)	0.053 m²K/W
	Resistance of cavity	(R)	0.176 m²K/W
	Resistance of internal surface	(R)	0.123 m²K/W

Sectional view of brick exterior with timber frame interior.

STEP ①

Draw a diagram representing the information.

STEP ②

Draw a table and fill in the known values.

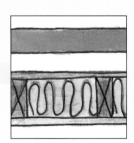

Fig. 16.6 Sectional view of brick exterior with timber frame interior.

TABLE 16.7

Element	Conductivity $k = \frac{1}{r}$	Resistivity $r = \frac{1}{k}$	Thickness (m)	Resistance $R = r \times T$ $R = \frac{T}{k}$
External surface	–	–	–	0.053
A Brick	0.77		0.1	
B Cavity	–	–	–	0.176
C Ply sheathing	0.13		0.012	
D Insulation	0.024		0.150	
E Studs	0.13		0.150	
F Plasterboard	0.25		0.013	
Internal surface	–	–	–	0.123

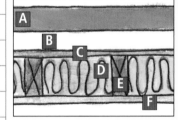

STEP ③

Next calculate the resistivity values and resistance values as shown (in red) in Table 16.8.

TABLE 16.8

Element	Conductivity $k = \frac{1}{r}$	Resistivity $r = \frac{1}{k}$	Thickness (m)	Resistance $R = r \times T$ $R = \frac{T}{k}$
External surface	–	–	–	0.053
A Brick	0.77	1.3	0.1	0.129
B Cavity	–	–	–	0.176
C Ply sheathing	0.13	7.69	0.012	0.092
D Insulation	0.024	41.67	0.150	6.25
E Studs	0.13	7.69	0.150	1.153
F Plasterboard	0.25	4	0.013	0.052
Internal surface	–	–	–	0.123

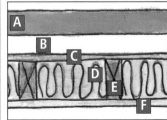

STEP 4

To find the total resistance, an upper (higher) and lower resistance value are calculated. The two heat paths are treated separately. The resistance values are taken from Table 16.8 above, and a total resistance for each combination of materials is determined by calculating an average, as shown in Tables 16.9 and 16.10.

TABLE 16.9

INSULATION PATH (1)	
Element	**Resistance**
External surface	0.053
Brick	0.129
Cavity	0.176
Ply sheathing	0.092
Insulation	6.25
Plasterboard	0.052
Internal surface	0.123

INSULATION PATH (2)	
Element	**Resistance**
External surface	0.053
Brick	0.129
Cavity	0.176
Ply sheathing	0.092
Studs	1.153
Plasterboard	0.052
Internal surface	0.123

TABLE 16.10

Total Resistance (insulation path) 6.87m²K/W	**Total Resistance** (stud path) 1.78m²K/W

$$R_u = \cfrac{1}{\left[\left(\cfrac{F_1}{R_1}\right) + \left(\cfrac{F_2}{R_2}\right)\right]}$$

Where:

F_2 is the fractional area of heat flow through Path 1 (i.e. the percentage make-up of that material)

F_2 is the fractional area of heat flow through Path 2

R_1 is the total resistance of Path 1

R_2 is the total resistance of Path 2

In this case the timber studs are 50mm at 400mm centres. Therefore their fractional area = 50/400 = 0.125, which means that the insulation will be 0.875 (in order to make 1).

$$R_u = \cfrac{1}{\cfrac{0.875}{6.87} + \cfrac{0.125}{1.78}} \qquad R_u = \cfrac{1}{0.197}$$

$R_u = 5.07m^2K/W$

CHAPTER 16

STEP 5

To calculate the lower resistance, the insulation and studs are combined to find a bridged resistance value (i.e. a combination of insulation and stud). This value is then added to the other materials' resistance values.

Use the following formula to find the bridged resistance value.

$$R_b = \dfrac{1}{\dfrac{F_1}{R_1} + \dfrac{F_s}{R_s}}$$

Where:

F_1 is the fractional area of heat flow through Path 1   0.875

F_s is the fractional area of heat flow through Path 2   0.125

R_1 is the resistance of the insulation   6.25

R_s is the resistance of the studs   1.153

$$R_b = \dfrac{1}{\dfrac{0.875}{6.25} + \dfrac{0.125}{1.153}} \qquad R_b = \dfrac{1}{0.248} = 4$$

$R_b = 4\text{m}^2\text{K/W}$

STEP 6

Feed the 'bridged' value back into the table in place of both insulation and studs in order to find the lower resistance value, as shown in Table 16.11.

TABLE 16.11

Element	Resistance
External surface	0.053
Brick	0.129
Cavity	0.176
Ply sheathing	0.092
Bridged section	4
Plasterboard	0.052
Internal surface	0.123

Total lower resistance (R_L) = 4.62m²K/W

STEP 7

The upper resistance and lower resistance values are fed into the following formula in order to find the total resistance of the building element:

$$R^T = \frac{R_U + R_L}{2}$$

$$R^T = \frac{5.07 + 4.62}{2} \quad R^T = \frac{9.69}{2} = 4.845$$

$R^T = 4.845 \text{ m}^2\text{K/W}$

STEP 8

Use the total resistance to find the U-value.

$$\frac{1}{R^T} = \text{U-value}$$

U-value = 0.2W/m²K (This value meets the current building regulations.)

CALCULATING COSTS

It is very hard to talk about the cost of running a central heating system, due to the number of variables that are present, e.g. the type of heating system, type of fuel, cost of fuel, size of dwelling, etc. But whether the dwelling is a one-bedroom apartment or a four-bedroom detached house, the price of central heating is a major issue for a householder. Householders can calculate the energy efficiency (or inefficiency) of the dwelling to figure out how much money they are losing – and could potentially save.

Fig. 16.7 Turning down the thermostat can save up to 10 per cent on household energy costs.

There are a number of things that can be done to save money on the annual heating costs of a dwelling:

- Delay switching on the boiler
- Turn down the thermostat

CHAPTER 16

- Replace the boiler with a condensing boiler
- Zone areas of the dwelling so that heating can be turned on in some rooms but not in others (e.g. in the bedrooms but not the kitchen)
- Install double or triple glazing
- Install insulation.

The heat loss can be calculated when the U-value, the area of the building element and the temperature difference between outside and inside is known. Given a fuel type and its price, the cost of that heat loss can be found. Take the following example, using Table 16.12.

Calculation

Calculate the cost of oil used as a result of losing heat through a wall, using the following information.

TABLE 16.12 THERMAL DATA

Area of external wall	152m²
Average internal temperature	290.15 kelvin
Average external temperature	279.15 kelvin
U-value of wall	0.1645
Heating period	11 hours per day, 41 weeks per year
Cost of oil	88 cent per litre
Calorific value of oil	37350kJ per litre
1000 Watts	1kJ per second

STEP 1

Find the total heat loss using the formula:

> **Total heat loss = U-value x area x temperature difference**

Total heat loss is measured in watts (a unit of power defined as one joule (unit of energy) per second).

> **Total heat loss = 0.1645 x 152 x 11**

= 275.044 watts

1 watt = 1 joule per second, therefore 275.044 watts = 275.044 joules per second.

Now that the amount of heat lost per second is known, we can calculate how much is lost per year. To do so, we need to know the heating period. This is measured in seconds.

Heating period = (weeks per year) x (days per week) x (hours per day) x (minutes per hour) x (seconds per minute)

= 41 x 7 x 11 x 60 x 60 = 11365200 seconds

STEP 3

Then the total number of kilojoules (kJ) per year is calculated:

$$= \frac{11365200 \times 275.044}{1000}$$

= 3125930kJ per year

Now the number of litres of oil consumed per year can be found by:

$$\frac{\text{Total oil}}{\text{calorific value}} = \frac{3125930}{37350} = 83.69 \text{ litres}$$

= 83.69 litres

STEP 4

Finally, the price itself can be calculated using the following formula:

Cost per year = number of litres x price per litre

= 83.69 x 0.88

= €73.65

It is important to note that this monetary value relates solely to the wall and not the amount lost through the entire building.

ELEMENTAL AND OVERALL HEAT LOSS

A U-value measures the heat lost through various elements of a dwelling. It does not give an overall indication of how much heat is lost. Two other heat loss calculations can give a more accurate depiction of the amount of heat lost over the entire area of the dwelling.

TABLE 16.13

Area of heat loss elements/ building volume m²	Maximum average U-value
1.3	0.39
1.2	0.40
1.1	0.41
1.0	0.43
0.9	0.45
0.8	0.48
0.7	0.51
0.6	0.56
0.5	0.62
0.4	0.72
0.3	0.87

OVERALL HEAT LOSS

This heat loss calculation is relevant to new buildings and extensions to existing buildings. This method considers all measurable U-value elements. The maximum acceptable U-value is based on the ratio of the total area of all measurable elements to the building volume. Table 16.13 shows the maximum U-values in relation to the area of building elements/building volume in the current building regulations.

ELEMENTAL HEAT LOSS

This heat loss calculation is initially based on the specific U-values of individual building elements. If each element satisfies building requirements (see Table 16.1, page 258), the next step can be carried out. The floor area is calculated along with the combined area of external doors, windows, rooflights, etc. The combined area of the openings must not exceed 30 per cent of the floor area.

HEAT GAIN

Heat gain can originate from a number of sources, namely the sun, body heat and incidental heat from appliances. Heat gain is a disadvantage in countries with a warm climate, and a number of methods can be employed to reduce its effects, e.g. awnings, special glass, etc. In Ireland the climate is usually quite cool, which means that it is necessary to maximise heat gain. The best way to do this is at the design stage of a build. Some of the ways of maximising heat gain are:

- Orientation
- Large areas of south-facing glazing
- Draught-proofing
- High levels of insulation.

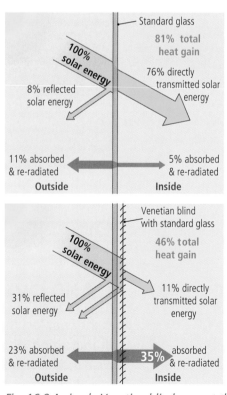

Fig. 16.8 A simple Venetian blind can cut the total heat gain from the sun.

SOLAR HEAT GAIN

Solar heat gain is the rise in temperature which comes from radiation from the sun. Most solar heat gain comes through windows and doors. In Ireland, solar heat gain is used to heat space passively and as a free source of energy.

Solar Panels

A solar panel is a collection of photovoltaic cells joined together to form a panel. A photovoltaic cell converts solar (sun) energy into electricity. The reason a number of these cells are joined together is to increase the productivity of the panel. Solar panels are very expensive to buy, but they offset this price tag over their lifetime in energy savings. Depending on the time of year, they can provide 40–60 per cent of the energy required to heat water. Solar panels do

Fig. 16.9 The larger groupings of panels are photovoltaic. The smaller installations are evacuated tubes for heating water.

not need direct sunlight to operate, though they are most effective if they are positioned within 15 degrees of south. They reduce dependency on fossil fuels such as oil, coal and gas, which in turn results in a reduction of CO_2 output.

PRACTICE QUESTIONS

1. What is a U-value?

2. List the maximum acceptable U-values for building elements.

3. How can a U-value be improved?

4. What is the difference between overall heat loss and elemental heat loss?

5. Describe how heat gain can be maximised.

SAMPLE EXAMINATION QUESTIONS

2012 Higher Level Question 5 (a) and (b)

A house built in the 1970s has an un-insulated solid concrete ground floor with a sand/cement fine screed finish.

(a) Calculate the U-value of the concrete ground floor given the following data:

Sand/cement fine screed	thickness	60 mm
Concrete floor slab	thickness	100 mm
Damp proof membrane (DPM)	thickness	0.25 mm
Sand blinding	thickness	50 mm
Hardcore	thickness	225 mm
Subsoil	thickness	300 mm

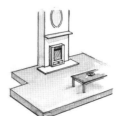

Thermal data of concrete ground floor:

Resistance of internal surface	(R)	0.104	m²	°C/W
Resistivity of fine screed	(r)	0.710	m	°C/W
Conductivity of concrete floor slab	(k)	0.160	W/m	°C
Conductivity of DPM	(k)	0.250	W/m	°C
Conductivity of sand blinding	(k)	0.160	W/m	°C
Conductivity of hardcore	(k)	1.330	W/m	°C
Conductivity of subsoil	(k)	1.800	W/m	°C

(b) Using the U-value of the concrete ground floor obtained at **5(a)** above and the following data, calculate the cost of heat lost annually through the un-insulated concrete floor slab:

Dimensions of floor	9.0 metres × 7.0 metres
Average internal temperature	20° C
Average external temperature of subsoil	5° C
Heating period	12 hours per day for 40 weeks per annum
Cost of oil	85 cent per litre
Calorific value of oil	37350 kJ per litre
1000 Watts	1 kJ per second.

2011 Higher Level Question 5 (a) and (b)

The external wall of a house built in the 1970s is constructed using a single leaf 215 mm hollow concrete block. The wall is rendered externally and plasterboard is fixed to the internal surface using dabs of plaster adhesive, as shown in the accompanying sketch.

(a) Calculate the U-value of the external hollow block wall, given the following data:

External render	thickness	15 mm
Concrete hollow block	thickness	215 mm
Air space between plasterboard and block	width	10 mm
Internal plasterboard	thickness	12 mm

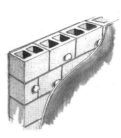

Thermal data of external wall of house:

Resistance of external surface	(R)	0.048	m²	°C/W
Resistivity of external render	(r)	2.170	m	°C/W
Resistance of hollow block	(R)	0.210	m²	°C/W
Resistance of airspace	(R)	0.170	m²	°C/W
Conductivity of plasterboard	(k)	0.160	W/m	°C
Resistance of internal surface	(R)	0.104	m²	°C/W

SAMPLE EXAMINATION QUESTIONS

(b) It is proposed to upgrade the thermal properties of the wall by fixing expanded polystyrene to the external surface. Given the thermal conductivity (k) of expanded polystyrene as 0.037 W/m °C, calculate the thickness of expanded polystyrene required to achieve a U-value of 0.27 W/m² °C to meet the requirements of the current Building Regulations.

2009 Higher Level Question 5 (a) and (b)

(a) Calculate the U-value of the external wall of a new dwelling house, given the following data:.

External render	thickness	12 mm
Concrete block outer leaf	thickness	100 mm
Cavity	width	150 mm
Insulation	thickness	100 mm
Concrete block inner leaf	thickness	100 mm
Internal plaster	thickness	15 mm

Thermal data of external wall of new house:

Resistance of external surface	(R)	0.048	m²	°C/W
Conductivity of external render	(k)	1.430	W/m	°C
Conductivity of concrete blocks	(k)	1.440	W/m	°C
Resistance of cavity	(R)	0.170	m²	°C/W
Conductivity of insulation	(k)	0.018	W/m	°C
Conductivity of internal plaster	(k)	0.430	W/m	°C
Resistance of internal surface	(R)	0.122	m2	°C/W

(b) Using the thermal data below and the U-value obtained at 5(a) above, calculate the cost of the heat lost annually through the walls of:
- the new house specified at **5(a)** and
- a house built in the 1970s with an external wall U-value of 1.80 W/m2 °C.

Thermal data:

Area of external wall	152 m²
Average internal temperature	17 °C
Average external temperature	6 °C
U-value of wall of new house	as calculated at 5(a) above
U-value of wall of 1970s house	1.80 W/m² °C
Heating period	11 hours per day for 41 weeks per annum
Cost of oil	65 cent per litre
Calorific value of oil	37350 kJ per litre
1000 watts	1kJ per second.

CHAPTER 16

CHAPTER 17
INSULATION AND VENTILATION

LEARNING OUTCOMES:

After studying this chapter students will:

- Understand the need for insulation and ventilation.
- Recognise the different qualities of materials used as insulation.
- Understand thermal bridging, where it commonly occurs and how to combat it.
- Discover how to improve insulation in older buildings.
- Be able to explain different methods of ventilation.
- Understand how mould and rot form and flourish.

KEYWORDS:

- **INSULATION • VENTILATION • HEAT LOSS • CONDENSATION • THERMAL BRIDGING**
- **MINERAL WOOL • EXPANDED POLYSTYRENE • EXTRUDED POLYSTYRENE**
- **INTERSTITIAL CONDENSATION • RETRO-FITTING • AIR CHANGE PER HOUR (ACH)**
- **NATURAL VENTILATION • MECHANICAL VENTILATION WITH HEAT RECOVERY (MVHR)**
- **EXTRACT FAN • MOULD**

INTRODUCTION

Heat loss is a huge problem in buildings. As oil prices continue to rise, the cost of heating homes, offices and other buildings can be enormous. Insulation plays a major part in reducing the cost of heating a dwelling because it prevents heat escaping. Fig. 17.1 shows the percentage heat lost through each element of a dwelling. A build-up of heat and moisture also leads to the formation of condensation, and ventilation is required in order to counteract this.

INSULATION

Insulation is used to prevent heat being lost through the building fabric. Insulation is a high-density material that does not allow heat to pass easily through it.

Fig. 17.1 Heat loss from a building.

In the 1970s, due to lack of knowledge of the value of insulation, it was not commonly installed in the cavity walls of new buildings. In the 1980s and 1990s insulation to a thickness of 50mm was installed against the inner leaf of the cavity wall. The thickness increased to 60mm in the

Roof 0.16

Roof ≤ 0.15

Window 1.6

Window ≤ 0.8

Wall 0.21

Wall ≤ 0.15

Floor 0.21

Floor ≤ 0.15

Fig. 17.2 The progression of building standards means that more energy-efficient homes are being built by increasing the insulation of the external envelope. Here we see current insulation (ABOVE LEFT) and passive (ABOVE RIGHT).

Fig. 17.3 Inner leaf cavity wall insulation.

early 2000s, and nowadays the regulations require a minimum of 100mm of insulation within a cavity wall. For passive houses, insulation thicknesses can be as wide as 200mm. Fig. 17.2 shows a comparison between these two insulation standards.

Insulation is placed horizontally under the floor slab, and vertically around the inside edges of internal rooms. A layer of insulation is also placed vertically inside the cavity along the inner leaf of the cavity wall. This insulation is held in place using wall ties. Fig. 17.3 shows inner leaf cavity wall insulation.

Where a suspended floor is to be used as the ground floor of the house, insulation is placed between the joists as described in Chapter 8, and netting or timber battens are used to make sure that it stays in place. Fig. 17.4 shows insulation in a suspended timber floor.

All new residential and commercial buildings must have thermal insulation to control the transfer of heat through the building materials. This use of insulation reduces the amount of energy required to maintain a comfortable temperature in the building.

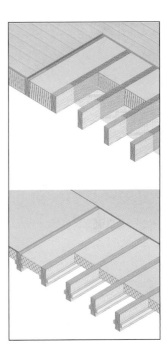

Fig. 17.4 Insulation in a suspended timber floor.

INSULATION MATERIALS

There are a number of materials used in insulation manufacture, each with its own particular properties. Some of these materials are outlined below.

Mineral Wool

Mineral wool comes in different forms, including fibreglass, basalt rock and slag wool. They all work by trapping air between their fibres. Mineral wool is

Fig. 17.5 Mineral wool insulation.

Fig. 17.6 Cross-laid insulation over beams.

Fig. 17.7 Cellulose insulation being applied to a timber frame wall.

manufactured in a furnace. The source material is mixed with coke and fired until it becomes molten rock, industrial slag or glass. To convert this liquid into glass, it is spun at extremely high speeds and forced through a fine mesh using centrifugal force. Tiny strands are formed as the material passes into cool air.

On its own, mineral wool conducts heat very well, but when it is woven into a blanket with many layers, air pockets are formed, which makes the material a very good heat insulator and sound absorber. Around 2 per cent of the mineral wool's make-up consists of a thermosetting resin binder (adhesive) and oil to help make it resistant to water.

Mineral wool also acts as passive fire protection – it has the ability to contain or slow down the spread of fire. Fig. 17.5 shows mineral wool insulation.

Mineral wool is supplied in rolls which are pre-scored to make cutting and fitting easy. The wool is fitted loosely in position and is generally stiff enough to hold itself in place. Where the wool is likely to slip, netting is used to prevent movement. In order to ensure complete coverage, cross-laid layers of insulation must be used in the attic space. This means that the bottom layer is laid parallel with the joists and the next layer at right angles to it, as shown in Fig. 17.6.

Cellulose

Cellulose is one of the cheapest forms of insulation. It is made from recycled materials, including newspaper and other paper, wood and cotton textiles. These materials are turned into fibres through a system using hammers, shredders and pulverisers. Fire-retardant chemicals are blended into the fibres to ensure that the cellulose offers passive fire protection. Fig. 17.7 shows cellulose insulation being installed.

Cellular Plastics

Plastic insulation comes in several different forms, including sprayed-in expanded foam and rigid boards. Polystyrene is one of the most widely used plastics in the world. It is manufactured from petroleum and is a thermoplastic (i.e. it can be reheated and reused). Examples of everyday uses of polystyrene include CD and DVD cases, stereo units and disposable drinking cups. The advantage of polystyrene is that it can be reused again and again.

Polystyrene insulation is available as expanded or extruded polystyrene and as beads.

Expanded Polystyrene: Also known as EPS, this material consists of pre-expanded polystyrene closed-cell foam beads, which are moulded and pressed together with heat to form a rigid board. The numerous pockets of air within the board make it an excellent insulator. The boards are suitable for insulating cavity walls and sub-floors. They come in various thicknesses, most commonly 100mm. Boards for use in cavity walls are tongued and grooved (T&G), improving rigidity and preventing any gaps. Although EPS is white as standard, grey boards are available: these have a graphite coating, which gives better thermal performance. Fig. 17.8 shows an expanded polystyrene board.

Fig. 17.8 Expanded polystyrene board.

Extruded Polystyrene Foam: Sometimes known as XPS or styrofoam, this material is a closed-cell foam. It is denser, more moisture-resistant and stiffer than expanded polystyrene. It also tends to be more expensive. Because of its better thermal performance and greater strength it is used for dry-lining internal walls as well as lining floors.

The material starts off as crystals, which are fed into an extruder with other additives along with a blowing agent. The extruder heats and mixes the materials into a plastic fluid, which is then forced through a die. Emerging from the die, the material expands into a foam and it is then shaped, cooled and trimmed to its final measurements.

Fig. 17.9 Extruded polystyrene foam board.

The extrusion process results in a product that is consistent throughout its structure, which gives it an advantage over other insulation types. Fig. 17.9 shows extruded polystyrene foam being fixed in place.

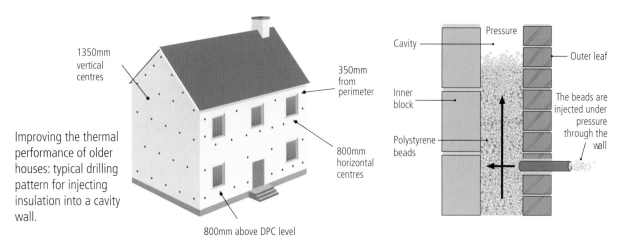

Improving the thermal performance of older houses: typical drilling pattern for injecting insulation into a cavity wall.

1350mm vertical centres

350mm from perimeter

800mm horizontal centres

800mm above DPC level

Pressure

Cavity

Outer leaf

Inner block

The beads are injected under pressure through the wall

Polystyrene beads

Fig. 17.10 LEFT: *Location and elevation of hole centres for pumping insulation.* RIGHT: *Insulation pumped into the cavity.*

Polystyrene Beads: Polystyrene beads can be used to insulate cavity walls which were originally built without insulation. These beads are the raw material used in the expanded polystyrene boards described above. Holes are drilled into the cavity wall and the beads are pumped in. The main disadvantage of this insulation type is that the wall cavity is filled, and therefore a cold bridge is created between the outer and inner leaf. Fig. 17.10 shows how polystyrene beads are pumped into an existing cavity wall.

WHERE IS INSULATION NECESSARY?

Where best to position insulation is a much studied topic. Over time, buildings have been required to adhere to stricter guidelines regarding heat loss, so insulation placement is a top priority.

Thermal bridging, also known as cold bridging, has led to improvements in the placement and required dimensions of insulation. A thermal bridge is an area where there is an opportunity for heat to transfer from inside the building

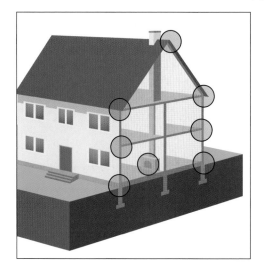

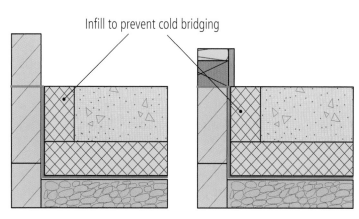

Infill to prevent cold bridging

Fig. 17.11 LEFT: *Key thermal bridge areas in buildings.* RIGHT: *Concrete floor with vertical insulation around the floor slab and the internal slab.*

straight to the outside, with no air gaps in between. This can be caused by insufficient insulation and it leads to condensation. Vertical insulation around the floor slab prevents heat transfer between the external layers of building and the internal slab (Fig. 17.11). Examples of where cold bridges occur within dwellings, and how insulation combats them, are shown in Fig. 17.12.

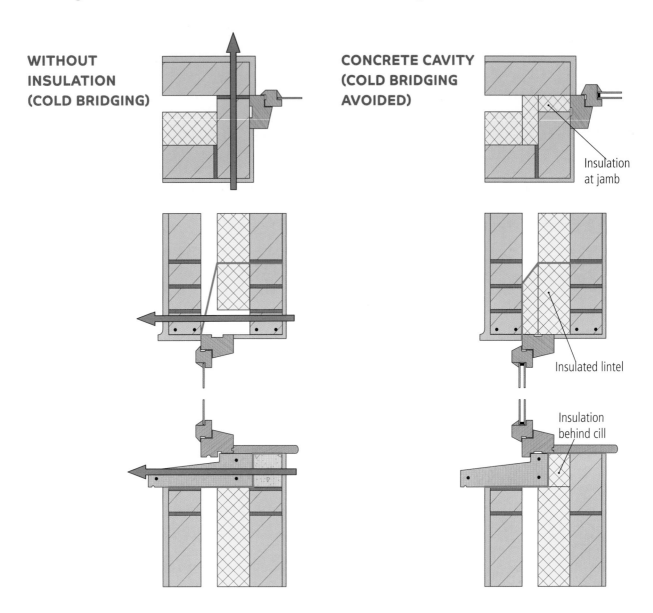

WITHOUT INSULATION (COLD BRIDGING)

CONCRETE CAVITY (COLD BRIDGING AVOIDED)

Insulation at jamb

Insulated lintel

Insulation behind cill

Fig. 17.12 Counteracting cold bridging using insulation.

Insulation is placed around the house so that the entire building is enveloped by the material. Key areas in need of insulation, other than those mentioned above, are:

- Ceiling joists
- Floor joists
- Attic space
- Stud partitions
- Around pipework and services.

CHAPTER 17

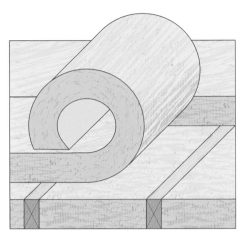

Fig. 17.13 Cross laying the insulation closes any gaps in the first layer of insulation.

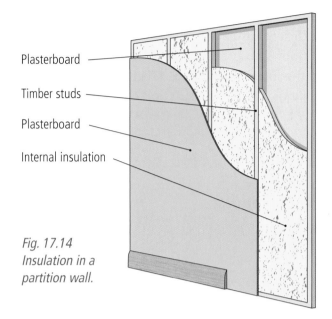

Plasterboard

Timber studs

Plasterboard

Internal insulation

Fig. 17.14
Insulation in a
partition wall.

Fig. 17.15 Insulated pipework.

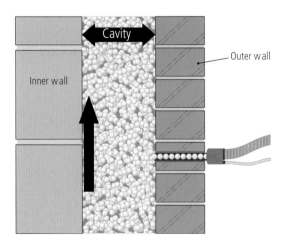

Cavity

Outer wall

Inner wall

Fig. 17.16 Cavity is filled with insulation to increase the thermal mass of the wall.

The attic space is a particularly important area because a lot of heat is lost through the attic, and here the material is double layered. Fig. 17.13 shows double-layered attic insulation.

Internal partition walls are not always insulated. Where insulation is used it is fitted before the wall is covered with plasterboard. Fig. 17.14 shows an internal partition wall with insulation in place.

Pipework and services are insulated to protect against the cold as well as to retain heat. Fig. 17.15 shows insulated pipework.

IMPROVING THERMAL PROPERTIES OF EXISTING HOUSES

As a result of increasing energy costs, improving the thermal properties of their homes has become a priority for many people. There are a number of ways this can be done. The most common method of retrofitting an existing home is to increase insulation to the walls. This can be done either by filling a cavity wall (where one exists), as discussed earlier, or by providing a new layer of wall insulation. Fig. 17.16 and Fig. 17.17 show both methods.

External wall insulation (EWI) is a popular choice because it improves the building's thermal properties but does not affect the internal dimensions of the house. Materials that can be used for EWI include mineral wool, polystyrene and wood fibre.

To begin, a starter board is laid at the same level as the DPC, to provide a level platform on which to install the insulation. The insulation is fixed above and below the starter board to maintain the lines of the building. The chosen insulation material (generally polystyrene) is then fixed to the wall using a chemical adhesive and mechanical fixings. It is important that walls are clean and dry to ensure adequate bonding between the wall and the insulating material.

In order for the insulation to be effective, windows, doors and other breaks in the wall (for pipework, cables, etc.) must be dealt with. Window and door cills are removed and replaced (after rendering) so that the extra thickness of the insulation does not interfere with the aesthetics of the building. Pipework and cables are lengthened and any spaces left in the insulation material are filled with expanding foam to prevent a cold spot forming.

Finally, the entire surface is rendered. A special mesh is used to allow the render to move slightly without cracking. Three coats of render are applied, and then finally painted. Fig. 17.18 shows the final structure in place, along with the new window cills.

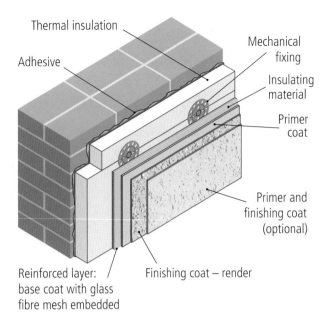

Fig. 17.17 Insulation is attached to the wall with adhesive and placed on a track. Mechanical fixings also keep the insulation panels in place.

INEFFECTIVE INSULATION

Whatever type of insulation is used, if it is not installed properly or fails at a later date it will not reduce heat loss effectively, and may in fact cause problems within the building fabric.

Condensation happens when moist, warm air comes into contact with a colder surface, or when the air reaches a temperature below dew point – the temperature at which saturated air condenses. Condensation leads to rot and mould growth, so it needs to be prevented as much as possible.

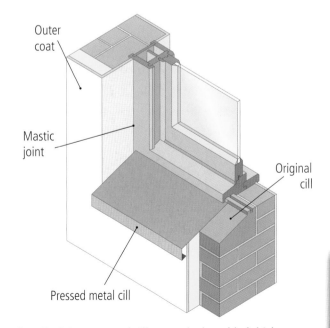

Fig. 17.18 A new metal cill conceals the added thickness of the insulation on the wall.

CHAPTER 17

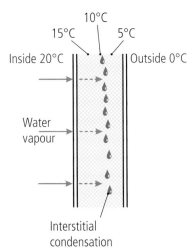

Inside 20°C   15°C   10°C   5°C   Outside 0°C

Water vapour

Interstitial condensation

Fig. 17.19 Interstitial condensation at the point where the material hits the dew point.

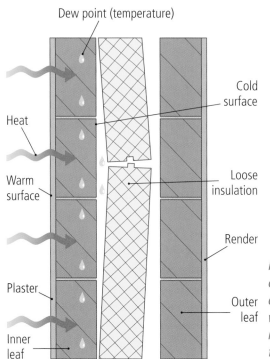

Dew point (temperature)

Heat

Warm surface

Plaster

Inner leaf

Cold surface

Loose insulation

Render

Outer leaf

Fig. 17.20 Interstitial condensation can occur within a cavity wall if insulation is not properly fixed to the inner leaf.

Interstitial condensation occurs within a fabric rather than on it. Interstitial condensation happens when warm, moist air travels through a building fabric and cools to dew point while still within the material. This creates condensation in the material itself, which leads to structural defects and makes insulation ineffective. Fig. 17.19 illustrates interstitial condensation.

Interstitial condensation also occurs where rigid insulation comes away from the wall, creating a cold surface, as shown in Fig. 17.20.

Interstitial condensation is prevented by placing a polythene sheet on the warm side of the insulation, the inner surface of the wall next to the plasterboard, or by using a foil-backed plasterboard. Each of these measures prevents warm, moist air passing through the wall and therefore eliminates the problem.

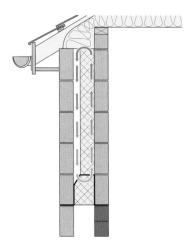

Fig. 17.21 Thermal looping.

THERMAL LOOPING

Thermal looping is the movement of air between the inner leaf of the cavity and the insulation within the cavity. A thermal loop is created when air is allowed to circulate between the inner leaf and the insulation, due to dropped mortar, insufficient use of wall ties, etc. The circulation of air in the cavity draws heat from the inner leaf, and as a result increases the energy requirements of the wall. Fig. 17.21 shows how a thermal loop works.

VENTILATION

Ventilation is the process by which air is circulated and replaced in a building or other environment. Ventilation is necessary to remove moisture-laden stale air and replace it with fresh air. Traditionally dwellings were ventilated unintentionally during the building process – small gaps were inadvertently left in the building fabric, and around windows and doors, etc. Because newer construction methods are more efficient at making houses airtight, modern buildings must include ventilation. Ventilation methods include vents in windows, doors and walls, and mechanical ventilation systems.

The ventilation system that is used can affect a building's Building Energy Rating (BER) (see Chapter 16), and this is something that must be considered at the design stage of the build.

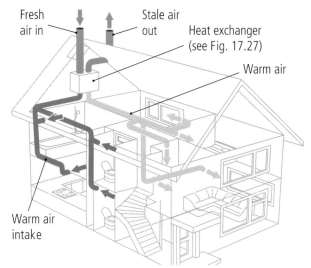

Fig. 17.22 Mechanical ventilation system. Hot air from warm rooms such as the kitchen and bathroom are extracted while cooler rooms such as sitting rooms have air pumped into them.

REQUIREMENTS OF VENTILATION

There are two main types of ventilation used in Ireland: natural ventilation; and mechanical ventilation with heat recovery. Whichever system is used, there are a number of functional requirements that the ventilation system must satisfy. It must:

- Dilute or remove pollutants
- Provide a sufficient air change per hour (ACH) to control condensation
- Quickly ventilate kitchens, bathrooms and utility rooms to remove pollutants and excess moisture
- Include purge ventilation to rapidly remove pollutants and excess moisture in habitable rooms
- Provide a fresh supply of air to eradicate problems posed by any pollutants and moisture that are not removed by extraction.

Pollutants

Pollutants are substances that can cause long- or short-term damage. Types of pollutant found in dwellings include odours, aerosol chemicals, carbon monoxide and carbon dioxide.

As we saw in Chapter 9, radon is a pollutant that, if present in air, can be cleared with good ventilation.

Fig. 17.23 A mechanical extract fan carries away heat and steam from cooking.

Air Change per Hour (ACH)

ACH is a measure of how many times per hour the stale air in a room is replaced by fresh air. A rate of 0.5–1.5 ACH is sufficient to control condensation in the entire building.

Mechanical Extract Fans

Mechanical extract fans are used in wet or very humid rooms, such as bathrooms and kitchens. They rapidly extract moisture from the air and direct it outside the building. These fans are located on the ceiling and can be operated either manually or automatically. Fig. 17.23 shows a type of mechanical extract fan that can be found in a kitchen.

Purge Ventilation

Purge ventilation (formerly known as rapid ventilation) is a means of ventilation in which air is circulated directly through an open window or door.

Fig. 17.24 Wall vents can be opened or closed as required.

Wall Vents

Wall vents are used to allow air circulation between rooms and the outside. The wall vent crosses the cavity and is closed at each end to allow a degree of ventilation control. Fig. 17.24 shows a wall vent.

NATURAL VENTILATION

Natural ventilation depends on weather conditions outside the dwelling. This means that natural ventilation can lead to under- or over-ventilation.

Over-ventilation means that too much warm air is being lost, which puts more pressure on the heating system and leads to draughts.

Under-ventilation means that insufficient air change is taking place, and that leads to mould growth, condensation and generally poor air quality.

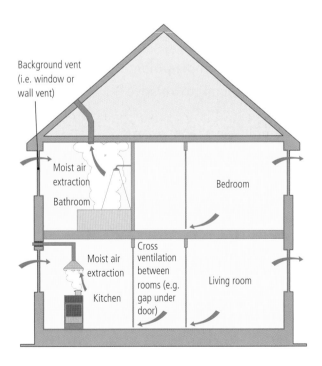

Fig. 17.25 Ventilation in the home using a combination of mechanical vents and natural ventilation.

Natural ventilation uses vents in windows, walls, doors, etc. in conjunction with extract fans and purge ventilation options. The efficiency of modern building methods has led to increased airtightness, so ventilation has become a more important issue: modern buildings that use natural ventilation are more prone to under-ventilation. Fig. 17.25 shows mechanical and natural ventilation.

MECHANICAL VENTILATION WITH HEAT RECOVERY

Mechanical ventilation with heat recovery (MVHR) is an alternative to natural ventilation. This system does not rely on the weather so it is more reliable. It uses ductwork to direct air around the dwelling. As this air is directed around the house it passes through a central unit, which heats the incoming fresh air using the outgoing warm stale air. Fig. 17.26 shows an MVHR system.

The central unit is designed to allow heat to exchange between ducts without allowing stale and fresh air to mix. Fig. 17.27 shows this in detail.

Because there is ducting to each room, vents to the outside of the building are not necessary. This makes the building more airtight, which reduces energy costs. The air change per hour (ACH) can also be controlled. The elimination of vents in the windows, walls, doors, etc. also means that:

- There is less risk of condensation and mould growth
- Cold draughts are eliminated
- Pollutants are effectively removed from rooms.

The control unit is usually placed in the attic of the dwelling. It must be easily accessible to perform maintenance, such as cleaning the filters.

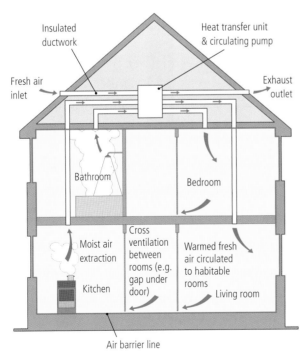

Fig. 17.26 Mechanical ventilation using a heat recovery unit.

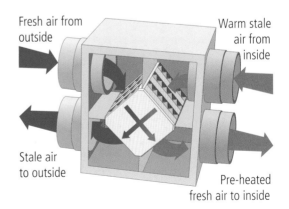

Fig. 17.27 Air exchange unit. Cold air enters from the top left of the exchange and passes through the exchange to the bottom right. As it does so, air coming from the building passes by the cold air coming in and warms it.

MOULD GROWTH

Mould growth and rot are consequences of poor insulation and/or ventilation techniques that lead to condensation and a build-up of moisture on and in fabrics. Mould grows on many surfaces, most commonly on plaster, timber and wallpaper.

The growth of mould is usually associated with condensation, but it can be caused by other factors, such as rising damp as a result of insufficient damp proof membrane (DPM) or damp proof course (DPC) in the substructure. Mould also grows in cold areas where there is a high level of humidity on a regular basis. The undesirable properties of mould growth in the home include appearance, odour and health considerations.

Mould is made up of fungi, which need a number of conditions to survive. Spores are the first essential element of mould growth. Spores are found in high numbers in the outside air and are easily transported indoors. Fungi require organic matter to thrive. This organic matter is found in the building materials used to construct the dwelling. Although fungi require food, oxygen and suitable temperatures to thrive, it is the presence of moisture that leads to rapid mould growth. Fig. 17.28 shows mould growth on a wall.

Mould can lead to significant damage to indoor furnishings as well as respiratory problems for the people living in a building. It can be removed by cleaning, but to prevent it returning the problem must be addressed at source, by preventing condensation and by installing the DPM/DPC correctly.

Fig. 17.28 Mould on a wall caused by poor ventilation.

PRACTICE QUESTIONS

1. Explain the importance of insulation in dwellings.

2. Describe using notes and neat freehand sketches the different insulation materials and how they are used.

3. Explain using notes and neat freehand sketches the term 'thermal bridging' and how to combat it.

4. A house built in the 1970s needs to be insulated. Decribe in detail two methods of achieving this.

5. What is interstitial condensation?

6. What is thermal looping and how can it be prevented?

7. Why is ventilation necessary?

8. What are the functional requirements of a ventilation system?

9. Describe using notes and neat freehand sketches how a natural ventilation system operates.

10. Describe using notes and neat freehand sketches how a mechanical ventilation with heat recovery system works.

11. What are the conditions required for mould growth?

12. How can mould growth be prevented at the initial stages of the build?

SAMPLE EXAMINATION QUESTIONS

2012 Ordinary Level Question 2

A dwelling house, as shown in the sketch, has a 300 mm external block wall with 50 mm expanded polystyrene insulation in the cavity. The wall has a smooth external render finish. It is proposed to improve the insulation properties of the wall by adding an external system of insulation.

(a) Using notes and *neat freehand sketches*, show **one** suitable method of applying an external insulation system to the wall. Specify the insulation material used, indicate its typical thickness and include details of the external surface finish to the insulation.

(b) List **two** advantages of applying an external system of insulation to the walls of an existing house.

2011 Higher Level Question 9

Careful design detailing is necessary in order to design a building envelope which is free of thermal/cold bridges. The drawing shows an outline section through a single storey house having a 350mm external concrete block wall with an insulated cavity. The ground floor is an insulated solid concrete floor.

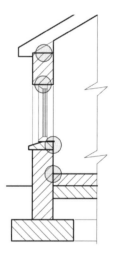

(a) Select any **three** locations from those circled on the sketch, and show clearly, using notes and *annotated freehand sketches*, the typical design detailing which will prevent the formation of thermal bridges at each location selected.

(b) Discuss in detail **two** advantages of designing a building envelope which is free of thermal bridges.

2010 Higher Level Question 3

The external wall of a dwelling house built in the 1970s is a 300mm concrete block wall with 40 mm expanded polystyrene insulation in the cavity. It has been decided to upgrade the thermal properties of the external wall by using either:

- an internal insulation system or
- an external insulation system.

(a) For **each** of the insulation systems outlined above, show using notes and *freehand sketches*, one method of applying the insulation material. For **each** insulation system, include the following in your sketches:

- method of fixing
- insulation material and its thickness
- surface finish.

(b) Discuss in detail **two** advantages of each system of insulation and recommend a preferred system of insulation for the house outlined above.

SAMPLE EXAMINATION QUESTIONS

2009 Ordinary Level Question 2

The arrows show three areas through which heat is lost in a poorly insulated dwelling house. The house has a slated roof, concrete block external walls with a cavity and a solid concrete ground floor.

(a) Select any **two** areas of the dwelling house and, using notes and *neat freehand sketches*, describe how you would insulate the areas selected to reduce the heat loss. Indicate on your sketches the type of insulation and give the typical thickness of the insulation.

(b) Discuss **two** advantages of increasing the thermal insulation levels in a dwelling house.

2008 Higher Level Question 3

Poor design detailing or workmanship can result in the formation of thermal (cold) bridges, causing significant heat loss through the external fabric of a building.

(a) Outline **three** areas in a dwelling house where thermal bridges are likely to occur and using notes and *freehand sketches*, show the correct design detailing which will prevent the formation of thermal bridges in each location outlined.

(b) A house built in the 1980s has 50mm expanded polystyrene insulation in the cavity of the external wall. Using notes and *freehand sketches,* show **two** methods of upgrading the thermal properties of the external envelope of the house to meet the requirements of the current Building Regulations.

2008 Ordinary Level Question 6

Thermal insulation is used to reduce heat loss through the external walls of a dwelling house.

(a) Using notes and *neat freehand sketches*, show the location of a rigid insulation board in the cavity of an external wall of concrete block construction.
Show the typical thickness of the insulation board.

(b) Using notes and *neat freehand sketches* show how the insulation board is held in place in the cavity.

(c) Using notes and *neat freehand sketches* show another method of insulating the external wall of the house.

2007 Ordinary Level Question 8

Thermal insulation is important in the construction of a dwelling house.

(a) Using notes and *neat freehand sketches*, show the position of the thermal insulation quilt in the attic of a new house.

(b) On your sketch, show clearly the position of a vapour barrier and give **one** reason why it should be placed in the position outlined.

(c) Outline **two** safety precautions that should be observed when placing an insulation quilt in an attic.

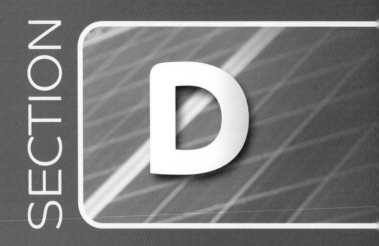

SERVICES AND SUSTAINABILITY

CHAPTER **18**
ACCESSIBILITY

LEARNING OUTCOMES**:**

After studying this chapter students will:

- Understand the importance of making residential buildings accessible to all.
- Know the basic dimensional requirements needed to make different areas accessible.
- Be able to sketch various dimensional requirements and layouts that make areas accessible.

KEYWORDS**:**

- ACCESSIBILITY • OPENINGS • APPROACH • ACCESS • SLOPE • STEPS • GRADIENT
- WHEELCHAIR • MOBILITY • LANDING • GRAB RAIL • NON-SLIP FLOORING
- THRESHOLD • DOOR SADDLE

INTRODUCTION

Lifetime use, in terms of building, refers to designing a building so as to create easy access for all users over its lifetime.

Buildings must be designed so that they are easily accessible to everyone. Building regulations set out specific accessibility requirements for many different parts of buildings. These regulations, which offer simple, inclusive designs and specifications, help to make buildings easy to navigate and use. They are particularly important for elderly people, people with disabilities, and young children. All new dwellings, and public buildings such as schools, libraries, shopping centres, etc., are subject to these regulations.

ACCESS AND USE

New building regulations governing the accessibility of dwellings came into effect in 2010. To comply with the regulations, a dwelling must be designed and constructed to allow people to independently access a building and use its facilities in a safe manner. The design must also avoid creating potential hazards for people with impaired vision, hearing or mobility.

The main entrance to a dwelling must be suitable for wheelchair users. For this reason, it must have a minimum opening of 800mm to allow a person in a wheelchair to pass through. The approach to the main access is equally important; in order to go through the door, a person must first be able to reach it. A clear, level area of 1200mm by 1200mm must be provided at the main access to allow a wheelchair user room to manouevre, while the access route must be a minimum width of 900mm.

The threshold that a person must cross to gain entry to the dwelling cannot exceed a height of 15mm and must be rounded or chamfered; this reduces the risk of someone tripping, and it makes the threshold less difficult to cross in a wheelchair or other mobility aid. Fig. 18.1 shows these basic accessibility requirements.

ACCESS

- Minimum opening of 800mm
- Level manoeuvering area of 1200 x 1200mm
- Maximum threshold height of 15mm
- Minimum headroom on approach of 2.1m
- Minimum width of access route 900mm

Main entrance – should be suitable for use by wheelchair users

Minimum 1200 × 1200m clear level area in front of every accessible entrance

Access route – level, gently sloped, ramped or stepped, min. 900mm wide, firm, even surface to reduce risk of slipping. May form part of a driveway of min. width 3600mm

Point of access minimum 900mm wide

Raised kerb minimum 100mm high if ground is not graded to the approach

Boundary wall

Fig. 18.1 Accessibility requirements at the entrance of a building.

APPROACH TO THE DWELLING

The approach to the dwelling's main entrance must be flat or have at most a gentle slope. The pathway must have a firm and even surface to reduce the risk of slipping for people with mobility aids. The edges of the pathway must have a kerb of a minimum 100mm height where the gradient between the pathway and other areas changes. If the approach to the main entrance passes under an archway, stairs, projecting window or low balcony, a minimum headroom of 2100mm must be provided. Openings of less than this height must be boxed off to prevent the risk of people injuring themselves.

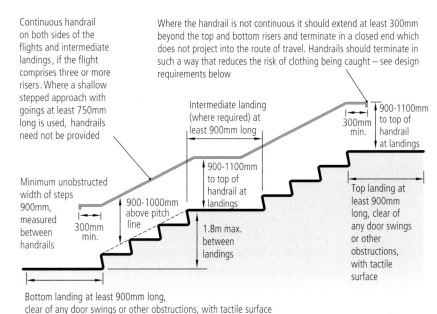

Continuous handrail on both sides of the flights and intermediate landings, if the flight comprises three or more risers. Where a shallow stepped approach with goings at least 750mm long is used, handrails need not be provided

Where the handrail is not continuous it should extend at least 300mm beyond the top and bottom risers and terminate in a closed end which does not project into the route of travel. Handrails should terminate in such a way that reduces the risk of clothing being caught – see design requirements below

Intermediate landing (where required) at least 900mm long

900-1100mm to top of handrail at landings

300mm min.

900-1100mm to top of handrail at landings

Minimum unobstructed width of steps 900mm, measured between handrails

300mm min.

900-1000mm above pitch line

1.8m max. between landings

Top landing at least 900mm long, clear of any door swings or other obstructions, with tactile surface

Bottom landing at least 900mm long, clear of any door swings or other obstructions, with tactile surface

Fig. 18.2 Step profiles and handrail specifications for external use.

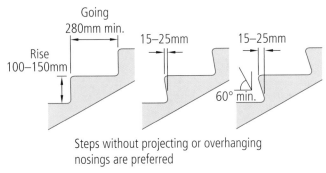

Fig. 18.3 External step profiles which can be used.

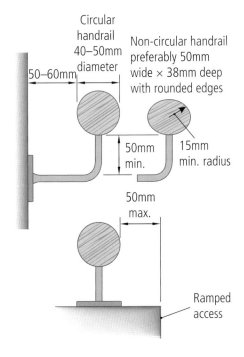

Fig. 18.4 Access regulations for handrails.

Ideally, the approach to the dwelling should be level. Level means that the area has a maximum gradient of 1:50 (i.e. for every 50 units of measurement in length, the height rises by one unit). Where the gradient is not level, a gentle gradient is recommended. A gentle gradient is one where the slope is 1:20 at most. When the approach to the dwelling has a gradient of between 1:20 and 1:12 it is considered a ramp. A ramp must have a landing after a distance of 7m, and at each change of direction. The landing provided must have a minimum width of 1200mm to allow a wheelchair user to move comfortably.

Steps may be used where it is not possible to install a level, gentle or ramped approach. Steps must satisfy several regulations. The rise of each step must be between 100mm and 150mm, and the maximum rise of the flight overall cannot exceed 1800mm. Tapered steps are not advised, because of the possibility that the user might fall as a result of misjudging the distance from one step to the next. Handrails must be available on both sides of the steps, and they must be no more than 900mm apart. Landings must be built where necessary, and must have a minimum length of 900mm, with no obstructions caused by, for example, door swing. Figs 18.2, 18.3 and 18.4 show acceptable step profiles and handrail specifications for external use in a dwelling.

APPROACH

- Must be a flat or gentle slope (maximum gradient 1:50)
- Pathway: minimum width 900mm
- Kerb height: minimum 100mm
- Minimum headroom: 2100mm
- Ramps: landings every 7m
- Landing: minimum width 1200mm
- Steps: 100–150mm rise
- Handrails: maximum 900mm apart
- Flight of steps: maximum rise 1800mm

INTERNAL CIRCULATION

Having entered the dwelling, it is important that a person with impaired mobility is able to navigate through the building and use all its facilities. Dwellings of more than one storey must allow this freedom across the entire floor level. For wheelchair users, an accessible bathroom, and bedroom if required, must be located all on one storey. The person should not have to navigate steps to use any facilities in the building. Where there is a split-level floor, at least one habitable room and a bathroom must be accessible to a wheelchair user.

Corridors must be a minimum of 900mm wide to allow a person with impaired mobility to move through the building. Permanent fixtures such as radiators and structural elements must not make the passageway less than 800mm wide, and they cannot be located along the wall opposite a door opening. The walls adjoining each side of the doorway must be kept clear for a minimum distance of 400mm. When a door leads to a part of the dwelling that can only be accessed by steps or stairs, a minimum opening of 775mm is suitable, because in this case a wheelchair does not have to pass through it. These regulations are illustrated in Fig. 18.5.

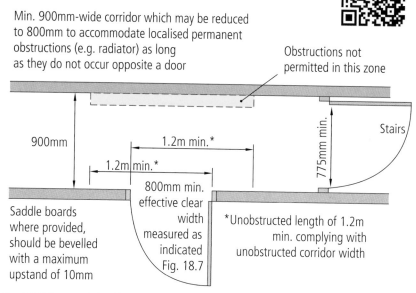

Min. 900mm-wide corridor which may be reduced to 800mm to accommodate localised permanent obstructions (e.g. radiator) as long as they do not occur opposite a door

Obstructions not permitted in this zone

900mm

1.2m min.*

1.2m min.*

800mm min. effective clear width measured as indicated Fig. 18.7

775mm min.

Stairs

Saddle boards where provided, should be bevelled with a maximum upstand of 10mm

*Unobstructed length of 1.2m min. complying with unobstructed corridor width

Fig. 18.5 Internal circulation requirements for corridors and doors.

Doors must be designed so that someone in a wheelchair can use them easily. Not only is the width of the door important, the position of the handle and the type of saddle also affect how well the door works. A saddle at the base of a doorway must not rise higher than 10mm, and it must be chamfered so that it is not difficult to clear it. Door handles must be located within easy reach. An optimum height of 900mm is recommended, though the handle can be positioned anywhere between 800mm and 1200mm from the ground. Fig. 18.6 shows this detail. The clearances at door openings are shown in Fig. 18.7.

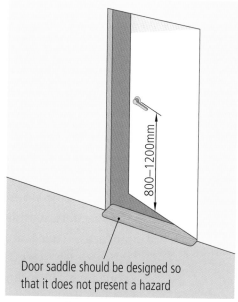

800–1200mm

Door saddle should be designed so that it does not present a hazard

Fig. 18.6 Easily accessible door.

(i) Effective clear width
(door stop to projecting
ironmongery)

Handle height
between 800mm
and 1200mm

(ii) Effective clear width
(door stop to door leaf)

(iii) Effective clear width
for sliding door (door
stop to door leaf)

Fig. 18.7 Determination of effective clear widths at door openings.

INTERNAL CIRCULATION

- Corridors: minimum 900mm wide
- Radiators/permanent fixtures: must not make corridor less than 800mm wide
- Radiators/permanent fixtures: must not be opposite doorways
- Door opening: minimum clearway of 400mm on either side of door opening
- Door saddles: maximum height 10mm
- Door handles: optimum position 900mm

ROOM LAYOUTS

For some rooms there are additional regulations for access and use so that anyone can enjoy them. The kitchen and bathroom are given specific attention in relation to ease of use for wheelchair users because both rooms are used frequently.

Kitchen

The regulations outlined above also apply to the kitchen, but there are also some additional recommendations for kitchens. The floor must have a non-slip surface, and a turning circle of not less than 1500mm diameter. Worktops and sinks must be no higher than 800mm from the floor, and appliances such as dishwashers, washing machines and ovens should be installed under the work surfaces. There must also be a space underneath the workspace so that wheelchair users have enough room for their knees. Sockets and small appliances, including kettles, toasters and microwaves, must be positioned at an accessible height.

The sink, cooker and fridge must be laid out to form a triangle, with a maximum distance of 1800mm between the cooker and sink. Workspace must be made available on either side of the cooker. (See work triangle, Chapter 3.)

The regulations recommend that a kitchen table should be oval or circular in shape as these are easier for people with impaired mobility to use. The table should be lower than usual; a maximum height of 700mm is set out in the guidelines. Fig.18.8 shows the layout of a kitchen suitable for a wheelchair user.

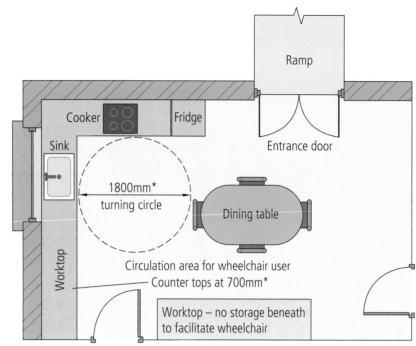

*Fig. 18.8 Kitchen layout suitable for a wheelchair user. Key work areas such as hobs, sinks and food preparation areas should have knee clearance provided below or adjacent to them. (*Irish Wheel Chair Association Access Guidelines)*

KITCHEN

- Non-slip floor
- Allow turning circle of 1500mm (optimum 1800mm)
- Worktop/sink: maximum height 800mm (optimum 700mm)
- Sockets at accessible heights
- Cooker to sink: maximum distance 1800mm
- Round or oval table: maximum height 700mm

Bathroom

The bathroom is used by one occupant at a time, and for this reason it has a number of specific regulations to ensure a user's safety. The floor must be of a non-slip material to prevent any slipping or sliding, and the space should have a turning circle of not less than 1500mm diameter. The wash-hand basin must be fixed to the wall rather than on top of a pedestal – this leaves room underneath for a wheelchair user. The taps attached to the sink must be lever operated. For a person with reduced mobility, it is easier to operate a lever than twist a tap.

The toilet must have a clear space of 750mm by 1200mm beside it, to allow a wheelchair user sufficient space to transfer sideways from the wheelchair to the WC.

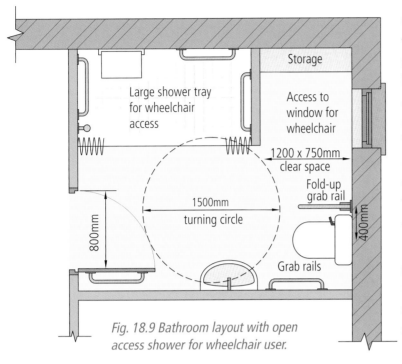

Fig. 18.9 Bathroom layout with open access shower for wheelchair user.

Grab rails are an important aid for wheelchair users. These 600mm-long rails are placed either vertically or horizontally at strategic locations around the room. Horizontal grab rails are best set at a height of 700mm off the floor. A fold-up grab rail positioned 400mm from the centre line of the toilet is provided for grip and stability.

The entry into the shower must be level to allow ease of access, and a shower seat should also be installed. Grab rails must be provided in the shower, and the height of the shower-head should be adjustable. Fabric shower curtains are recommended. Fig. 18.9 shows a bathroom layout suitable for a wheelchair user.

BATHROOM

- Non-slip floor
- Turning circle: minimum 1500mm
- Wash-hand basin: fixed to wall
- Lever taps rather than screw taps
- Toilet: 750mm by 1200mm space beside it
- Grab rail: 400mm from toilet
- Grab rails: at height of 700mm for length of 600mm
- Level entry into shower with shower seat provided
- Grab rails in shower
- Adjustable height shower-head

SWITCHES AND SOCKETS

Every room in a building is furnished with switches and sockets for lighting and various appliances. In order for a wheelchair user to use switches and sockets with ease, they must be installed according to the regulations set out in the technical guidance documents.

Equipment used near the main entrance, including doorbells, intercoms, keyholes, etc., must be located between 900mm and 1200mm from floor level. The same dimensional requirements apply to all light switches in the accessible area of the dwelling.

Sockets for general use must be at a height of between 400mm and 1200mm from floor level. Specific-purpose sockets such as sockets for cookers, washing machines, etc. that are in continual use do not have to comply with these regulations.

SWITCHES AND SOCKETS

- Main entranceway (doorbell, intercom) at height of 900–1200mm

- Sockets at height of 400–1200mm from floor

- Light switches at height between 900–1200mm

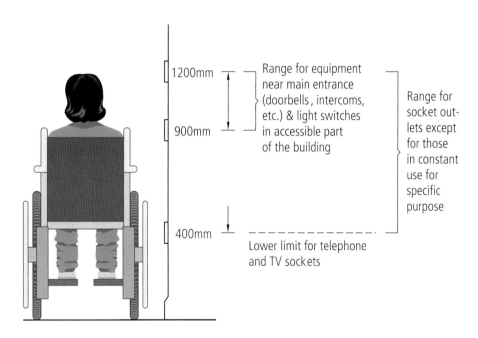

Fig. 18.10 Heights to the centre of socket outlets, switches and controls.

PRACTICE QUESTIONS

1. Discuss in detail the regulations regarding the approach to and the main access point of a dwelling. Use sketches where appropriate.

2. Describe using notes and neat freehand sketches the regulations in relation to internal circulation within a dwelling.

3. Neatly sketch a layout for a kitchen suitable for a wheelchair user. Annotate the sketch to show the dimensional requirements.

4. Neatly sketch a layout for a bathroom suitable for a wheelchair user. Annotate the sketch to show the dimensional requirements.

SAMPLE EXAMINATION QUESTIONS

2012 Higher Level Question 2

(a) Discuss in detail, using notes and freehand sketches, **two** functional requirements of a dwelling house designed for lifetime use. Refer in particular to the:

- main entrance **and**
- internal corridor layout.

(b) The layout of a bedroom and an adjoining bathroom, which is 2.3 m × 2.9 m, is shown in the accompanying drawing. The hot press is also shown.

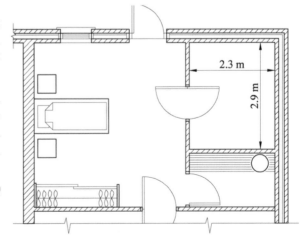

Using notes and freehand sketches, show a preferred layout for the bathroom space to ensure that it is suitable for a person in a wheelchair. Indicate in your design sketches the location of the following:

window, shower area, toilet, wash hand basin and grab rails.

Include **three** typical dimensions.

(c) Discuss your preferred location for the bathroom items listed at **2(b)** above.

SAMPLE EXAMINATION QUESTIONS

2010 Higher Level Question 2

The accompanying diagram shows an open-plan living, dining and kitchen space suitable for a person in a wheelchair. The floor is an insulated solid concrete ground floor.

(a) Using notes and *freehand sketches* show the design detailing at the entrance door to ensure that rainwater is removed from the threshold area and that the entrance is suitable for a person in a wheelchair.

(b) From the given diagram, select any **two** areas that need specific consideration to ensure suitability for a person in a wheelchair. For **each** area selected, using notes and *freehand sketches*, show the specific design detailing that ensures ease of use for a person in a wheelchair. Indicate on your design sketches typical dimensions as appropriate.

CHAPTER **19**
PLUMBING AND WATER

After studying this chapter students will:

- Understand how water is treated so that it is usable in the home.
- Understand how water is distributed around a dwelling.
- Be able to sketch the hot and cold water supply line diagrams.
- Be able to explain the different elements that make up the water systems in dwellings.
- Understand the different hot water systems available.
- Understand the benefits of rainwater harvesting.

KEYWORDS:

- WATER TREATMENT • DISTRIBUTION • DIRECT SYSTEM • INDIRECT SYSTEM
- VENTED • UNVENTED • SOLAR PANELS • LIMESCALE • FITTINGS • STORAGE TANK
- VALVES • CYLINDER • BOILER • RADIATOR • EXPANSION VESSEL • UNDERFLOOR HEATING
- ONE-PIPE SYSTEM • TWO-PIPE SYSTEM • RAINWATER HARVESTING

INTRODUCTION

Clean drinking water is essential for life. Throughout history, towns have been located near freshwater sources, such as rivers and lakes, because they provide a supply of clean drinking water. Today's towns and cities demand huge amounts of water. In Ireland, each person uses an average of 150 litres of water per day. However, because of pollution, it is no longer safe to take water directly from natural sources, so water reservoirs are needed to store and treat this water before it is used.

Fig. 19.1 Water meter attached to a home's incoming water main.

A new public water utility called Irish Water has been set up as part of a national programme to upgrade the supply and distribution of water throughout the country. And, for the first time, Irish households will now pay for the water they use. Water meters, which measure the quantity of water used, will become a basic feature in Irish homes.

WATER SOURCES

Our water supplies start as rainfall. Most rain soaks into the ground; the water that does not is referred to as surface water. Surface sources include lakes, streams and rivers, reservoirs, and the run-off from roofs and paving. This water is easily polluted by farm and industrial waste, so it must be treated before being supplied to households. Water from shallow, fast-flowing rivers is purer, but there is no guarantee that it is safe to drink, so it must also be treated.

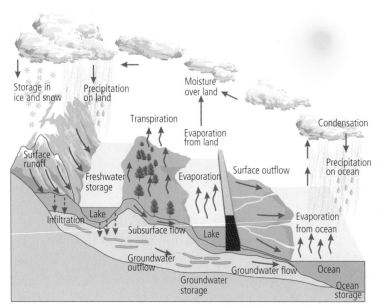

Fig. 19.2 The hydrological water cycle.

Rainfall that soaks into the ground filters through the soil and eventually reaches an impermeable layer; a layer of rock or clay that will not allow the water to go further. At this point it either collects and forms an underground reservoir, or flows along the surface of the impermeable material to form an underground stream. Layers of water formed underground are known as aquifers. Wells are bored to reach the supplies of water in underground aquifers. It is essential that wells are protected from contamination by untreated surface water that could enter through the upper section. Springs and natural

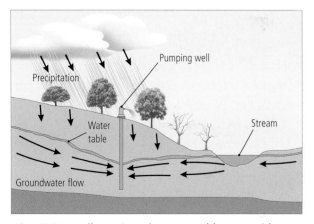

Fig. 19.3 A well taps into the water table to provide a fresh source of water.

wells originate from underground water. However, water is purified as it flows through the ground, so spring water is generally pure.

Local authorities use water from all these water sources. They store it, treat it, and eventually distribute it through pipes to local households. Each local authority is responsible for ensuring that every dwelling house in its area has access to clean water for domestic purposes. Dwellings that are not reached by the local authority supply use a local group water scheme. This is a water supply shared between a number of households and is typically sourced from wells.

WATER TREATMENT

The water that local authorities supply to households must be safe to drink. The water has to be treated to remove any particles and bacteria in the water, as well as adding minerals such as chlorine and fluoride to improve its quality. There are a number of steps involved in treating water for human consumption.

Treatment Process

1. Water is pumped from surface water and underground supplies into a treatment facility.

2. **Screening**. The water passes through a stainless steel mesh, which filters large debris, such as twigs, leaves and other particles. Most groundwater does not need to be screened as it has been filtered naturally by the soil.

3. **Flocculation**. Aluminium potassium sulphate (alum) is added to the water. This chemical attracts small particles, and as the particles attach to each other they grow heavy and fall to the bottom of the treatment tank.

4. **Sedimentation**. The water flows into sedimentation tanks, which are located as close as possible to the flocculation tanks so that there is as little agitation as possible. In the sedimentation tanks, particles are allowed to settle at the bottom, where they form a layer of sludge. This sludge is removed from the tank.

5. **Filtration**. While most particles in the water have now been removed, suspended particles still remain. The water is now filtered to remove all of these. The filter is made up of layers of stone, gravel and sand. The spaces between the filtration material allow the water to flow through them, leaving the particles behind. These spaces get gradually smaller over the depth of the filter.

6. **Disinfection**. Chlorine is added to the water to kill off any bacteria or microbes that have survived up to this point. Enough chlorine is added to ensure that contamination will not occur between the treatment facility and individual households, but not so much that the water gives off a smell or taste as it comes through the household tap.

7. **Fluoridation**. In Ireland, unlike most European countries, fluoride is added in a controlled manner to the water to reduce tooth decay.

The water is now safe to drink.

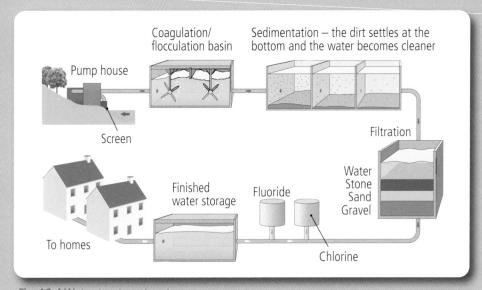

Fig. 19.4 Water treatment system.

COMPONENTS OF A WATER SYSTEM

Whatever system is chosen to distribute water in a dwelling, its components need to be chosen carefully to make sure that it works efficiently.

Water storage tanks. One storage tank is needed in a direct hot water system. This tank must have a capacity of 230 litres. A secondary storage tank is needed in an indirect hot water system. It must have a capacity of 45 litres. Fig. 19.5 shows a cold water storage tank.

Cylinder. The cylinder stores the hot water produced by the boiler. The standard size is 135 litres. It is made from copper and heavily insulated to prevent the water losing heat. Fig. 19.6 shows a cut-away of a hot water cylinder covered in insulation foam. A lagging jacket can also be used for insulation.

Pipework. Pipes can be made from copper or plastic. Plastic pipes are generally preferred because: plastic is a better insulator than copper; plastic pipes have push-to-fit junctions, which make them easier to install; and plastic is cheaper than copper. Copper pipe is shown in the coil (Fig. 19.6) and plastic pipes in Fig. 19.7.

Valves. A number of types of valve are used in plumbing. Some of the common types are:

Ball valve. This is a type of stop valve. Inside is a ball with a hole through the centre. The hole allows water to flow through only when it is aligned with the pipe. Ball valves are used to turn the supply on and off and are commonly located next to appliances such as boilers.

Fig. 19.5 Cold water storage tank, insulated against cold weather.

Fig. 19.6 Insulated hot water cylinder with cut-away to show internal copper coil.

Fig. 19.8 Ball valve.

Fig. 19.7 Copper or plastic pipes can be used for pipework. The plastic pipes here are laid for underfloor heating.

CHAPTER 19

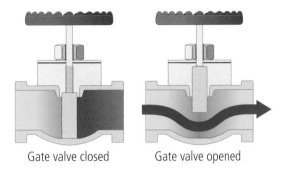

Fig. 19.9 Gate valve showing how the valve operates.

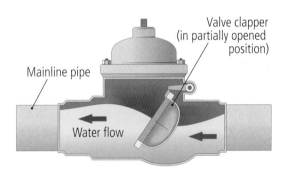

Fig. 19.11 Check valve.

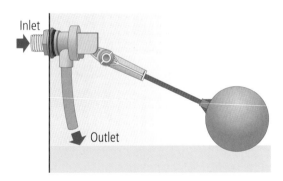

Fig. 19.12 Float valve.

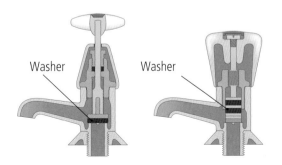

Fig 19.13 Two common types of tap.

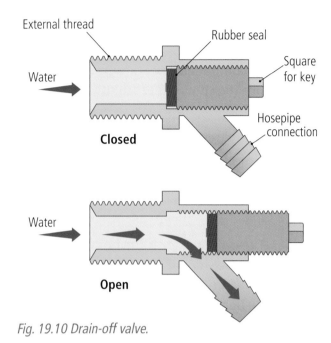

Fig. 19.10 Drain-off valve.

Gate valve. This is a type of stop valve. As the wheel is turned, the pin inside the valve closes. This type of valve can either stop or restrict the flow of water through the pipes and is used near appliances. Fig. 19.9 shows a gate valve.

Drain-off valve. This type of valve allows some or all of the system to drain off without needing to disconnect pipework. Drain-off valves are commonly located on boilers and cylinders. Fig. 19.10 shows a drain-off valve.

Check valve. A check valve or non-return valve is a one-way valve that only allows water to flow through it in one direction. This prevents pressure loss and back siphonage (water flowing in the wrong direction) in the system. Fig. 19.11 shows a check valve.

Float valve. A float valve cuts off the supply of water when it reaches a certain height. The valve works in conjunction with a hollow sphere that floats and triggers the valve. It is typically found in the toilet cistern. Fig. 19.12 shows a float valve.

Taps. Taps are used in sinks, bathtubs, etc. to control the supply of water. There are many tap designs; two are shown in Fig. 19.13.

Fig. 19.14 Various types
of pipe fittings.

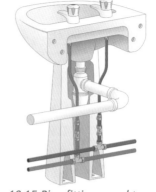

Fig. 19.15 Pipe fittings used to
connect a sink to the water supply
of the home.

Fittings. Fittings connect the different parts of the pipework. They are available in many shapes and sizes, and made from many different materials, including plastic, copper and cast iron. They are used to split the connections, change direction and/or extend pipework. Figs 19.14 and 19.15 show common fittings and how they are used to manipulate pipework.

DISTRIBUTION OF WATER

Water enters the house through the mains pipe, as shown in Fig. 19.16. The mains connection is located in a chamber under the pavement outside the dwelling. From here, the water goes straight to the kitchen sink. Stop valves are situated at the connection to the mains pipe outside the property and under the sink. Drain valves are fitted above the stop valves in order to drain water from the system if necessary.

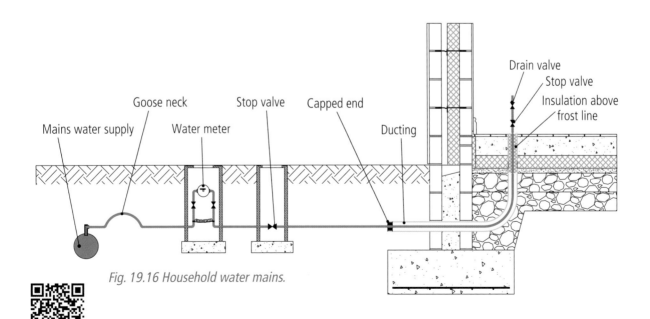

Fig. 19.16 Household water mains.

COLD WATER

There are two systems for supplying a dwelling with cold water: the direct cold water supply system and the indirect cold water supply system. Each has its advantages and disadvantages.

Direct Cold Water Supply System

The direct system uses the mains feed to supply all the appliances in the house. This means that all sinks, showers, toilets and washing machines draw water from the same source. The water in the taps is suitable for drinking (drinking water is also called potable water). A non-return check valve must be used at taps in this system to prevent the drinking water being contaminated as a result of back flow. Fig. 19.17 illustrates the direct cold water system.

The advantages of the direct cold water system include:

- Ease of installation
- Low cost
- No large water storage cistern needed in attic
- Drinking water available from all taps
- Less pipework (which is susceptible to freezing) in attic.

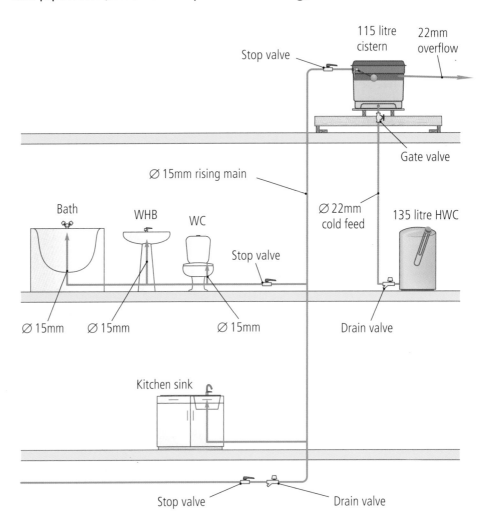

Fig. 19.17 Direct cold water supply system.

The disadvantages of the direct cold water system include:

- Reduced pressure at peak times
- High failure rate of fittings due to increased pressure
- No reserve supply if mains fail.

Indirect Cold Water Supply System

The indirect cold water supply system directs the mains water coming into the house in two directions, one up to a storage tank or the cistern in the attic and the other to the kitchen tap. It is fed off to individual appliances from the cistern. The only outlet coming directly from the mains is the kitchen tap. This tap is the source of clean drinking water for the household. The tap is also the only high-pressure outlet in the system.

The storage tank for a typical four-bedroom house has a recommended capacity of 340 litres. A storage tank is heavy when it is full of water, and it is essential that the load is spread evenly over at least four joists. The tank must also be insulated to protect the water in the pipes from freezing in cold weather. Figs 19.18 and 19.19 show the details necessary for supporting the water storage tank as well as the necessary insulation. Fig. 19.20 shows the layout and technical specifications of the indirect cold water system.

The advantages of the indirect cold water supply system include:

- Reserve supply of water if mains fail
- Constant pressure on all taps, except the kitchen tap
- Overflow fitting fitted to storage tank to prevent water damage due to overflow.

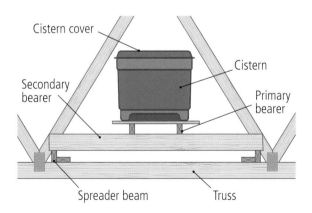

Fig. 19.18 Cold water storage tank, supported to spread the load over a mimimum of four joists.

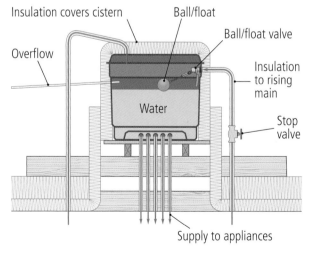

Fig. 19.19 Cold water storage tank, with tank and pipework insulated.

Fig. 19.20 Indirect cold water supply system.

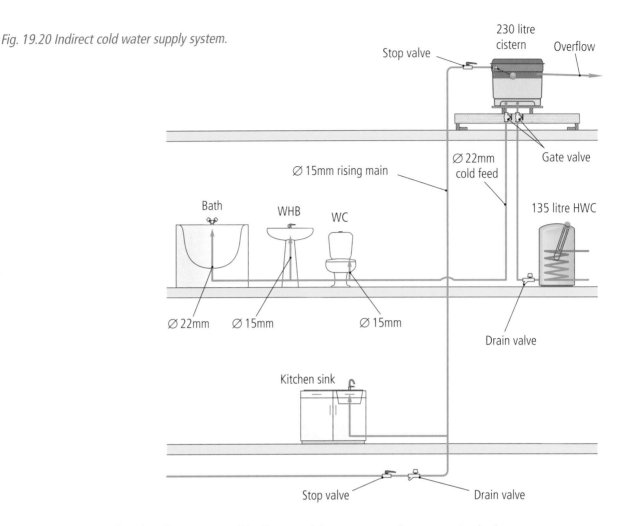

The disadvantages of indirect cold water supply system include:

- Higher cost – more pipework and fittings are needed
- Large water storage tank required
- Drinking water is only available at kitchen sink.

HOT WATER

Hot water is not just needed in the taps around the house; it is also used to heat the building. Different appliances can be used to heat water, but some of the common ones in Irish homes are:

- Boiler (solid fuel, oil or gas)
- Back boiler (open fire or stove)
- Immersion (electric heating element fitted inside cylinder).

Fig. 19.21 Insulated hot water cylinder.

After it has been heated, the water is stored in a hot water cylinder. The cylinder must be well insulated to prevent the water losing heat while being stored. Fig. 19.21 shows an insulated hot water cylinder. An efficient hot water system is easy to maintain and will provide enough hot water to meet the demands of the household.

The three types of hot water system used in Ireland are the direct, the indirect and the unvented system. Solar panels are also becoming increasingly popular as part of the hot water system.

Direct Hot Water System

In the direct hot water system, cold water is fed from the tank in the attic into the hot water cylinder. A cold feed also runs from the cylinder to the boiler. The boiler heats the water in the cylinder, which begins to rise as it grows hotter. As it is used, the hot water in the cylinder is drawn off from the top, where the water is hottest. When water is drawn off, the cylinder refills with cold water from the storage tank. This cold water must then be fed through the boiler and heated before returning to the cylinder to be used. Briefly, this is how the system works:

- Water fed from tank to cylinder
- Water fed from cylinder to boiler
- Boiler heats the water
- Hot water fed back into cylinder
- As water is used the cylinder is refilled from the storage tank.

Fig. 19.22 shows the main components of the direct hot water system.

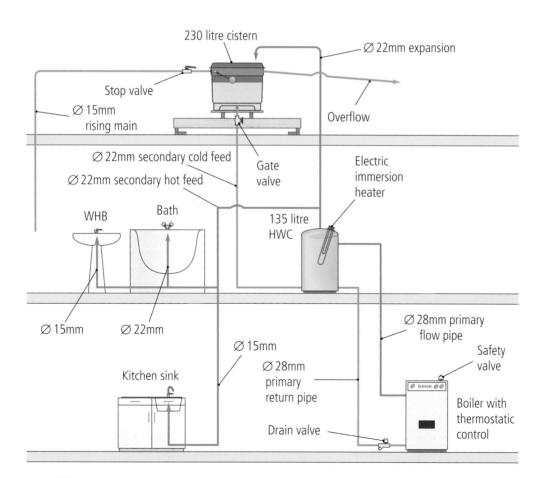

Fig. 19.22 Main components of the direct hot water system.

The main advantages of the direct hot water system are:

- Low cost of installation
- Ease of installation.

The disadvantages of this system outweigh the advantages, particularly because:

- Radiators cannot be attached to this system
- Keeping a large volume of water hot places a lot of strain on the boiler
- It is expensive to run
- Due to the constant heating of new water, in hard water areas limescale builds up and blocks the pipes.

Indirect Hot Water System

The indirect system is much more commonly used. In this system, as in the direct system, water is fed into the hot water cylinder from the cold water storage tank. This water does not feed into the boiler. A separate storage tank in the attic provides the boiler with water. This storage tank is known as a feed expansion tank and has a capacity of 45 litres.

A coiled pipe is placed in the cylinder. The hot water from the boiler feeds through this coil and heats the water in the cylinder. This system heats the water in the cylinder more evenly and economically, because, unlike the direct system,

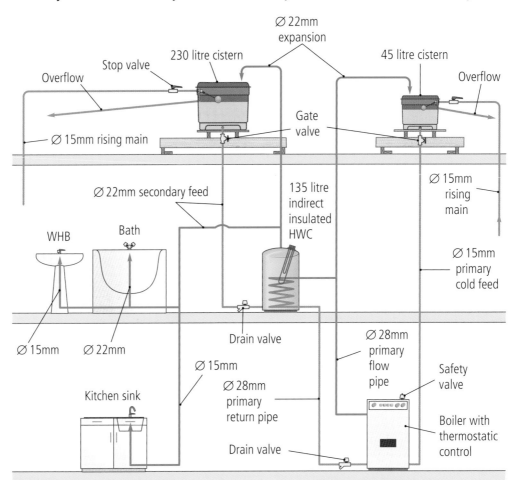

Fig. 19.23 Main components of the indirect hot water system.

CHAPTER 19

the water in the cylinder is not constantly being replenished. Fig. 19.23 shows the main components of the indirect hot water system.

The water in the cylinder can also be heated directly using an immersion, which is an electrical element in the cylinder. Fig. 19.24 illustrates a hot water cylinder with its hot water coil and immersion.

The advantages of the indirect hot water system are:
- Reduced stress on boiler due to regulated temperatures
- No build-up of limescale as the same water is being reused
- Radiators can be connected to the system.

The disadvantages of the indirect hot water system are:
- Storage tank necessary in the attic
- Higher installation cost because more pipework is used.

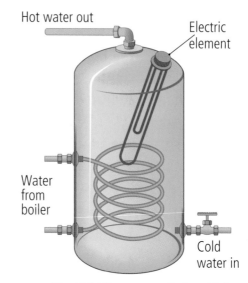

Fig. 19.24 Hot water cylinder with hot water coil from boiler and electric immersion heater element.

Solar Power

The sun is the main source of energy for the planet. This energy can be harvested and used to heat water in the home. A solar panel mounted on the roof warms

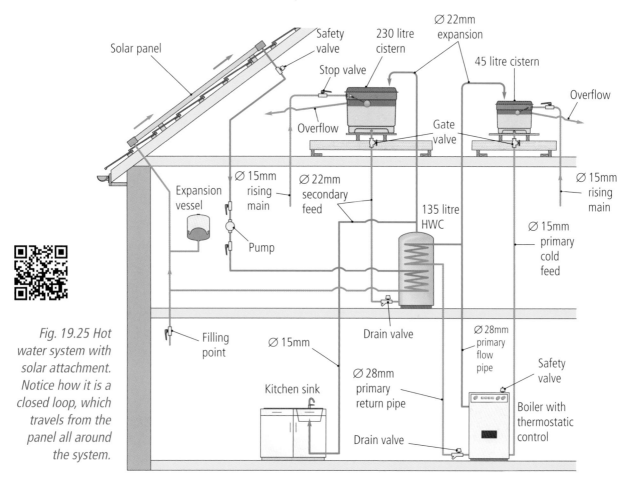

Fig. 19.25 Hot water system with solar attachment. Notice how it is a closed loop, which travels from the panel all around the system.

fluid in a closed circuit of pipework that passes through the hot water cylinder in coils. The cylinder also contains a coiled pipe, into which hot water flows from the boiler. Because the solar coil at the bottom of the cylinder maintains a constant warm temperature, the boiler uses less energy to convert the water from warm to hot. Fig. 19.25 shows how the solar panel is tied into the hot water system.

The advantages of using a solar coil system are:
- Less stress on the boiler, as water in the cylinder is not being heated from cold
- Less expensive to heat water.

The disadvantages of solar coil system are:
- Expense of solar panels
- Amount of sunlight varies during the year.

Geothermal

A geothermal system uses the heat stored in the ground to heat space and/or water in a dwelling. Pipework laid underground absorbs heat from the surrounding soil, which stores the heat from the sun. The pipework is laid below the frost point, so that it maintains a constant temperature, and does not get cold. The system then circulates this warmth into the heating system, the hot water system or a venting system. The pipework can be looped, rather than laid in straight lines, so that it absorbs as much heat as possible. The main loop types are shown in Fig. 19.26.

The advantages of using a geothermal system are:
- Low operating cost
- Environmentally friendly.

The disadvantages of a geothermal system are:
- Installation extremely expensive and intensive
- Reduced heat of soil over time. In effect, the system eventually absorbs all the heat out of the ground.

Figs 19.27 shows how geothermal systems are integrated with hot water systems.

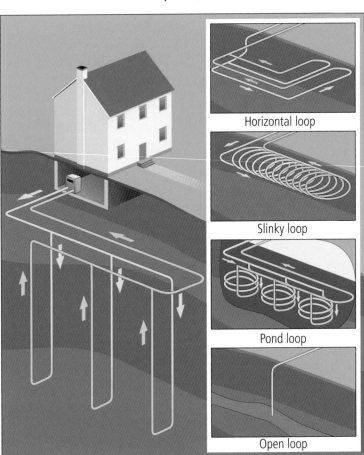

Horizontal loop

Slinky loop

Pond loop

Open loop

Fig. 19.26 Different configurations of pipework in a geothermal system.

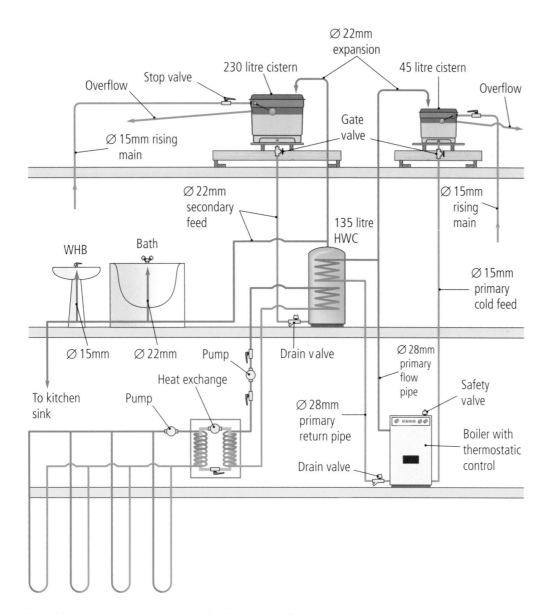

Fig. 19.27 Integration of geothermal collection and hot water system.

Unvented System

Unvented systems connect the hot water cylinder to the mains instead of using a storage tank. The unvented system has been around since the late 1980s, but it has only recently become popular in Ireland. 'Unvented' refers to the fact that the system is closed, i.e. air has no access. This is a closed system operated from mains water, so there is no need to have a water storage tank in the attic. The method of heating is the same, but because the water comes from the mains, the pressure is much higher. Due to the pressure and expansion of water involved in this system, a number of safety features are built into it. Fig. 19.28 shows the main components of the unvented system.

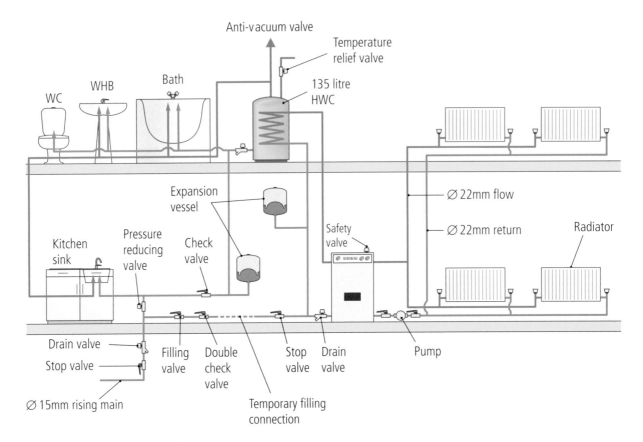

Fig 19.28 Main components of the unvented system.

The advantages of the unvented hot water system are:

- Even water pressure supplied to all appliances
- Consistent water temperature
- No water storage needed in attic.

The disadvantages of the unvented hot water system are:

- High cost of installation
- Reliance on mains supply
- Wear on fittings due to high pressure.

Safety Features of an Unvented System

Many safety features are necessary in an unvented system. Some of these are outlined here.

Expansion vessel. Water increases in volume as it is heated. The expansion vessel is a large metal chamber containing a rubber diaphragm which is filled with nitrogen. As water in the system expands, it pushes against the diaphragm, which expands to allow for more room in the system without creating a drop in pressure. The diaphragm expands and contracts, keeping the system balanced. Fig. 19.29 shows how the expansion vessel works.

Pressure relief valve. This valve opens automatically once a set pressure level is reached. When too much pressure builds up, the valve allows hot water to pour off. This prevents other fittings being damaged by the high pressure in the system. Fig. 19.30 shows how the valve works.

Temperature relief valve. Like the pressure relief valve, the temperature relief valve is set to a predetermined temperature, and when the element in the valve reaches this level, it opens the valve to allow water that is too hot to escape the system.

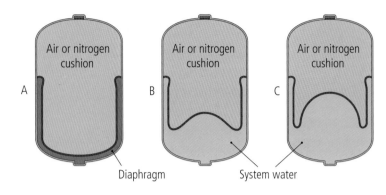

A. When system is filled, no water enters tank when cushion and water pressure are in equilibrium

B. As temperature increases, diaphragm moves to accept expanded water

C. When water rises to maximum, full acceptance of expansion is achieved

Fig. 19.29 Expansion vessel in an unvented system.

Whichever water system is used, there are a number of basic matters to take care of to make sure that it functions efficiently:

- **Sizes**: Using the correct fittings and pipework will help the system run efficiently.

- **Leaks**: Pipework must be properly sealed to prevent leaks, which cause damp. The seals also prevent a drop in water pressure or water levels.

- **Isolating appliances**: Appliances must be capable of being isolated from the water supply so that maintenance and repairs can be carried out.

- **Safety**: Safety measures must be put in place to prevent accidents.

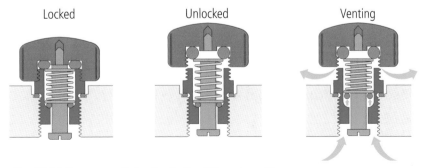

Fig. 19.30 Pressure relief valve in its different positions.

HEATING

The heating system in a house provides warmth in each room. The three most popular heating systems in Ireland are the one-pipe system, the two-pipe system and underfloor heating.

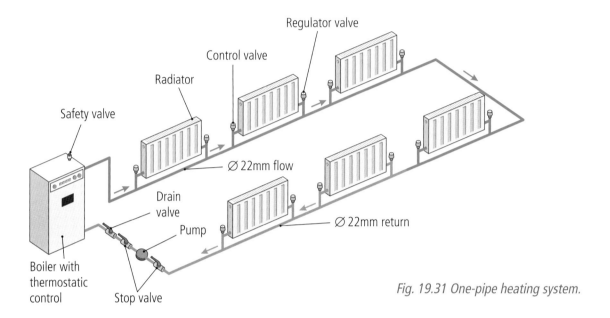

Fig. 19.31 One-pipe heating system.

ONE-PIPE SYSTEM

Hot water taken from the boiler runs through the first radiator and out the other side, and carries on to the next radiator and the next, finally returning to the boiler. Fig. 19.31 shows the one-pipe heating system.

The advantages of the one-pipe system are:

- Low cost of installation
- Ease of installation
- Low maintenance requirements.

The disadvantages of the one-pipe system are:

- Temperature difference between radiators
- Reduced control over radiators.

TWO-PIPE SYSTEM

Hot water is taken from the boiler and fed into each of the radiators. A second pipeline is connected to the end of each radiator and feeds back into the boiler. Fig. 19.32 shows the two-pipe heating system.

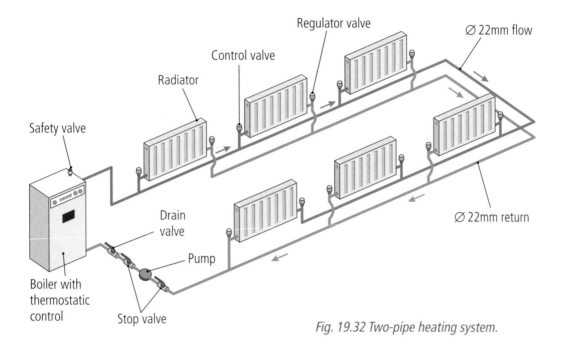

Fig. 19.32 Two-pipe heating system.

The advantages of the two-pipe system are:

- Radiators operate at the same temperature
- Radiators heat up at the same time
- Greater control over individual radiators.

The disadvantages of the two-pipe system are:

- High cost – it uses more materials
- Lengthy installation as more connections and preparations are required.

UNDERFLOOR HEATING

Another method of heating a dwelling is underfloor heating, which has grown in popularity in one-off houses in Ireland. Underfloor heating essentially turns the whole floor into a radiator which performs at a low temperature. Pipes that carry the hot water to and from the central manifold (the central distribution of all hot water) are built into the floor slab when the slab is being poured. Each run of pipe is referred to as a zone. These typically take up one room each, though a large room can use up to three zones, which allows the temperature to be adjusted for different parts of the room. Underfloor heating heats the water in the pipes to 30°C compared to radiators' 60°C. Fig. 19.33 shows an underfloor heating system.

The advantages of the underfloor heating system are:

- Warm conditions, with cool air temperatures
- Warmth stays in the room

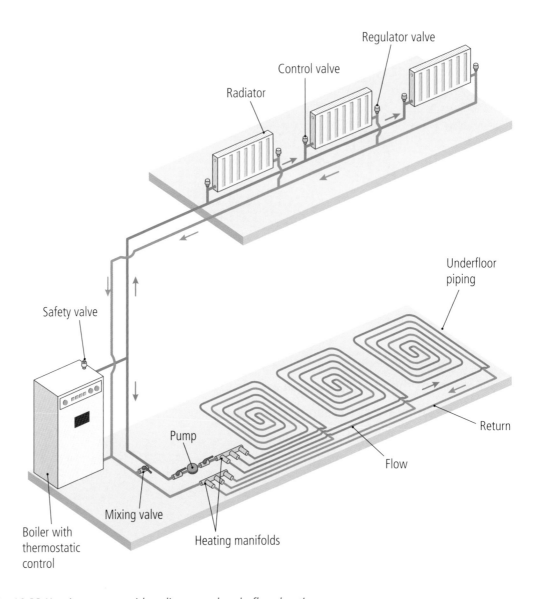

Fig. 19.33 Heating system with radiators and underfloor heating.

- Better energy efficiency
- More space in rooms because there are no radiators
- Increased comfort of radiant rather than convection heat.

The disadvantages of the underground system are:

- Costly installation
- Costly repairs
- Slow build-up of heat.

Cold water, hot water and heating systems work together to make a dwelling more habitable. Fig. 19.34 illustrates the combined water and heating system.

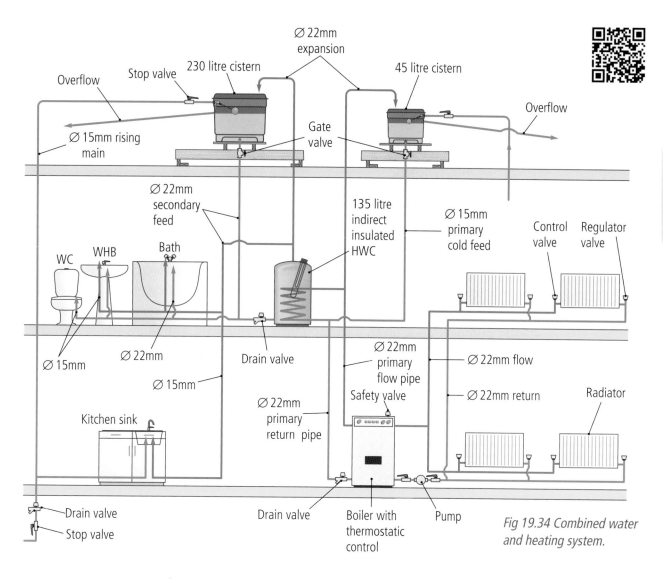

Fig 19.34 Combined water and heating system.

SAFETY FEATURES OF HEATING SYSTEMS

Because they involve hot water, special safety features are needed for heating systems. Boilers are fitted with thermostats which prevent the water heating above a pre-determined temperature, while temperature relief valves and drain-off valves are also connected.

SUSTAINABLE USE OF WATER

Water is a precious commodity, and as water meters are introduced it will also have to be paid for. Water use can be reduced in the home in a number of ways, including:

- Using dual flush toilets: these use more or less water as necessary
- Not over-filling kettles
- Choosing showers over baths
- Turning taps off instead of leaving them running while washing teeth, etc.

RAINWATER HARVESTING

To reduce costs further, rainwater can be harvested and used in some appliances and certain areas in the house. This water is not potable (drinkable), so it is important that it is not connected to taps. Rainwater can be used instead of mains water for:

- Flushing toilets
- Washing clothes
- Gardening
- Outside taps.

As its name suggests, rainwater harvesting means collecting and redistributing rainwater for domestic use. The roof of a house acts as a collector of rainwater, but this is usually collected in gutters and directed away from the building. A rainwater harvesting system collects water in the guttering at roof level, filters it, and pumps it back up to a storage tank in the attic. The rainwater is stored in a separate storage tank to prevent contamination with mains water. It also allows for a reservoir to build up to be used when necessary. Fig. 19.35 shows how this process takes place.

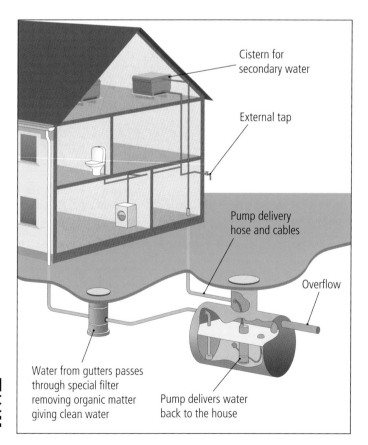

Fig. 19.35 Rainwater harvesting system.

This recycled water can be used in any of the areas outlined earlier. Fig. 19.36 shows how a rainwater harvesting system is attached to a cold water supply.

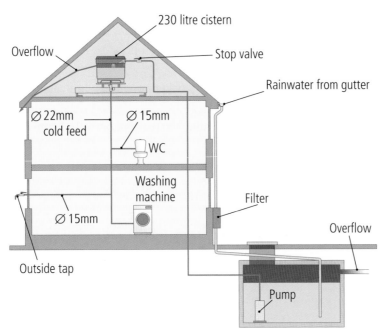

Fig. 19.36 Rainwater harvesting system connected to a cold water supply.

PRACTICE QUESTIONS

1. Explain the steps taken to treat water for use in domestic dwellings.
2. Using a line diagram, show how the direct cold water supply system operates. Indicate on the diagram the typical size of each element.
3. Using a line diagram, show how the indirect cold water supply system operates. Indicate on the diagram the typical size of each element.
4. Outline the advantages and disadvantages of the direct and indirect cold water supply systems.
5. Show, using a line diagram, how the direct hot water supply system operates. Indicate on the diagram the typical size of each element.
6. Using a line diagram, show how the indirect hot water supply system operates. Indicate on the diagram the typical size of each element.
7. Sketch a line diagram which illustrates how the solar supply system operates. Indicate on the diagram the typical size of each element.
8. Using a line diagram, show how the geothermal water supply system operates. Indicate on the diagram the typical size of each element.
9. Using a line diagram, show how the unvented hot water supply system operates. Indicate on the diagram the typical size of each element.
10. Outline the advantages and disadvantages of each of the hot water supply systems.

PRACTICE QUESTIONS

11. Using a line diagram, show how the one-pipe heating system operates. Indicate on the diagram the typical size of each element.

12. Using a line diagram, show how the two-pipe heating system operates. Indicate on the diagram the typical size of each element.

13. Using a line diagram, show how the underfloor heating system operates. Indicate on the diagram the typical size of each element.

14. Outline the advantages and disadvantages of the different heating systems.

15. Using a line diagram, show how the rainwater harvesting system operates. Indicate on the diagram the typical size of each element.

SAMPLE EXAMINATION QUESTIONS

2011 Higher Level Question 8

(a) A wood burning stove, as shown in the sketch, is used to heat two independently controlled heating zones, one on each floor, in a two storey dwelling house. Using notes and a single-line diagram, show a typical design layout for the pipework necessary to independently heat each zone. Show **three** radiators on each floor, indicate the control valves and give the typical sizes of the pipework.

(b) It is proposed to connect a solar collector, as shown in the sketch below, to the system at 8(a) above to heat domestic water. Show a design layout for the pipework necessary to connect the solar collector to the existing system and outline the modifications required to the existing system to accommodate the solar collector.

c) Using notes and freehand sketches, show a preferred location for the solar collector and discuss in detail **two** factors that influenced your choice of location.

2011 Ordinary Level Question 7

The sketch shows an outline of a single storey house, an underground rainwater storage tank and a separate rainwater storage tank in the attic of the house.

(a) Using notes and *neat freehand sketches* show the pipework necessary to pump the rainwater from the underground storage tank to the tank in the attic. Label the components and give their typical sizes.

(b) Stored rainwater may be used in both a toilet and a washing machine. Show, using notes and *neat freehand sketches*, the pipework necessary to connect **one** of these appliances to the storage tank in the attic. Show the necessary valves.

(c) Discuss **one** reason why the rainwater is stored in a separate storage tank in the attic.

SAMPLE EXAMINATION QUESTIONS

2009 Ordinary Level Question 3

(a) Using a *single-line labelled diagram*, sketch a system to supply hot **and** cold water to a kitchen sink, as shown in the accompanying sketch.
Include the following in your diagram:
- rising main
- water storage tank
- hot water cylinder
- pipework to hot and cold taps
- all necessary valves
- typical sizes of pipework.

(b) Using notes and *neat freehand sketches*, show one method of ensuring that the water in the cylinder stays hot for as long as possible.

2009 Ordinary Level Question 7

(a) Describe, using notes and *neat freehand sketches*, how rainwater is collected and discharged to ground level from a pitched roof of a dwelling house, as shown in the accompanying sketch. Label the components and give their typical sizes.

(b) In order to conserve water, it is recommended that rainwater be stored for use. Suggest **two** suitable uses for the stored rainwater.

2008 Higher Level Question 8

(a) An oil-fired central heating and hot water system for a two storey dwelling house is designed to provide independent control of hot water and space heating. Using notes and a *single-line diagram*, show a typical layout for such a system. Show **three** radiators on each floor, indicate the necessary control valves and give the typical sizes of the pipework.

(b) On a separate diagram show an alternative system for providing domestic hot water which is not dependent on fossil fuels. Discuss **two** advantages of the proposed system.

2007 Ordinary Level Question 3

The sketch shows an oil-fired boiler and an indirect cylinder for a hot water system in a dwelling house.

(a) Using a *single-line labelled diagram*, show the pipework required to connect the boiler, cylinder and expansion tank.
Your diagram should include the following:
- boiler and cylinder;
- expansion tank;
- rising main;
- pipework;
- insulation;
- valves.

(b) On the diagram, use arrows to indicate the direction of flow of the hot water between the boiler and the cylinder.

LIGHT

LEARNING OUTCOMES:

After studying this chapter students will:

- Understand the basic concept of how humans see using light.
- Be able to describe the physics of light.
- Be able to calculate window size using the degree of efficiency method.
- Be able to identify various lamp types and the common characteristics of each.

KEYWORDS:

- **SPECTRUM • REFLECT • ABSORB • TRANSMIT • WATT • LUMEN • LUX**
- **DEGREE OF EFFICIENCY METHOD • FENESTRATION • DAYLIGHTING • NATURAL LIGHT**
- **BRISE SOLEIL • GLARE • ARTIFICIAL LIGHT • INCANDESCENCE • LUMINESCENCE**
- **HALOGEN • TUNGSTEN • LED**

INTRODUCTION

Light is a basic need, which people depend on to go about their daily lives. We need light to view the world and interact with it. Natural daylight has even been shown to increase people's mental wellbeing. For these reasons, light is important when planning a build.

LIGHT

Light is energy which is part of the electromagnetic spectrum. Light is a range of colours or frequencies which, when combined, join to form what is called white light. Newton's colour wheel in Fig. 20.1 is made up of a range of colours; however, when spun at high speed it appears as white only.

White light can be divided into its constituent colours. Droplets of water in the air split white light in this way, forming a rainbow. Light can also be split into the various colours using a prism.

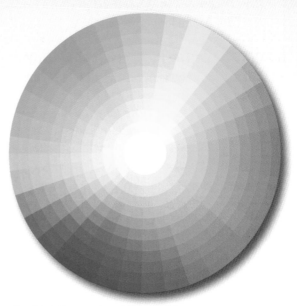

Fig. 20.1 Newton's colour wheel.

Surfaces reflect, absorb or transmit light. Which one of these effects happens is determined by the surface properties of the material that the light comes into contact with. The reaction of light to the surface enables the eye to differentiate the colours, textures and finish of these surfaces.

- **Reflection** occurs when light changes direction after meeting a surface. Shiny surfaces like mirrors reflect light particularly strongly.

- **Absorption** is when the object soaks up some of the light energy. Objects with rough black surfaces, such as coal, absorb light.

- **Transmission** of light is like absorption, except that the object allows the light to pass through it. An example of this is a frosted glass window.

Fig. 20.2 White light split by droplets of water forms the colours of the rainbow.

Light travels in straight lines. When it comes into contact with a shiny surface, it bounces off it at the same angle that it originated from. The incoming angle is known as the angle of incidence; the outgoing angle is known as the angle of reflection. Both angles are equal, as shown in Fig. 20.3.

When light hits a matt surface, which is not glossy or polished, the light is scattered and diffused in many directions.

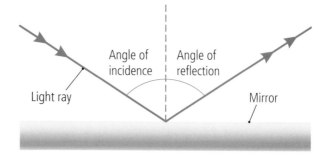

Fig. 20.3 Light reflection.

MEASURING LIGHT

Lighting for dwellings is governed by standards which ensure that the lighting provided is sufficient in each room. Key terms used in the measurement of light are watt, lumen and lux.

Watt: This is the international standard unit of power. One watt equals one joule per second, and measures the rate of energy conversion, that is the rate at which electrical energy changes to light energy. Lamps are measured by their wattage; that is, the rate of energy used by the lamp. This is also referred to as the radiant flux.

Lumen: The light given off from a source (whether a bedside lamp or the sun) is called the luminous flux. It is measured in lumens. The higher the lumens, the brighter the light. Lumens are a more efficient measure of the light output of a bulb than wattage. For example, a 230V 40 watt tungsten bulb has a value of 400–500 lumens. A 230V fluorescent lamp also reaches 400–500 lumens, but it needs only 7 watts to reach this lumen value.

Lux: This is the measurement of how illuminated an area is as a result of the light sources working in it. It is calculated as lumens per square metre. The measurement is taken using a lux meter (Fig. 20.4). With this device, it is possible to map the lighting levels of an area, showing the distribution of light in that space. The process can be seen with a simple experiment.

Fig. 20.4 A lux meter.

Experiment: Recording a light map using a lux meter

CONTEXT OF EXPERIMENT:

The purpose of this experiment is to map the lux levels of a room using various types of lights.

EQUIPMENT NEEDED:

Prepare the room with different lighting scenarios: daylight only, all lights on, one light on. You also need a lux meter.

PROCEDURE:

STEP 1

Divide the room into grids 1m square.

STEP 2

Draw a map of the room showing these grid lines.

STEP 3

Take lux readings at all the intersections of the gridlines and record them on your map.

STEP 4

Join any corresponding lux levels to form lighting contours.

STEP 5

Repeat for each different lighting scenario.

ANALYSIS:

Examine the differences between the maps, taking note of where lux levels have risen in areas of the room, and also where results have not changed following the different lighting scenarios you have created. You may also identify areas that need more light.

DEGREE OF EFFICIENCY METHOD

Lux is also used to determine appropriate window sizes for a dwelling, using the degree of efficiency method. Windows must provide the appropriate daylight factor, that is the amount of natural light needed to carry out everyday activities in a room. The degree of efficiency method calculates the appropriate window size using the following formula:

$$Li = Lo \times WF \times E \times (WA/FA)$$

Where:

Li = lux inside – the required amount of light inside.

Lo = lux outside. Standard overcast sky = 5000 lux.

WF = window factor – reduction of light due to window being vertical (0.5) (Note that this is not a unit of measurement, rather the proportion of light lost.)

E = efficiency coefficient – reduction of light due to glazing, reflections, obstructions, etc. (0.4). (Again, this is a proportion of light lost rather than a unit measurement.)

WA = window area – area of the window in square metres.

FA = floor area – area of the floor in square metres.

Take the following as an example:

Determine, using the degree of efficiency method, the area of glazing required for a room 5m by 4m and needing an illumination of 150 lux.

$$Li = Lo \times WF \times E \times (WA/FA)$$
$$150 = 5000 \times 0.5 \times 0.4 \times (WA/20)$$
$$150 \times 20 = 5000 \times 0.5 \times 0.4 \times WA$$
$$3000 = 1000WA$$
$$3m^2 = WA$$

STANDARDISATION OF LIGHT

The Commission Internationale de l'Éclairage (CIE) has established lighting standards which are used to compare different lighting conditions. A typical overcast sky is taken as the norm and is given a value of 5000 lux. The various lux levels are shown in Table 20.1.

TABLE 20.1 TYPICAL LUX LEVELS

Description	Typical lux levels
Irish sunny day	50,000
Overcast day	5000
Well-lit office	500
Typical roadside lighting	5
Clear night sky	0.3
Moonlit cloudy sky	0.1

NATURAL LIGHT

Natural light from the sun enters a building through its windows, rooflights and other openings – collectively called its fenestration. The practice of positioning windows and other openings, and reflective surfaces, so as to maximise the natural daylight gain in a building is called 'daylighting'. If planned correctly, the amount of artificial lighting that will be needed during daylight hours can be greatly reduced. This reduces the amount of electricity used, too, of course. Fig. 20.5 shows a building which makes maximum use of natural light.

Fig. 20.5 Natural light is captured by tall windows.

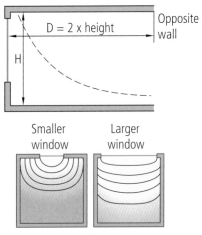

Fig. 20.6 Different windows allow different levels of light to penetrate a room.

The availability and quality of natural light that enters a building is governed by four factors:

- The brightness of the sky
- The external element (direct light and external reflective surfaces)
- The size and position of the fenestration
- The internally reflected element.

As a rule of thumb, useful daylight is such that its depth into the room is twice the height of the room. This is under ideal conditions, with clear glass, no external obstructions and the window cills at working plane level (that is at a comfortable height for a person). Fig. 20.6 illustrates the penetration of daylight into a room.

THE EXTERNAL ELEMENT

The external element refers to everything outside the dwelling that influences the amount of light it receives. Natural light is best harnessed by planning the orientation and glazing of the building around the path of the sun. A south-facing house will harness the most light, while a north-facing building will harness the least.

External obstructions, and reflection off nearby surfaces, also play a role in the amount of daylight that reaches the building. A tall building to the south of a property can cast a shadow and thereby reduce the available sunlight, for example, while a tall galvanised building such as a shed will reflect light into the property.

FENESTRATION

Window and door size affects the quality and amount of natural daylight a building receives. Increasing the glazing area in both doors and windows increases the amount of natural daylight allowed in. Fig. 20.7 shows fenestration on a modern Irish house. Its large bay windows are designed to bring light into the living and dining rooms downstairs, while the porch makes maximum use of natural light too.

Fig. 20.7 The size and style of windows help to determine how much light shines into a dwelling.

THE INTERNALLY REFLECTED ELEMENT

Light-coloured surfaces reflect light, to the extent that an internal space which is finished with light-coloured matt paint can maximise the light from the light source in the room by up to 80 per cent more than a room painted in dark colours. How well light is reflected also depends on the area of the room, as well as the colours and textures of the wallpaper, wall hangings and furniture used in it.

CONTROLLING AND HARNESSING NATURAL LIGHT

There are many ways of controlling the amount of natural light shining into a building. Simple controls include hanging blinds, net curtains or curtains to block or reduce the amount of sunlight coming through the windows. More elaborate methods include installing overhangs outside the windows or using brise soleil. Brise soleil, which comes from the French and translates as 'sun breaker', are a permanent fixture to a property. They diffuse sunlight, and so reduce its intensity. Fig. 20.8 shows a modern brise soleil.

Bringing sunlight into a room that does not have natural light can be difficult. One product that addresses this problem is the light tube. The light tube works by using reflection. A reflective material is rolled into a cylinder, which bridges the gap between outside and inside, and a dome is placed on top. Light hits the dome and travels down the reflective tube to a diffused ceiling panel which spreads the light throughout the room. Fig. 20.9 shows a light tube.

Fig. 20.8 A modern office block, with a brise soleil to reduce the glare of the sun.

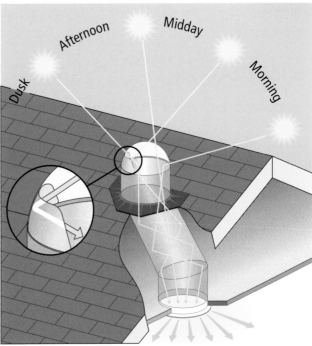

Fig. 20.9 Light is reflected from the top of the dome and the sides of the light tube to the interior of the house.

GLARE AND GLARE INDEX

When too much light shines into a room it creates glare, or light which is too intense for the naked eye. Glare makes it difficult for the eye to see the contrast between objects and light, so the eye has to work harder to prevent this. The result is tired eyes or eye strain. Glare is most commonly a problem in well-lit areas with highly polished glass-like surfaces, such as windows, table tops, or even computer screens. Glare can be combated by introducing soft furnishings as well as the control methods outlined earlier.

**TABLE 20.2
SOME TYPICAL
GLARE INDEX VALUES**

GLARE INDEX	
7 or less	Unnoticeable glare
10	Noticeable glare
16	Acceptable glare
22	Uncomfortable glare

A glare index has been developed to set standards for acceptable and unacceptable levels of glare. It works from the point of view of a typical person in a room, and analyses the glare they might experience. However, the index only considers average annual sunlight, which is misleading because it does not represent particular problems with glare that occur during the summer. Table 20.2 shows typical glare index values.

ARTIFICIAL LIGHTING

It is important to plan the lighting of a dwelling and how it will be controlled. There are many types of light fittings and fixtures, although they can be classified into two groups: architectural and non-architectural.

- **Architectural** fittings refer to those that are planned during the build; these include coving lights, pendant lights and recessed lights.

- **Non-architectural** fittings are usually non-permanent and can be moved, e.g. table and floor lamps.

In a dwelling, people must be able to control the lighting as they move from room to room, and of course it is essential at night, particularly in hazardous areas such as the stairs. The earliest form of artificial lighting was fire. Nowadays, 'fire' comes in various forms and styles, such as fluorescent, tungsten or halogen lighting. Most take their names from the elements or methods they use to create light. Different styles of lighting are used around the home, depending on the particular purpose they are meant for. While there are many kinds of artificial lighting, most can be classified under two headings:

- **Incandescence:** an object is heated to such a high temperature that it emits light (for example, the element inside a light bulb).

- **Luminescence:** a lamp that produces light, not from heat, but as a result of chemical reactions, electrical energy or subatomic motion in a substance.

GENERAL LIGHTING SERVICE (GLS) LAMPS

Otherwise known as the common light bulb, in this product an electric current heats a metal filament until it glows. The metal is usually tungsten, and it sits in a vacuum or partial vacuum contained within a glass exterior. This vacuum prevents the bulb from overheating. The common light bulb is incandescent: it produces light through heat. In fact, typically 90 per cent of the bulb's energy is released as heat rather than light. The glass enclosure can be of different shapes, sizes and colours, and can be frosted to diffuse or soften the light from the bulb.

Fig. 20.10 Common light bulb.

HALOGEN LAMPS

Fig. 20.11 Halogen lamp.

Like the GLS, this type of lamp has a gas within the glass envelope, typically iodine or bromine, which extends the life of the tungsten filament. It also allows it to operate at higher temperatures and so has a higher colour temperature, which creates a blueish-white light. Because of its high temperature, the lamp becomes very hot, and is a fire and burn hazard. For that reason, strict guidelines govern their installation, particularly in recessed ceiling fittings. Halogen lamps come in high-voltage and low-voltage forms, although it is the lamp's wattage which has most impact on the amount of energy it uses. Halogen lamps are often small, which is an advantage in many areas around the home, e.g. under kitchen units.

Fig. 20.12 Fluorescent lamp.

FLUORESCENT TUBES

Fluorescent tubes are filled with gas, and when electricity is passed through the gas it produces light. Generally the gas is inert – commonly argon or mercury vapour. The tubes are coated in phosphor, which absorbs the light and glows (fluoresces) to produce light.

Fig. 20.13 Compact fluorescent lamp.

COMPACT FLUORESCENT LAMPS

Compact fluorescent lamps (CFLs) operate in the same way as fluorescent tubes, and use the same chemicals. The main difference between the two is the shape: CFLs are typically curved rather than straight. These lamps are beginning to replace the GLS lamp or common light bulb because they are more energy-efficient and have a longer life span than the tungsten-lit bulb.

A fluorescent lamp produces light rather than heat. For that reason, fluorescent lamps are four or five times more efficient than incandescent lamps, and a 25 watt fluorescent lamp can replace a 100 watt tungsten lamp.

LIGHT-EMITTING DIODES (LEDs)

A light-emitting diode is most commonly seen on circuit boards for electronics. The little red light on televisions and other appliances is an example of a coloured LED. They come in a variety of colours and sizes. An LED is made up of two terminals, the positive and negative. As the current passes from the negative to the positive terminal, photons of light are produced.

The benefits of LEDs are: their long life span of up to 100,000 hours; the time taken from turning on the lamp until it reaches its maximum output is shorter than the fluorescent equivalents; and LEDs can be adjusted to dimmer or brighter light levels as needed. The drawback, however, is that the cost of high-power LEDs can be five times that of fluorescent lamps.

Fig. 20.14 An LED.

LAMP AND BULB SUMMARY TABLE

A summary of the details of each lamp type is shown in Table 20.3.

TABLE 20.3

		Common names	Normal range	Life expectancy (hours)	Features	Typical lumens per watt[1]	Colour temperature[2]
General Lighting Service (GLS) Lamp		Light bulb, common bulb	40–150 watts	1000–2000	General purpose bulb. Comes in a range of colours and shapes.	12–18	2800
Decorative GLS		Candle bulb, globe bulb, ornamental bulb	25–60 watts	1000–2000	Bulb for ornamental use (chandeliers, decorative light fittings).	7–12	2800
Fluorescent Tube		Bar light, tube light	13–125 watts	6000–7000	Provides even and bright illumination. Economical to run. Comes in a range of colour tones.	35–100	2700–6300
Compact Fluorescent Tube		Low energy bulb, energy saver	48–69 watts	6000–8000	Used as a replacement for the common light bulb. Can be fitted with a screw or bayonet fitting.	6–30	2700–6300
Mains-voltage Halogen Lamp			20–50 watts	2000–4000	Popular for size and ease of installation. Popular for wall lights and recessed lighting.	12–16	3050
Low-voltage Halogen Lamp			10–50 watts	2000–4000	Widely used for recessed ceiling lighting. Reflective internal case to project light forward.	14–19	2900–3000
Light-emitting Diode		LED	Up to 10 watts per light fitting	100,000	Often used for decorative fittings.	30–35	5500

[1] Lumens per watt: the higher the number the greater the efficiency of the bulb (more light output per electrical input).

[2] Colour temperature (in degrees kelvin): the higher the number the cooler (bluer) the light.

LUMINAIRE

A luminaire is a complete lighting unit, consisting of one or more lamps, along with the socket and other parts that hold the lamp in place and protect it, wiring that connects the lamp to a power source, and a reflector that helps direct and distribute the light. Fluorescent fixtures usually have lenses or louvres to shield the lamp (thus reducing glare) and redirect the light emitted. Luminaires include both portable and ceiling- or wall-mounted fixtures.

PRACTICE QUESTIONS

1. Describe how the human eye interprets light.

2. Explain how light reacts to surfaces.

3. Use the degree of efficiency method to determine the area of glazing required for a room 5m by 3m and needing an illumination of 200 lux.

4. What does the term 'daylighting' mean?

5. Using notes and neat freehand sketches, explain how natural light entering a dwelling can be controlled.

6. What is glare and how can it be combated?

7. What is incandescence?

8. What is luminescence?

9. Describe, using notes and neat freehand sketches, the different lamp types available.

10. Explain what a luminaire is.

SAMPLE EXAMINATION QUESTIONS

2010 Higher Level Question 8

(a) Determine by degree of efficiency method, or by any other suitable method, the approximate size of a vertical window for a living room 5.0 metres long by 3.8 metres wide requiring an average illumination of 150 lux on the working plane.

Assume an unobstructed view and the illumination of a standard overcast sky to be 5000 lux.

(b) Discuss in detail, using notes and *freehand sketches*, **two** design considerations for a contemporary window frame and glazing system that will ensure the high thermal performance of both:

- the window frame **and**
- the glazing system.

(c) Outline **two** environmental considerations that should be taken into account when recommending a preferred material for the window frame.a

CHAPTER 21
SOUND

INTRODUCTION

Sound is a series of vibrations which travel through the air in waves. Sound can travel through solids, liquids and gases, but it cannot travel through a vacuum.

Sound waves have a high or low pitch, depending on their frequency. A guitar string demonstrates this very simply. When it is plucked, the string resonates (moves up and down). The frequency at which this happens depends on the tightness of the string. As the string moves, it vibrates the air around it, creating a wave. The energy used to strum the guitar has, in effect, been converted into sound energy. Fig. 21.1 shows high and low frequency graphically.

HOW HUMANS HEAR

When humans hear a sound, this is the last in a number of complex steps as the sound travels from the source through the person's ear. The first part of the ear that the sound reaches is the eardrum. The eardrum is a taut membrane, which vibrates when sound waves reach it. These vibrations are channelled to the three smallest bones in the body: the hammer, the anvil and on to the stirrup. After

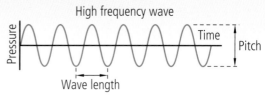

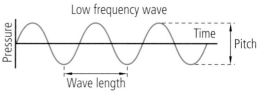

Fig. 21.1 Sound waves of different frequencies. Frequency refers to the number of waves which appear over a given time scale.

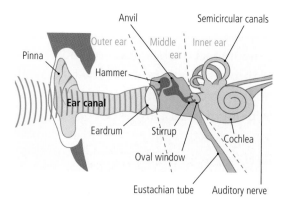

Fig. 21.2 Human hearing converts sound waves into electrical signals which are interpreted by the brain.

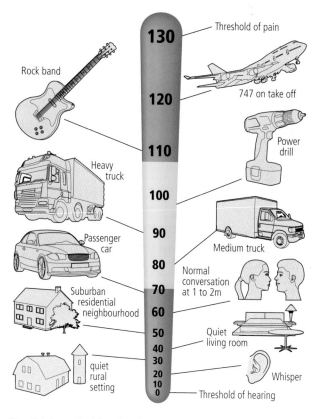

Fig. 21.3 Decibel levels of various everyday noises.

passing through these bones, vibrations reach the cochlea, a tube containing thousands of fine, hair-like nerve endings. As the cochlea vibrates, these hairs move, sending a message to the brain, which in turn translates the vibrations into sound. Fig. 21.2 shows the inner parts of the ear used to interpret sound.

Volume is measured in decibels (dB). High volumes can have a detrimental effect on the human ear. Fig. 21.3 shows some typical sources of sound or noise with their decibel values.

TRANSMISSION OF SOUND

Sound is transmitted directly and indirectly. In direct transmission the sound travels through materials in straight lines. In indirect transmission it travels around a material, or from one material to another. Indirect transmission is also known as flanking transmission. Fig. 21.4 shows both direct and indirect transmission of sound in a home.

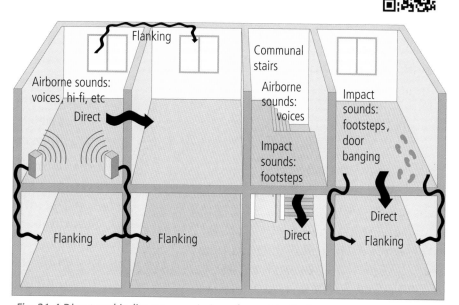

Fig. 21.4 Direct and indirect transmission of sound in the home.

SOUND SOURCES

The two sources of sound are airborne and impact. Airborne sound radiates in the air and is transmitted either directly through a wall or indirectly by way of flanking. Airborne sources include the human voice, the sound from televisions, radios, etc. Impact sound travels from the point of impact either directly through walls or by flanking through the building's structure. Impact sources include banging doors, footsteps, fallen objects, and so on.

HOW SOUND WAVES REACT

No matter where sound originates, its waves travel in all directions equally. Sound waves are affected by objects in their path, and react in a number of ways depending on the shape, size and texture of the object they come into contact with. The main reactions are known as sound absorption, sound reflection and reverberation time.

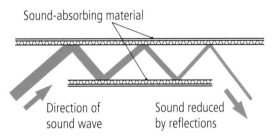

Fig. 21.5 Surfaces absorb sound, reducing the sound each time it hits a surface.

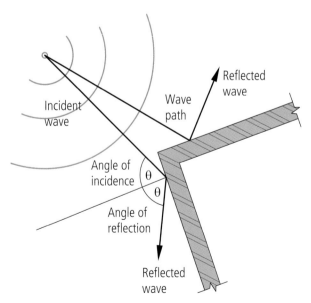

Fig. 21.6 Sound reflection works on similar principles to light reflection.

Sound absorption: This is the amount of sound soaked up by the surfaces and materials in a room. Hard surfaces absorb very little sound. More often, they reflect sound, which causes it to echo. Soft surfaces, including furnishings, wallpapers, curtains, etc., absorb sound rather than reflecting it. As sound waves bounce off a material, they grow less and less intense. Fig. 21.5 shows how sound is absorbed.

Sound reflection: Sound reacts in the same way as light in the sense that the angle of reflection and the angle of incidence (see Chapter 20) to a surface are equal. Sound reflection is used to alter the acoustics in a room, to ensure that the distribution of sound is even. This even distribution of sound is essential in theatres, though not so in domestic dwellings. Fig. 21.6 shows how sound reflection takes place.

Reverberation time: This is the amount of time it takes for a sound to decline by 60dB. The time will vary from room to room, depending on both the size of the room and the furnishings in it. Surfaces that reflect sound have a longer reverberation time than soft, sound-absorbing surfaces. Fig. 21.7 shows how reverberation time is measured.

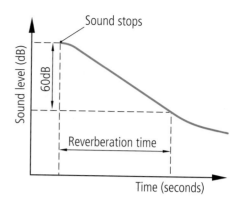

Current building regulations in relation to sound (1997) require that reasonable resistance to airborne sound through party walls and to airborne and impact noise between shared floors (i.e. apartments) be provided.

PRINCIPLES OF SOUND INSULATION

There are four principles of sound insulation which ensure that the transmission of sound is minimised. These are:

Fig. 21.7 Graph of reverberation against time. Reverberation time is the time taken for a noise to be reduced by 60dB.

1. Heaviness
2. Isolation
3. Flexibility
4. Completeness.

Heaviness: Heaviness is the principle that the more dense a material is, the better its sound-insulating properties will be. Heaviness is directly related to mass.

Isolation: Transmission of sound is reduced by separating (i.e. isolating) the surfaces of a wall or partition to create voids or cavities, which reduce the transmission of sound.

Flexibility: Refers to the placing of an absorbent quilted insulation material between voids in a partition. It is based on the principle that flexible materials absorb more sound than rigid ones.

Completeness: Completeness is the elimination of all small gaps in a structure, which increases its airtightness. The principle is based on the fact that the more complete the structure is, the less sound can travel through it.

NOISE CONTROL IN BUILDINGS

Noise is defined as loud, unwanted or unexpected sound. Semi-detached, terraced houses, and apartments, need noise insulation to prevent unwanted sound travelling from one dwelling to the next. The transmission of sound is reduced by making use of three of the principles outlined earlier, under the following headings:

1. Mass
2. Isolation
3. Completeness.

MASS

Mass is the amount of matter a material contains. The greater the density of a material, the greater its mass. Mass affects the transmission of sound by absorption, reflection and reverberation. As a sound wave passes through a dense material, its intensity decreases and the level of sound drops. The greater the mass of a material, the less sound will pass through it.

For that reason, one method of reducing sound transmission is to increase the mass of building materials. This can be done in a number of ways. One is to fix a second layer of plasterboard to either side of a wall. Another is to place insulation boards over ceiling joists to prevent noise travelling between floors. Figs 21.8 and 21.9 show these methods. Mass is also used to ensure good sound insulation in party walls, and between floors in a building, as shown in Fig. 21.10.

The amount of sound insulation that is needed depends on the frequency or pitch of the noise.

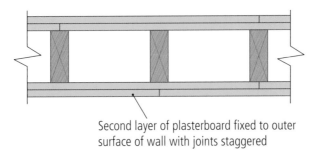

Second layer of plasterboard fixed to outer surface of wall with joints staggered

Fig. 21.8 Plasterboard is double layered on the outer surface, and joints are staggered to further reduce sound transmission.

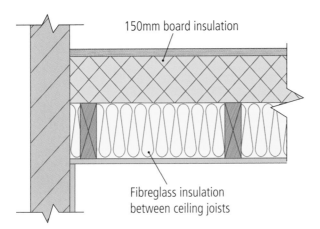

150mm board insulation

Fibreglass insulation between ceiling joists

Fig. 21.9 Ridged insulation board is placed over the ceiling joists, with fibreglass insulation between them.

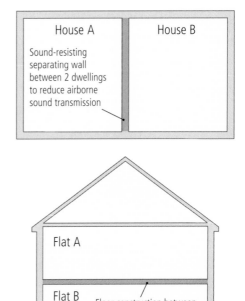

House A

House B

Sound-resisting separating wall between 2 dwellings to reduce airborne sound transmission

Flat A

Flat B

Floor construction between flats to resist both airborne and impact sound

Fig. 21.10 Top: party walls must be constructed so that they reduce airborne sound transmission. Bottom: floors must be constructed to resist both airborne and impact sound.

ISOLATION

Isolation reduces sound transmission by leaving voids or cavities between building materials. One method is to create a double partition wall, which has a cavity between the partitions. Another is to create a staggered partition, in which there is no material in contact with both sides of the partition. Figs 21.11 and 21.12 show these methods.

Placing an absorbent quilt in the cavity of either of these partitions increases the sound insulation even more. This is partly due to the flexibility of the material and partly due to the extra layer that the sound must travel through. Figs 21.13 and 21.14 show the addition of quilted insulation.

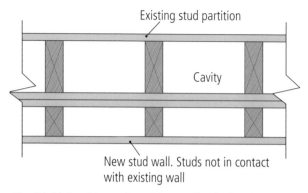

Fig. 21.11 Double stud partition wall, which is built independently so as to reduce the transmission of sound.

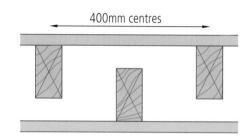

Fig. 21.12 Staggered studs, which are not in contact with each other.

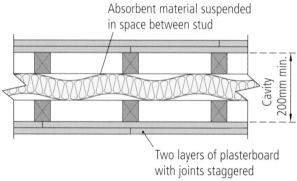

Fig. 21.13 Double stud partition wall with cavity and insulating quilt.

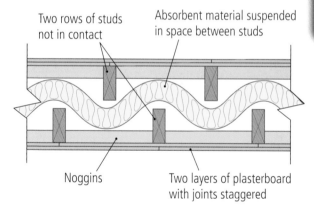

Fig. 21.14 Staggered stud partition wall with insulating material.

Sound insulating a floor is done in a similar manner; quilted insulation is floated – placed in position without being nailed – on a sound-absorbing material, allowing minimal sound to pass through. Fig. 21.15 shows how a floor is floated in this manner.

Fig. 21.15 Sound insulation of a first-floor room.

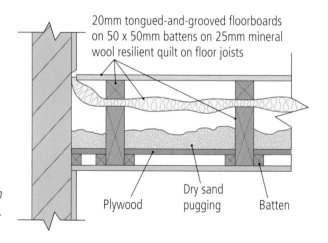

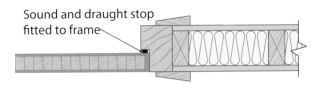

Fig. 21.16 Sound and draught stops should be fitted to living room and bedroom doors to reduce noise disturbance.

COMPLETENESS

The completeness of a material refers to the lack of voids or gaps inside it. It is essential that the structure, including walls, roof, floors, etc., is airtight to prevent sound being transmitted. Gaps around openings, pipes, ducts, etc. must be filled. Draught-proof strips are installed around doors, while windows are carefully sealed at junctions. All these measures help to ensure that no gaps are available for sound to travel through.

PRACTICE QUESTIONS

1. How does the human ear interpret sound?

2. Describe, using notes and neat freehand sketches, how sound is transmitted in a dwelling.

3. Explain each of the following terms as they relate to sound:
   (a) Sound absorption
   (b) Sound reflection
   (c) Reverberation time.

4. Explain the four principles of sound insulation.

5. Describe, using notes and neat freehand sketches, how noise is controlled in a dwelling.

SAMPLE EXAMINATION QUESTIONS

CHAPTER 19

2011 Higher Level Question 4

(a) Discuss in detail, using notes and freehand sketches, the importance of *each* of the following in reducing the transmittance of sound in a dwelling house:

- mass
- completeness
- isolation.

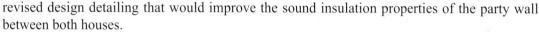

(b) The party wall between the two semi-detached houses shown in the sketch is of concrete block construction. The occupants of one house can hear everyday sounds from the adjoining house. Discuss **two** possible reasons why sound is transmitted between the houses, and using notes and freehand sketches, show the revised design detailing that would improve the sound insulation properties of the party wall between both houses.

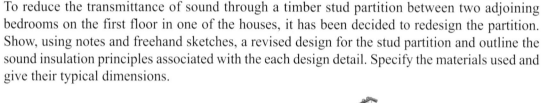

(c) To reduce the transmittance of sound through a timber stud partition between two adjoining bedrooms on the first floor in one of the houses, it has been decided to redesign the partition. Show, using notes and freehand sketches, a revised design for the stud partition and outline the sound insulation principles associated with the each design detail. Specify the materials used and give their typical dimensions.

2007 Higher Level Question 9

The accompanying sketch shows two semi-detached houses.

(a) Using notes and *freehand sketches*, show **two** design details that reduce the transmittance of sound between the two houses and explain the sound insulation principles associated with each design detail.

(b) The first floor consists of tongued and grooved softwood flooring on timber joists with a plasterboard ceiling beneath. Using notes and *freehand sketches*, show **two** design details that would increase the sound insulation properties of the first floor in order to minimise the transmittance of sound.

ELECTRICITY

LEARNING OUTCOMES:

After studying this chapter students will:

• Be able to identify the key elements of the energy cycle from production to dwelling.

• Understand the terminology used in relation to electricity.

• Appreciate the dangers of electricity and be aware of counter measures put in place to reduce risk.

• Be able to sketch typical circuit layouts as they would appear in a home.

KEYWORDS:

• SAFETY TURBINE • DYNAMO • WIND FARM • HYDROELECTRIC • PUMPED STORAGE
• NATIONAL GRID • TRANSMISSION STATION • TRANSFORMER • CURRENT • AMPERE
• VOLTAGE • RESISTANCE • OHM • WATTAGE • CIRCUITS • DISTRIBUTION BOARD
• CIRCUIT BREAKER • GROUNDING • CERTIFICATION

INTRODUCTION

Most services to the home, which provide us with modern comforts, rely on electricity to work. Electricity is a powerful force and one which should be respected. It must always be used correctly.

GENERATING ELECTRICITY

Before looking at where and how electricity is used in the home, it is important to understand how it is generated. Electricity generation in Ireland has changed and grown since it began in the late 19th century. In particular, the methods of generating electricity have become more reliable and efficient. Fig. 22.1 shows the different generation methods used in Ireland since 1990 and how their popularity has grown or diminished. Over time, burning coal and peat to produce electricity has declined, while the use of oil has increased. It can also be noted that from 2006 onwards there has been a small increase in renewable sources of electricity.

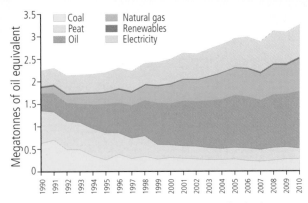

Fig. 22.1 Residential energy requirements by fuel (SEAI report, 'Energy in Ireland 1990–2010').

Electricity is generated in power stations, which are found across the country. Some of the main power station types in Ireland are:

- Fuel-burning
- Wind farms
- Hydroelectric
- Pumped storage.

FUEL-BURNING POWER STATIONS

Fuel-burning power stations are one of the oldest ways of producing electricity commercially. Fuel-burning plants burn raw materials, such as coal, peat, oil or gas, and the heat produced is harnessed and converted into electricity.

The burning fuel generates heat, which is used to turn water into steam. The steam, now under pressure, is directed through a turbine, causing it to spin. A large dynamo attached to the turbine converts the mechanical energy of the spinning turbine into electricity. The steam is cooled in cooling towers and then passed through the boiler once more to start the process again. Power stations of this kind are usually located near a large body of water, such as a lake or river, from which they draw their water supply. Fig. 22.2 shows the processes that take place in a fuel-burning power station.

The modernisation of fuel-burning power stations has made them more productive, and today there are tighter controls in relation to health and safety and the environment. Power stations are now required to clean the harmful emissions which build up in the stations' towers before they are released into the atmosphere. Even so, coal, oil, peat and gas are fossil fuels, and therefore non-renewable sources of energy.

CHAPTER 22

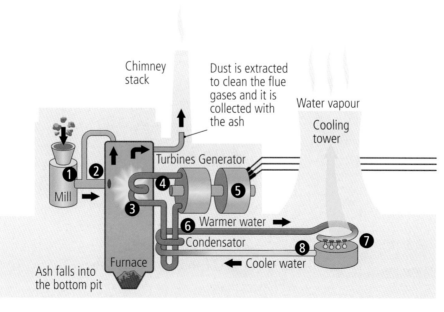

Chimney stack

Dust is extracted to clean the flue gases and it is collected with the ash

Water vapour

Cooling tower

Turbines Generator

Mill

Warmer water

Condensator

Cooler water

Ash falls into the bottom pit

Furnace

1. Fuel is fed into the system.
2. It is passed into the furnace.
3. The fuel is burned to create steam.
4. Steam passes under pressure through a turbine and makes it spin.
5. The spinning turbine turns a generator (dynamo), producing electricity which is fed to the grid.
6. Steam which has passed through the turbine is used to heat new steam.
7. Water condenses at base of cooling tower.
8. The cooled water is passed back into the system.

WIND FARMS

Fig. 22.3 Restored windmill, Blennerville, Co. Kerry.

Wind is abundant in Ireland, particularly on the western and southern coasts. People have traditionally harnessed this wind power to generate energy. Fig. 22.3 shows a restored 19th-century windmill at Blennerville, Co. Kerry.

While fuel-burning power stations use steam to turn turbines, modern wind turbines use the prevailing winds to turn their rotor blades, which then turn an electromagnetic generator. An electromagnetic generator is a rotating mechanical device that changes wind energy into electrical energy. Wind turbines can only work at low speeds, and for this reason a wind farm, which consists of several wind turbines all hooked up to a collector station, is needed to produce large amounts of electricity. Unlike fuel-burning stations, wind farms use a renewable source of energy, and have less environmental impact. They are criticised for being very noisy and disrupting the natural view, but they have become increasingly popular in Ireland due to our ability to exploit the potential of wind energy. Fig. 22.4 shows wind turbines on an Irish hillside.

Fig. 22.4 Wind turbines.

HYDROELECTRIC POWER STATIONS

Hydroelectric power stations rely on water as their source of energy. This is not a new source – mills have for centuries used water to generate the energy needed to crush grain and work machinery.

What is new in this technology, however, is the introduction of electrical inputs. A hydroelectric power station traps a large body of water behind an artificial dam, and then lets it flow through turbines which convert the potential energy of the water into electrical energy. Ardnacrusha, built on the Shannon in Co. Clare, is Ireland's largest river hydroelectric scheme.

Fig. 22.5 Water wheel harnessing the kinetic energy of water at Letterkenny, Co. Donegal.

Fig. 22.6 Ardnacrusha power plant, Co. Clare.

PUMPED STORAGE

Like a hydroelectric plant, this power generation plant uses the potential of a body of water to generate electricity. The water is pumped to a high point at night, when electricity is at its most abundant on the grid. The water is then released from this reservoir during the day as the demand on the grid increases. When the water is released it is passed through turbines to generate electrical energy. This cycle is repeated each day.

This type of system allows for greater control over the amount of electricity produced. Some pumped storage systems work in tandem with wind farms, which produce the energy to pump the water to the reservoir. The energy created from the hydroelectric process is then sold to the grid.

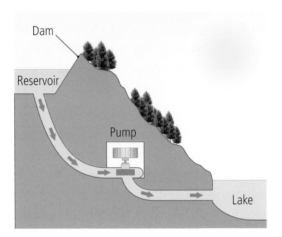 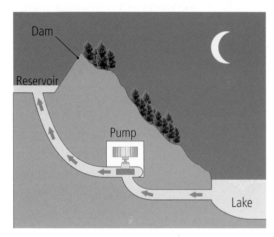

Fig. 22.7 Pumped storage. LEFT: water is released during the day. RIGHT: water is pumped back to the reservoir.

NATIONAL GRID

Power stations located around Ireland provide the country with its electricity. In order to deliver this energy to towns and cities, it must pass through the national grid (operated by Eirgrid), which supplies the country with electricity. Transmission System Operators (TSOs) are given the task of operating and maintaining the transmission of this electricity nationally. The TSO sells electricity to private companies for a wholesale price, and the private companies pass on the electricity, and the cost, to householders.

The valuable infrastructure that is the national grid consists of thousands of kilometres of high-voltage power lines,

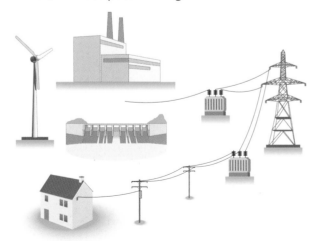

Fig. 22.8 Energy process from the power station to the home.

CHAPTER 22

Fig. 22.9 Local electrical substation.

Fig. 22.10 Step-down transformer.

running both above and below ground, along with numerous transmission stations. The grid can be likened to the country's road infrastructure, with lines, junctions and crossings linking up to bring electricity from power stations, wind farms and other sources to homes, business and industry. Fig. 22.8 shows the stages in this process.

Electricity is transmitted at a high voltage from its source to local substations (Fig. 22.9). It is sent at high voltages, and low current, to prevent energy being lost as the electricity travels over long distances. Energy is lost as heat – the cables heat up as electricity passes through them – and increasing the voltage ensures a higher delivery of energy. When the electricity reaches the substation, the voltage is reduced by a transformer – a device which is used to change the power of the electricity in the circuit – to between 220 and 240 volts. In cases where there is no local substation, the voltage is stepped down using a pole-mounted transformer similar to that shown in Fig. 22.10.

MEASURING ELECTRICITY

Electricity can sometimes seem like a mysterious force because we cannot see it. Electricity is the movement of electrons along a conductive material. Electrical energy is generated through a change in potential, kinetic or mechanical energy. The idea of electrons flowing in a circuit is similar to water flowing in a pipe. The amount of water passing through any given point in the pipe each second can be measured. In an electrical circuit, the amount of energy flow is referred to as the current. Fig. 22.11 demonstrates this.

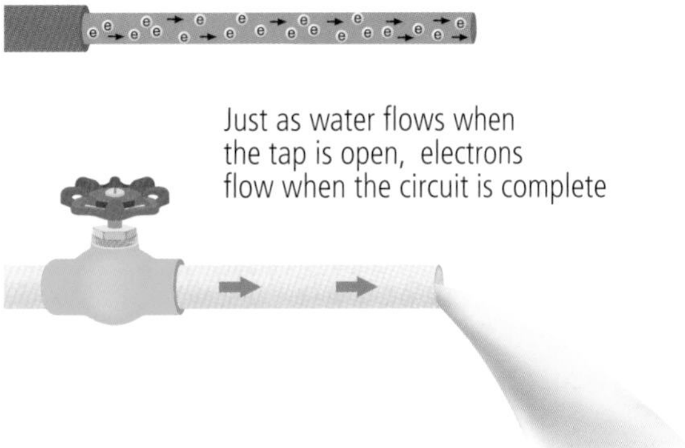

Just as water flows when the tap is open, electrons flow when the circuit is complete

Fig. 22.11 Electrons flow along a circuit like water in a pipe.

ELECTRICAL CURRENT

Electrical current is related to the flow of electrons, the small particles that orbit atoms. When enough electrical charge is applied, they leave the atom and begin to flow; this is what we know as electric current. The current is also related to the diameter of the wire along which it travels. Larger wire gives the capacity to carry more current without overheating.

The standard unit of measurement of current is the ampere (A), or amp for short. This unit measures the flow of electrons, much as a water meter measures the amount of water flowing through it.

VOLTAGE

Voltage (V) is the force of the current in an electrical circuit. Similar to water pressure, voltage is the push or force caused by the movement of electrons. The greater the voltage, the greater the pressure driving the current of electrons in a circuit.

RESISTANCE

The flow of electrons produces an electrical current. This flow, however, is obstructed by a force known as resistance. Resistance is measured in ohms. The amount of resistance varies from material to material. Due to its low resistance ratio, and its relative abundance, copper is the metal most commonly used for conducting electricity.

WATTAGE

Wattage measures the rate of conversion of electricity. It is a standard unit and is equal to 1 amp per second through a material of 1 ohm resistance. Wattage is often understood as a unit that measures the strength of light bulbs, which is incorrect as it does not measure the output of the lamp but the rate of conversion of the input of electricity, as shown in the formula:

Watts (W) = Voltage (V) x Current (Amps)

SIMPLE CIRCUITS

To see how electricity works in the home, it is important to understand that electricity flows in a circuit. A circuit is the path which electricity follows. It is laid out using copper cables, which supply fixtures and fittings with electricity when they are connected. Cables are insulated to prevent electric shock.

Fig. 22.12 shows a simple circuit. There are three main components: the battery, the light fitting and the switch. In the first diagram the switch is open and so the current is not flowing because there is a gap in the circuit. In the next diagram

CHAPTER 22

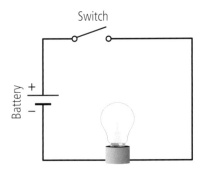

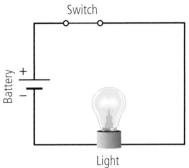

Fig. 22.12 LEFT: *Electric circuit.* RIGHT: *Current flowing through the circuit.*

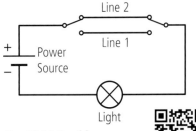

Fig. 22.13 Double light switch.

the circuit is closed, so the electrons can flow through the wire.

Understanding simple circuits is essential to the understanding of electrical layouts, the combined and linked circuitry in the home. Fig. 22.13 shows a simple circuit containing two switches. When the circuit makes a continuous loop, the light comes on; when the circuit is broken, the light will stay off. This circuit is used for two-way switches, which are used in halls and landings, where the light is usually controlled by two switches.

In these simple circuits, there is not much need for protective measures against shock or short circuiting, because the current is so low. Many installations in our homes, however, need a high degree of circuit safety.

WIRING A PLUG

There are many different types of cable and wire used in our homes. However, they follow a standard colour code: the brown wire in a cable is the live wire (L), the blue wire is the neutral (N) and the green and yellow wire is the earth (E). This colour code is standard in all electrical installations. The simplest example is the plug.

Most electrical installations in the home require consultation and use of a qualified electrician. Wiring a plug is not something that requires an electrician, but it is important to know what you are doing to carry out this task safely.

1. Strip down the three core flexes as in Fig. 22.14.

2. When the wires have been prepared, they can be connected to the terminals in the plug as in Fig. 22.15.

3. Tighten the cable using the cord grip – the black piece at the bottom of the picture. This ensures that the cable ends cannot be pulled from their terminals.

Fig. 22.14 Core flexes stripped down.

Remember that the brown is the live wire and must be connected to the live terminal. The fuse is always fitted to the live wire. The blue wire is the neutral wire and must go to the neutral terminal, and the earth is the green-and-yellow wire, which is connected to the earth terminal. To remember where to place them on a plug, the following may help:

Blue = BL = Bottom Left

Brown = BR = Bottom Right

Earth is the only other terminal left in the plug.

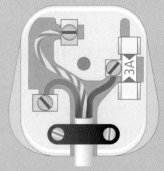

Fig. 22.15 Correct wiring for a plug.

ELECTRICITY IN THE HOME

The electrical connection to a home must be carried out by the Electricity Supply Board (ESB), now also known as ESB Networks. The connection is positioned on an external wall, in an enclosed external meter cabinet containing all the electrical connections and meters for the home (Fig. 22.16). The ESB connects a mains power cable from outside to this cabinet to provide electricity to the building. A meter in the cabinet tracks the electricity used, so that the connection company can charge the householder for the amount used. This meter is sealed and can only be accessed by ESB personnel.

If this cabinet is located more than 3m from the distribution board (the fuse board inside the house), it is also specified that there must be a separate miniature circuit breaker (MCB) fitted in an enclosure of non-conductive material, with a rating of not less than 63 amps.

The electricity is taken from the mains power cable to a distribution board in the house (Fig. 22.17). This board is filled with miniature circuit breakers (MCBs), residual current devices (RCDs) and fuses, which regulate and control the distribution of electricity in the home.

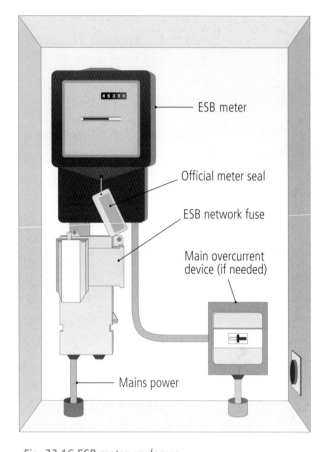

Fig. 22.16 ESB meter enclosure.

ESB meter

Official meter seal

ESB network fuse

Main overcurrent device (if needed)

Mains power

ELECTRICAL SAFETY

Every electrical connection in a home must have a safety device to protect users from electric shock. Safety devices also protect appliances from disruptions in power supply and damage from shock. The various kinds of devices are discussed next.

Fig. 22.17 Electrical distribution board.

Fig. 22.18 A fuse is a deliberately positioned weak link in a circuit.

Fuses

A fuse is a deliberate weak link in a circuit. If the current becomes higher than it should be, the fuse burns out and breaks the circuit, thereby saving the circuit and the appliances attached to it from burning. Fig. 22.18 shows a fuse in a plug.

CHAPTER 22

The main disadvantage of a fuse is that, once it has created the safety break, it has to be replaced. This means that it is not efficient as a primary safety device. Previously fuses were fitted to the main distribution board, but new standards have changed this system. Instead, the fuse is placed in the plug of the appliance, where it protects both the appliance and the user.

Miniature Circuit Breakers (MCBs)

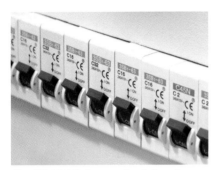

Fig. 22.19 Miniature circuit breakers.

Miniature circuit breakers monitor the amount of current flowing in the circuit. MCBs are set to a safe maximum current, and if the current exceeds the safe maximum they will trip. When an MCB 'trips' – physically, a switch flips from on to off in one-tenth of a second – it prevents current from flowing. The MCB will trip, for example, if the circuit is overloaded with too many appliances, or if there is a fault in the circuit. When the fault is solved, the trip switch can be flicked back to the On position, which will restart the current. Fig. 22.19 shows MCBs.

Different circuits have different maximum safe limits. For example, a lighting circuit needs far less current (5/6 amps) than a circuit serving sockets (30 amps). These are the maximum amount of amps (the maximum safe limit) for these applications. No more than ten connections can be made to a single circuit. This reduces the risk of overloading and of a complete cut-out (i.e. everything in the house turning off) in cases where the MCBs trip.

Residual Current Devices (RCDs)

Fig. 22.20 A residual current device, showing test button bottom right.

While the MCB will trip when there is an overload of current on a circuit, an RCD reacts to differences between current in the circuit. If a circuit is damaged, the current can leak and flow through nearby objects, creating a danger of electrocution. The RCD detects any leakage of current, and if there is a difference of 30 milliamps or more in the circuit it will trip in milliseconds and stop the current flow. Most RCDs have a test button, which allows a homeowner to test that the RCD works as a safety device (Fig. 22.20). RCDs must be fitted as standard on all socket, water heater and electric shower circuits.

Grounding the Circuit

Electricity travels along the path of least resistance to electrical ground. Electrical ground takes the current into the earth, and prevents high-voltage contact – that is, electric shock – if the electrical insulation fails in the circuit.

The electrical system is grounded by driving a conductive rod into the earth outside the home, and connecting the distribution board to it with a wire. Each circuit is connected through the distribution board to this ground wire and conductive rod. All electrical circuits must be grounded for safety. This feature offers a path for leaked current to travel safely to the earth, and works in conjunction with other safety devices on the system. Fig. 22.21 shows how the grounding rod is installed, as well as the green box that identifies the position of the rod.

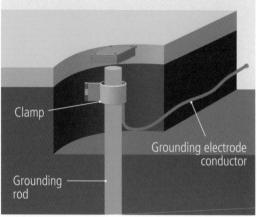

Fig. 22.21 Grounding rod and green box showing the position of the rod.

Appliance Isolation

Appliances that require higher than normal current need to have additional safety elements installed. This applies to electric cookers, water heaters and instantaneous electric showers. They need to have higher-gauge – i.e. higher diameter – wiring from the distribution board to the appliance and they also require a double pole isolation switch. This switch disconnects both the live wire and neutral wire at the same time. This facilitates the maintenance and installation of such appliances, as they can be disconnected from the electrical current without going near the distribution board. It also acts as a secondary safety device to those found on the distribution board, as it can be switched on and off independently.

Fig. 22.22 Double pole isolation switch.

Any appliance rated 3.6kW or higher must have a circuit of its own connected to the distribution board. Unlike a plug and socket, this connection is permanent, and is referred to as a dedicated circuit.

CIRCUITS IN THE HOME

Individual appliances require different amounts of current to run, but the majority are able to run from one circuit on the distribution board. To facilitate the increase or decrease of current flowing to an appliance, the cabling is either increased or reduced. A thicker wire can pass greater electrical loads than a thinner wire, without overheating.

Circuits in the home direct electricity from the distribution board through a number of circuits, ending in sockets or lighting.

Lighting Circuit

There will be generally one, but sometimes more than one, lighting circuit in the home, depending on the size of the dwelling. The lighting circuit starts at the distribution board and passes through all light fittings before returning to the distribution board. In comparison to other circuits, lighting is 'low drain', which is to say it uses little electricity.

CHAPTER 22

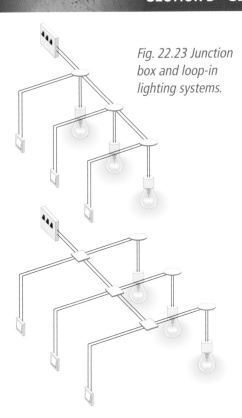

Fig. 22.23 Junction box and loop-in lighting systems.

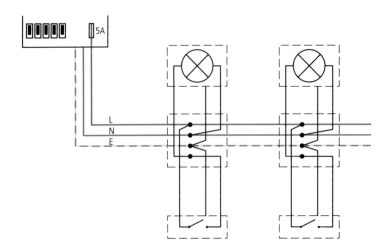

Fig. 22.24 Wiring of a radial circuit.

Radial circuits, which are used for lighting, can be either a junction box system or a ceiling rose (loop-in system). Each of these systems are shown in Fig. 22.23.

The wiring diagram for a radial circuit is shown in Fig. 22.24.

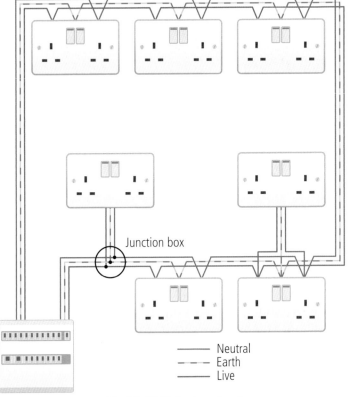

Junction box

Consumer unit

Neutral
Earth
Live

Fig. 22.25 Main ring circuit.

Ring Main Circuit

The ring main circuit is the loop of electrical outlets (sockets) which are used to power appliances around the home. Large houses may have more than one main ring circuit. The kitchen warrants having two dedicated ring main circuits because a high amount of heavy draw appliances are located here, and several of them may be in use at the same time.

The ring main circuit supplies sockets around the home with 13 amps of power. While the outlet is rated for 13 amps, the plug of the appliance has a cartridge fuse, which is rated to the appliance. The outlet will allow 13 amps through, and the plug will control whether

this can reach the appliance. Typically the fuse is 3 amps for low-usage items such as radios, while higher-rated fuses allow a higher draw for electrical devices such as microwaves, washing machines and irons.

There are general recommendations for the number of sockets which should be located in each area of the home. These are shown in Table 22.1.

TABLE 22.1 RECOMMENDED NUMBER OF ELECTRICAL OUTLETS PER AREA

Area	Number of Sockets
Kitchen	10
Dining room	6
Sitting room	5
Double bedroom	4
Single bedroom	3
Hall	2
Landing	1

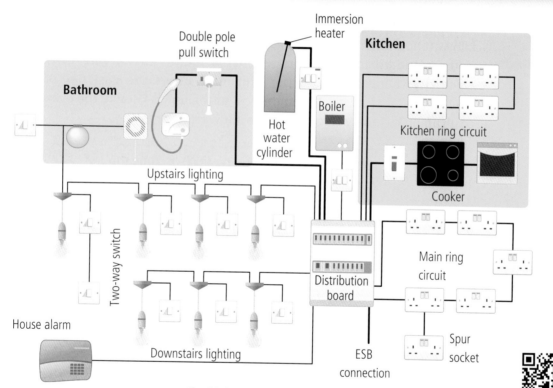

Fig. 22.26 An overview of electrical circuits in the home.

BATHROOMS AND ELECTRICITY

Water conducts electricity. For this reason, there are strict regulations governing the use of electricity in the bathroom.

When electric heaters are used in bathrooms, they have to be permanently fixed and wired. They must also be positioned more than 0.8m from the bath.

Where a switch is needed in the bathroom (e.g. for a shower) it should be positioned on the ceiling with a pull cord for switching on and off.

The only socket generally found in a bathroom is a low-voltage shaving socket. This should be installed where it will avoid direct spray from shower, taps and bath.

TABLE 22.2
TYPICAL APPLIANCE RATINGS

Appliance	Ratings
Light bulbs	40W, 60W, 100W, 150W
Electric fire	1kW, 2kW, 3kW
Television	200W
Electric kettle	1kW, 2kW,3kW
Hairdryer	1500W or 1.5kW
Electric cooker	8kW
Fridge	600W
Washing machine	920W
PC	300W

ELECTRICAL APPLIANCES

Appliances around the home use different amounts of power when they operate. Some appliances indicate their energy ratings, though others do not. The rating is given in watts or kilowatts. This energy rating is an indication of how much power the appliance will use when it is in operation. An A-rated appliance is typically 55 per cent more efficient than a D-rated appliance. Typical ratings are shown in Table 22.2.

Working out how much an electrical device costs to run can be done by calculating the kilowatt hour (kWh) of the appliance. Kilowatt hour (that is, 1000 watts an hour) is the standard unit in which energy is measured for sale to homes. The electricity supplier charges per unit, and shows the cost per unit on the dwelling's electricity bill. When the cost of the unit is known, the overall running cost can be found by calculating the kilowatt hour rating.

$$\text{kWh} = \text{Appliance Rating (kW)} \times \text{Time (hours)}$$

Question
Calculate the number of units used if an electric fire rated at 2 kilowatts is left on for 4 hours.

Solution

$$\text{kWh} = \text{Appliance Rating (kW)} \times \text{Time (hours)}$$
$$\text{kWh} = 2\text{kW} \times 4\text{h}$$
$$\text{kWh} = 8\text{kWh}$$

To find out how much this cost, you first need the current tariff. At 18.81 cent per kWh it would cost €1.50 (i.e. 18.81 x 8 = price in cents)

HOME CERTIFICATION

Electricity is a dangerous element, so it is important that a qualified electrician carries out all electrical work in the home. Whenever electrical contractors carry out a new electrical installation, or modify an existing installation, they are obliged to test and certify that it meets current standards set by the Electro-Technical Council of Ireland (ETCI). The client should receive a copy of this certification when the work is completed. The client passes this on to the ESB, who will in turn connect or reconnect the dwelling to the network.

PRACTICE QUESTIONS

1. Name the main types of power station in Ireland.

2. Explain, using notes and neat freehand sketches, how a pumped storage power station works.

3. Explain the following terms as they relate to electricity:
   a. Current
   b. Voltage
   c. Resistance
   d. Wattage.

4. Name and describe the different safety devices built into an electrical system to prevent shocks and failures.

5. What is a grounding rod and why is it necessary?

6. Describe the steps necessary to wire a plug.

7. Draw a simple circuit to include a two-way switch, a power source and a light bulb.

8. In terms of electrical safety, explain:
   a. Fuses
   b. MCBs
   c. RCDs
   d. Grounding
   e. Double pole isolation switch

   Refer in your answer to the places where these safety features are found.

9. Sketch an example of a ring and radial circuit for a home. On each sketch show three electrical outlets or light fittings.

10. Calculate the kilowatt hour units and cost used if a television of 200 watts is used for 8 hours at 18.81 cent per Kw/h.

11. Calculate the combined kilowatt hour units used if a light of 50 watts is used for 4 hours and an additional light of 100 watts is used for 2 hours.

12. Calculate the kilowatt hour units used if a cooker of 8 kW is used for 2 hours.

SAMPLE EXAMINATION QUESTION

2012 Higher Level Question 8

(a) Show, using notes and freehand sketches, the correct wiring layout for **two** electrical sockets in a ring mains circuit for a domestic electrical installation. Indicate on your sketch the sizes and the colour coding of all electrical cables used in the circuit.

(b) Show, using notes and freehand sketches, **two** safety features that should be incorporated into the design of the above circuit to ensure that the circuit is safe for all users..

(c) Discuss in detail **two** strategies that would ensure the economical use of electricity in the home.

2008 Higher Level Question 9

(a) Using notes and *freehand sketches*, show the electrical wiring layout for two lights and two switches in a radial circuit of a dwelling house.
Indicate on the sketch the typical sizes and colour coding of the electric cables.

(b) Using notes and *freehand sketches*, show **two** safety features in the design of the lighting circuit that ensure that it is safe for all users.

(c) Using notes and *freehand sketches*, show **two** features that should be incorporated into the design of the lighting system of a dwelling house to ensure the economical use of electricity.

CHAPTER 23
WASTEWATER DISPOSAL

LEARNING OUTCOMES:

After studying this chapter students will:

- Understand the difference between surface water and wastewater.
- Be able to explain how surface water is removed from a site.
- Understand how the guttering system works and identify its key components.
- Understand the main drainage systems and how they work.
- Be able to describe the different stack methods involved in above-ground drainage.
- Understand how a domestic septic tank works and sketch its operation.
- Appreciate the alternatives to septic tanks.

KEYWORDS:

- GUTTERING • WASTEWATER • SOAKAWAY • FOUL WATER • SOIL WATER • DRAINAGE
- TWO-PIPE SYSTEM • SINGLE-STACK SYSTEM • SIPHONAGE • WATER TRAP
- INSPECTION CHAMBER • MANHOLE • TEST • PERCOLATION • SEPTIC TANK
- DISTRIBUTION BOX • MECHANICAL AERATION • INTERMITTENT FILTER

INTRODUCTION

Surface water comes initially from rain, while wastewater is water that comes from the house. Dealing with this water is not a simple case of allowing it to flow from the site. All water contained on a site, or that runs onto a site, must be dealt with by the site owner. Rainwater and other surface water is directed to soak pits, while wastewater is directed to a private or public sewage system.

SURFACE WATER

In relation to domestic dwellings, surface water refers to the collection of precipitation (rainwater) on and around the dwelling. The two main places where surface water gathers are the roof and paved areas. Surface water has become more of a problem in recent years due to the increasing number of homes being built in urban areas. Siting buildings on previously undeveloped land means that the land absorbs less water than it would if there were no buildings, and this in turn increases the volume of surface water.

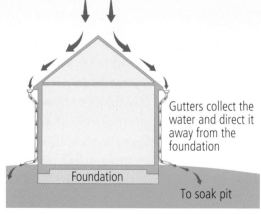

Fig. 23.1 Rainwater is carried away from the building via the gutter system.

CHAPTER 23

At roof level, guttering is placed under the eaves to collect rainwater as it runs off the roof. Guttering must be cleaned regularly to ensure that it functions well. Downpipes are the vertical members that direct the water down from the gutter to the drains. The drain leads to a soak pit, a large hole in the ground or precast concrete chamber designed to collect and drain a large amount of water. It is usually downslope from the dwelling and filled with stone, which helps collect the water and allow it to slowly drain away. Fig. 23.1 shows show how rainwater is transferred first from roof to gutter and from there to the soak pit. Fig. 23.2 shows a typical soak pit.

Installing the guttering is relatively straightforward. The guttering must be as close to the roof edge as possible. The roofing felt extends slightly into the gutter, so that water from underneath the tiles and slates will flow into the channel. The roof edge must not project outwards further than the centreline of the gutter; otherwise water from the roof will overshoot the gutter and spill onto the ground. Guttering can be installed level or slightly tilted (at a slight fall). When a fall is incorporated into the gutter, it helps to reduce the build-up of silt, and the gutter can also deal with a larger roof surface area.

The guttering itself is snapped into place and held with different kinds of bracket. Fascia brackets are fixed to the fascia, where they act as clips that hold the guttering. A union bracket is used to join two spans of guttering together. Angle brackets are used to change the guttering's direction. Stop ends prevent water spilling from the ends of the guttering.

The downpipe is attached to the guttering through an offset bend. Pipe brackets keep the downpipe in place on the wall. A rainwater shoe can be installed at the bottom of the downpipe to divert water away from the building; alternatively the pipe can be extended to the drainage channels using an adaptor. Fig. 23.3 shows a portion of guttering on a typical house.

Surface water on paved areas around the property must also be drained. Traditionally surface water is

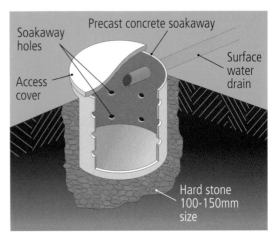
Fig. 23.2 Soak pit.

Fig. 23.3 Guttering.

Fig. 23.4 A trench and perforated pipe.

directed into drainage channels to get rid of it as quickly as possible. But while this works in cities and large towns, it is not a viable option for rural areas. In rural areas, surface water must be led to soakaway pits. There are two ways of doing this:

- Dig a trench to drain water away from the building.
- Set perforated pipes in the ground. The slope of the pipe drains water to the soakaway pit.

Fig. 23.4 shows a trench with perforated pipes, often called a French drain.

Surface water can also be reused. In this case the guttering will direct the water to a rainwater harvesting system. (See Chapter 19.)

DRAINAGE

Drainage is the term used to describe the system of pipework which takes wastewater from the house. The wastewater is directed to a mains sewerage system or to a septic tank. There are three types of wastewater:

Wastewater is water that comes from sinks, showers, dishwashers, washing machines, etc. This water has been contaminated with chemicals, food particles and other waste products.

Soil water is water that comes from the toilet. This is channelled directly into a sewer or septic tank.

Foul water is a mixture of wastewater and soil water. It is directed into a sewer or septic tank.

The wastewater flows through the drains to its disposal point. It is extremely important that the drainage system functions effectively. Important design features ensure that the system will:

- **Allow access.** The pipework must be accessible so that maintenance can be carried out.
- **Prevent leaking.** Pipes and fittings must be sound in order to prevent leaking, both inwards and outwards. If gaps appear in underground pipes, roots will penetrate and dirt and grit will build up.
- **Prevent the build-up of solids**. A build-up of solids will block the pipework.
- **Resist corrosion/abrasion**, which may be caused by chemicals transported in the pipe, or gravel outside the pipe.
- **Be at correct gradien**t. If the gradient is too steep, the liquid waste will flow too quickly through the pipework, leaving the solid waste behind. If the gradient is not steep enough, the waste will not flow through the pipework efficiently.

Drainage for domestic dwellings is divided into above-ground drainage and below-ground drainage. Above-ground drainage refers to all pipework associated with the dwelling that is above the ground; below-ground drainage refers to the pipework installed below ground level.

CHAPTER 23

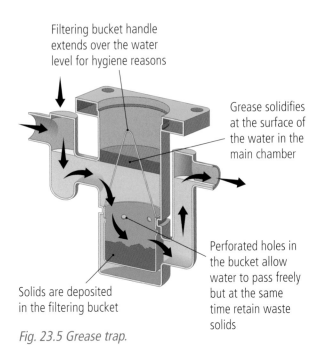

Filtering bucket handle extends over the water level for hygiene reasons

Grease solidifies at the surface of the water in the main chamber

Perforated holes in the bucket allow water to pass freely but at the same time retain waste solids

Solids are deposited in the filtering bucket

Fig. 23.5 Grease trap.

ABOVE-GROUND DRAINAGE

Above-ground drainage deals with all wastewater leaving the house and entering the drainage system. The kitchen and bathroom are usually the main focus here. There has to be a system for transferring water from kitchen and bathroom appliances (dishwashers, washing machines, kitchen sinks, showers and toilets) into the drainage system.

Grease and oils can build up in the drains from water draining from the kitchen sink. A fitting known as a grease trap can help prevent this. As the water passes through the trap, the grease/oils float to the top and solidify. A removable bucket is used to empty the trap at regular intervals. Fig. 23.5 shows a diagram of a grease trap.

Above-ground drainage can be designed using the two-pipe system or the single-stack system. Whichever method is used, it must carry waste efficiently and effectively, with a minimum risk of blockage.

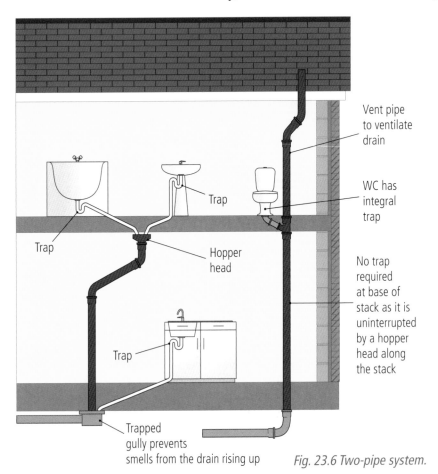

Trap

Trap

Trap

Hopper head

Trap

Trapped gully prevents smells from the drain rising up

Vent pipe to ventilate drain

WC has integral trap

No trap required at base of stack as it is uninterrupted by a hopper head along the stack

Fig. 23.6 Two-pipe system.

Two-Pipe System

The two-pipe system is more common in older buildings, and is not installed in new builds. Here the toilet waste is directed into the main stack (i.e. the main vertical component on the external wall), which is 100mm in diameter and vented to prevent the water being sucked out of – or siphoning from – the WC trap. From here the waste travels to the sewer or septic tank. Water from other appliances is discharged into an open hopper (a chute wide enough to accommodate numerous pipes) through 32–40mm diameter branch pipes, which have a maximum length of 1.7m. The branch pipes must slope at between 18mm and

90mm per metre. The hopper directs the water into a gully, where the kitchen water enters the drain. The gully then directs the water to the sewer/septic tank. Inspection chambers are positioned so that the pipes can be cleaned if blockages occur.

This system has the advantage of greater flexibility in the positioning of appliances, but is also costly to install due to the amount of pipework that is needed. Fig. 23.6 shows the two-pipe system configuration.

Single-Stack System

The single-stack system is more common than the two-pipe system. Here all appliances feed through branch pipes into one 100mm diameter stack. There are two ways to vent the stack. One is to attach a vent pipe to each appliance. For the vent pipes to work, they must be positioned as close as possible to the trap in the appliance. The second way to vent the stack is to extend the stack above the eaves and leave the top open. This prevents foul air escaping from the stack and entering the dwelling. The top of the stack must be capped to prevent debris getting into it. Fig. 23.7 shows the configuration of a single-stack drainage system.

To ensure that the single-stack system operates at its most efficient, the pipework must be carefully designed. Building regulations govern the dimensions, positions and slopes of pipework coming from the dwelling. They also determine the position of certain appliances in the dwelling. The connections of branch pipes to the stack are governed to prevent siphonage, a build-up of gases and other difficulties. Fig. 23.8 shows the requirements for attaching branch pipes to the main stack.

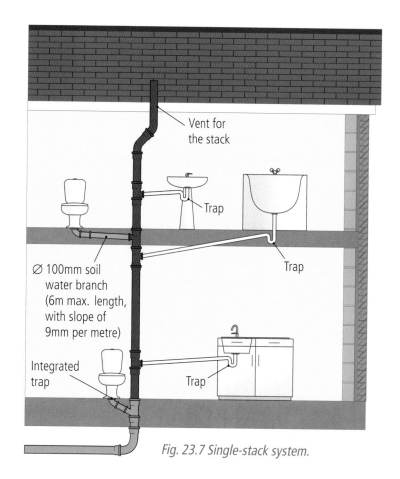

Vent for the stack

Trap

Trap

∅ 100mm soil water branch (6m max. length, with slope of 9mm per metre)

Integrated trap

Trap

Fig. 23.7 Single-stack system.

CHAPTER 23

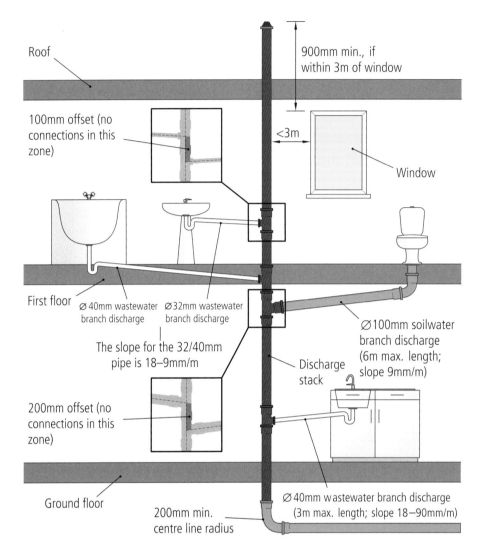

Fig. 23.8 The dimensional requirements for branch pipes.

Roof

900mm min., if within 3m of window

100mm offset (no connections in this zone)

<3m

Window

First floor

Ø40mm wastewater branch discharge

Ø32mm wastewater branch discharge

The slope for the 32/40mm pipe is 18–9mm/m

Ø100mm soilwater branch discharge (6m max. length; slope 9mm/m)

Discharge stack

200mm offset (no connections in this zone)

Ground floor

200mm min. centre line radius

Ø40mm wastewater branch discharge (3m max. length; slope 18–90mm/m)

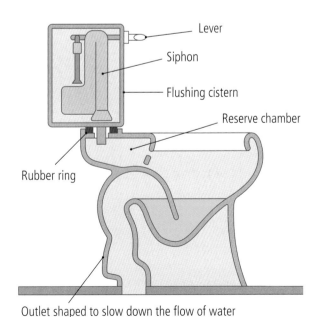

Lever

Siphon

Flushing cistern

Reserve chamber

Rubber ring

Outlet shaped to slow down the flow of water

Fig. 23.9 Single-trap type WC fitting.

Traps

In domestic drainage, a trap is a reservoir of water that prevents gases and odours escaping into the dwelling. Every appliance that drains water (sink, bath, WC) has a trap either built into the appliance or into the plumbing directly beneath it. The water in the traps prevents the passage of air, so odours cannot pass through. To function effectively, the trap must be located directly beneath the appliance and must be self-cleaning. Traps are required regardless of the piping used in the plumbing system. Fig. 23.9 shows a water trap in a bathroom fitting.

The water seal in an appliance can be broken by self-siphonage, induced siphonage and back pressure. Siphonage is a difference in air pressure that creates suction. These conditions must be prevented.

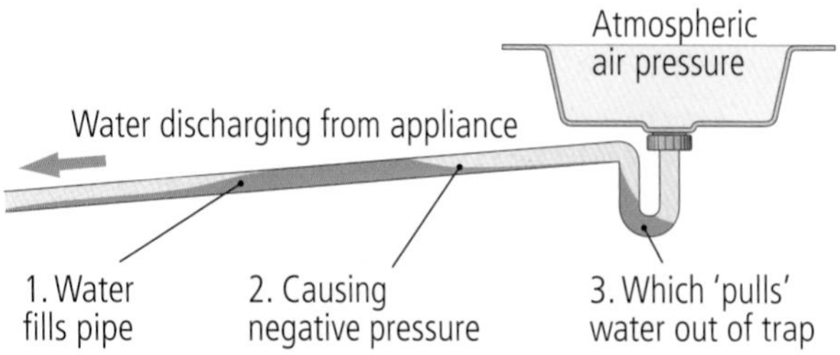

- **Self-siphonage** occurs when the pipe underneath the appliance runs at full bore (that is, across its full diameter) into the stack. As a result, the pressure inside the waste pipe is reduced, which causes siphonage from the trap. Fig. 23.10 shows this graphically.

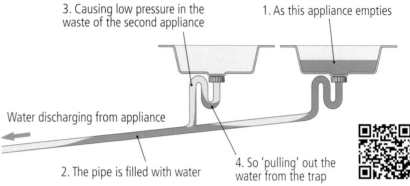

Fig. 23.10 Self-siphonage.

1. Water fills pipe
2. Causing negative pressure
3. Which 'pulls' water out of trap

Atmospheric air pressure

Water discharging from appliance

- **Induced siphonage** occurs when water passes down through the stack past the connecting waste pipe. The main flow causes suction in the waste pipe, thereby pulling the water from the trap (Fig. 23.11).

3. Causing low pressure in the waste of the second appliance

1. As this appliance empties

Water discharging from appliance

2. The pipe is filled with water

4. So 'pulling' out the water from the trap

Fig. 23.11 Induced siphonage.

- **Back pressure** begins at the base of the stack, usually where it turns. The slowdown in the flow through the stack increases the pressure, which builds up in the waste pipe and can blow out the seal in the appliance. Fig. 23.12 shows this graphically.

BELOW-GROUND DRAINAGE

The function of below-ground drainage is to transfer wastewater from where it enters the underground pipework into a sewer or septic tank. In urban areas, dwellings are usually connected to a local authority sewer. Most dwellings in rural areas use a septic tank, combined with a percolation area.

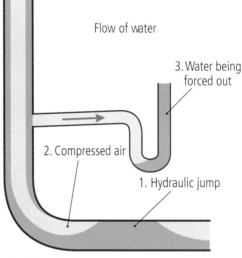

Flow of water

3. Water being forced out

2. Compressed air

1. Hydraulic jump

Fig. 23.12 Back pressure.

As the pipework is laid underground, it is important that it will not need regular maintenance. Ways of avoiding regular maintenance are:

- Keep layout simple
- Minimal change of direction or gradient
- Connections must be made in direction of flow
- Connections must allow branches to enter at oblique angles.

Pre-made sections of pipe and connectors, which can be bought in builders' providers, make the installation of underground drainage quicker and simpler,

Fig. 23.13 Pre-made pipes and connectors.

and ensure that fittings are airtight. If it is apparent that a blockage may occur and it cannot be cleared (i.e. at and after changes of direction, gradient, etc.), an access point must be provided. This allows essential maintenance to be carried out without disrupting the pipework. Fig. 23.13 shows some sections of pipework.

Where possible, pipes should be laid in straight lines between access points. Access points include inspection chambers, manholes, access junctions, etc. The main forms of access to underground drainage systems are outlined here (Figs 23.14, 23.15, 23.16, 23.17). Figs 23.18 and 23.19 show further access points in the below-ground system.

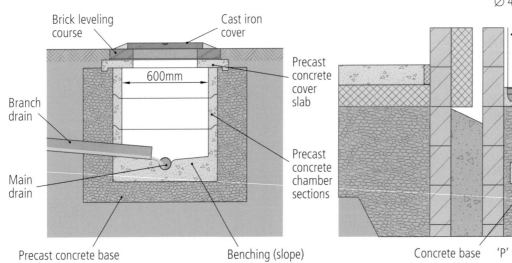

Brick leveling course — Cast iron cover — Precast concrete cover slab — 600mm — Precast concrete chamber sections — Branch drain — Main drain — Precast concrete base — Benching (slope)

Fig. 23.14 Manhole.

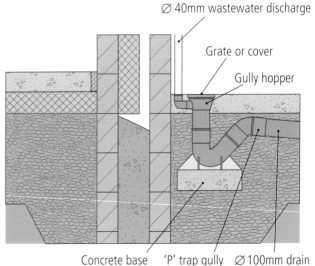

⌀ 40mm wastewater discharge — Grate or cover — Gully hopper — Concrete base — 'P' trap gully — ⌀ 100mm drain

Fig. 23.15 Gully grate.

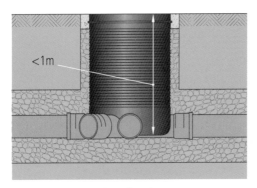

<1m

Fig. 23.16 Inspection chamber.

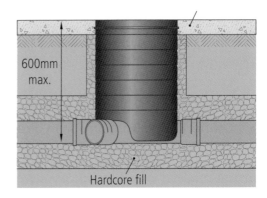

600mm max. — Hardcore fill

Fig. 23.17 Access junction.

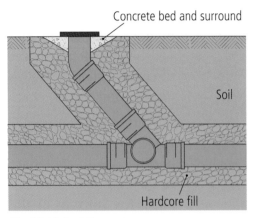

Fig. 23.18 Rodding point.

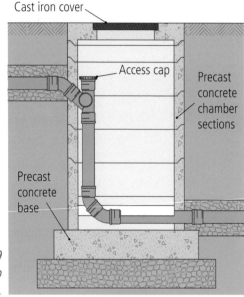

Fig. 23.19
Backdrop
manhole.

The drainage system needs to be ventilated when pipework connects to a number of houses (usually in an urban setting). Vents are installed at each house or where the branch length exceeds 6m. Where pipework is required to turn corners, it must turn with as large a radius as possible. This helps keep the flow free and gradual and reduces the risk of blockages.

Pipework must be watertight to prevent leakage either into or out of the system. Watertightness is achieved by installing rubber seals at the ends of the pre-formed pipes. The pipes must be connected square in order to prevent damage to the seal.

A number of things can be done at the design stage to prevent blockages building up.

- Internal surfaces must be smooth
- The diameter of the drain must be large enough (usually 100mm) for the volume it will be transporting
- Pipes must be laid at correct gradient
- Large radius should be used for turns
- Nothing should be allowed to project into the pipework.

Nowadays it is common to see plastic (uPVC) piping used for drainage. uPVC is popular because it is strong, flexible, reliable, resistant to chemicals and easy to install, but it is by no means the only material that can be used for underground drainage. Other materials include concrete, cast iron and clay. Although uPVC drains are generally used to connect to the house, it is usual to have a concrete pipe running along a row of houses, to which the uPVC drains can be attached. Fig. 23.20 shows an aerial view of the layout for the attachment of drains.

Drains that connect to a sewerage system must be laid at the correct gradient and depth. The drain itself (i.e. the pipe) is 100mm in diameter. The gradient of

CHAPTER 23

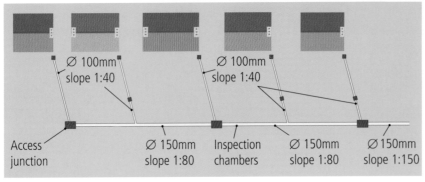

Fig. 23.20 Drains connected to a row of houses.

the drain depends on the number of dwellings that will be connected to the drainage system, as well as its span and use.

To lay drains correctly, a trench is dug and then backfilled with aggregate to embed the drainage pipe. The bottom of the drain must be 550mm below ground level. Topsoil is filled to a depth of 300mm, sitting on top of 500mm of aggregate. Fig. 23.21 shows these dimensions.

Inspection Chambers

Inspection chambers are installed to give access to the drain for periodic inspection and maintenance. Inspection chambers are placed along the length of the drain: at the head, at changes in level, at changes in direction, and where new connections are made to the main drain. An inspection chamber is used for depths of up to 1m. Where the depth to the drain exceeds 1m the chamber is referred to as a manhole.

The chambers can be made from a number of materials. Traditionally concrete and brick were used, while modern building has seen a rise in the use of uPVC products, which are easier, cheaper and quicker to install. The sides of the chamber are sloped or 'benched' to direct overflow from the system back into the drainage channel. Fig. 23.22 shows a section through an inspection chamber.

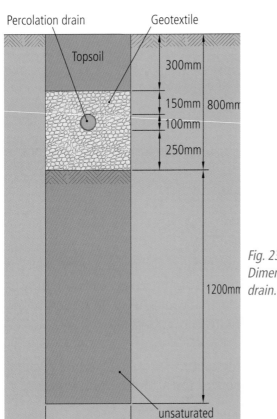

Fig. 23.21 Dimensions of a drain.

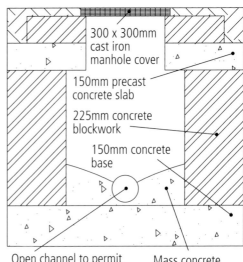

Fig. 23.22 Inspection chamber.

Manholes are constructed on a minimum 150mm concrete base. The minimum internal dimensions, which will depend on the manhole's depth, are between 1200 x 750mm and 1200 x 840mm. While an inspection chamber can be capped with uPVC, a manhole requires a cast iron, pressed steel or precast concrete capping. The stronger material is needed to ensure that no one can fall through the cover. A section through a manhole as well as its dimensional requirements are shown in Fig. 23.23.

TESTING THE SYSTEM

Underground drainage systems must be tested before they are backfilled. There are three common methods:

1. Air test
2. Water test
3. Smoke test.

To pass the test, the pipework must not allow the air, water or smoke to escape. The water test can be used to test an entire underground system, including access junctions, inspection chambers and manholes.

Air test. The section to be tested is fitted with temporary up-stands (vertical sections of pipe). One of the up-stands is sealed and a compressor or pump is attached to the other. Air is then pumped into the system and the pressure is maintained for three minutes. This test gives instant results as a drop in pressure immediately indicates an air leak. Fig. 23.24 shows how this test is carried out.

Water test. The section to be tested is fitted with temporary up-stands and filled with water. The level must be maintained for a period of 24 hours if the results are to be acceptable. The height of the

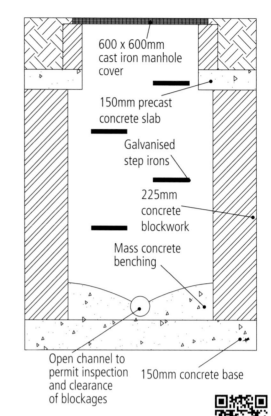

Fig. 23.23 Manhole.

600 x 600mm cast iron manhole cover

150mm precast concrete slab

Galvanised step irons

225mm concrete blockwork

Mass concrete benching

Open channel to permit inspection and clearance of blockages

150mm concrete base

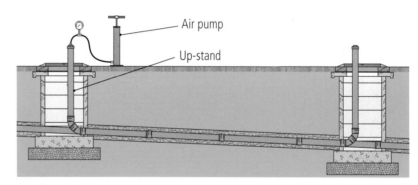

Fig. 23.24 Air test.

Air pump

Up-stand

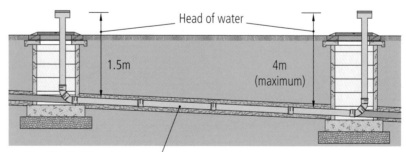

Fig. 23.25 Water test.

Head of water

1.5m

4m (maximum)

Pipe filled with water under pressure

CHAPTER 23

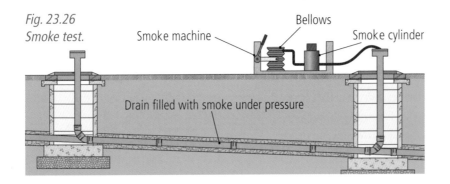

Fig. 23.26 Smoke test.

up-stands can be raised to increase the pressure on the drain. This is the most popular way of testing a drainage system, and any leaks can be addressed before backfilling takes place. Fig. 23.25 shows how this test is carried out.

Smoke test. This test is similar to the air test, but smoke rather than air is pumped into the drain. The smoke is pumped in through the length of the drain section, and the up-stand is sealed once the section is full of smoke. The pressure is maintained for a period of five minutes, while observation of pressure level and escaping smoke takes place. This test is preferable to the air test because it identifies the source of a leak, but it is not recommended for uPVC pipework. Fig. 23.26 shows how this test is carried out.

Fig. 23.27 Wastewater treatment plant.

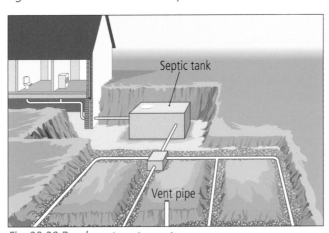

Fig. 23.28 Rural wastewater system.

TREATING WASTEWATER

Wastewater needs to be treated before it is allowed into the environment. Wastewater from houses connected to a sewer is treated at a treatment plant provided by the local city or county council. In a rural setting, a dwelling which does not have access to council-operated sewers must have its own wastewater treatment system.

A dwelling may need an individual wastewater treatment system to prevent wastewater coming into contact with people or animals; and to prevent it getting out of the drainage system and contaminating the soil or water sources. The system filters the solids and liquids in the waste, and allows controlled drainage into the ground.

The wastewater passes through a septic tank and then through a distribution box, and from there along a series of perforated pipes, through which it filters into the soil in the percolation area. A percolation test is carried out to determine the suitability of the soil on the site to filter waste, and the results of this determine the type of system that will be installed (see Chapter 5). Fig. 23.28 shows how the components of a rural wastewater system are laid out.

SEPTIC TANK

There are a number of ways of effectively treating wastewater coming from a dwelling. The need for proper treatment has increased as a result of our growing environmental awareness, and the systems themselves have been improved by technological advances.

The septic tank is the most common form of wastewater treatment for single dwellings in Ireland. Other less used but equally effective systems include the mechanical aeration system, the wetland system and the intermittent filter system.

EU legislation requires that septic tanks meet certain standards, and for this reason all owners of dwellings with a septic tank must register and pay a fee.

A septic tank is a precast unit designed to deal with sewage. The tank contains two chambers, which hold the sewage long enough to allow the solids to settle and a scum layer to form on top. A septic tank must have:

- A minimum capacity of 2725 litres
- A length three times its width
- A watertight and ventilated lid to prevent a build-up of methane gas.

The tank's first chamber collects all foul water coming from the dwelling. As the waste settles, anaerobic bacteria break down the solids, so their volume is reduced. Liquid from this chamber flows into the second chamber, where further settlement takes place. Excess liquid is directed out to the distribution box. Both the inlet and outlet pipes, which allow waste into the first chamber, and from there to the second chamber, are 100mm in diameter. The inlet pipe level is higher than the outlet level so that the wastewater flows easily from tank to distribution box. Fig. 23.29 shows a section through a conventional septic tank along with all relevant design details.

Having passed through the septic tank, the wastewater is carried to a distribution box. This box distributes the flow evenly to a minimum of four percolation pipes. Percolation pipes are perforated to allow liquid to filter out as it flows through them. The pipes are from 100mm to 110mm in diameter with 8mm perforation holes at 75mm centres around the circumference. The maximum length of a percolation pipe is 18m and they must be laid at least 2m apart.

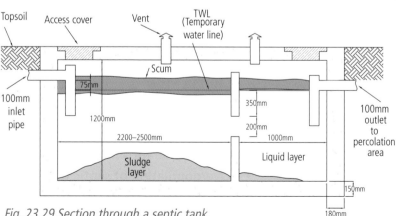

Fig. 23.29 Section through a septic tank.

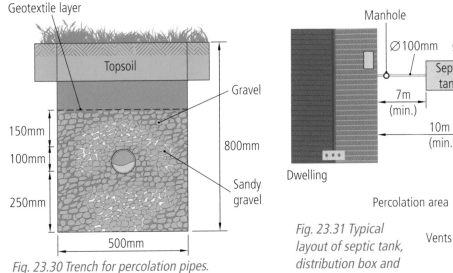

Fig. 23.30 Trench for percolation pipes.

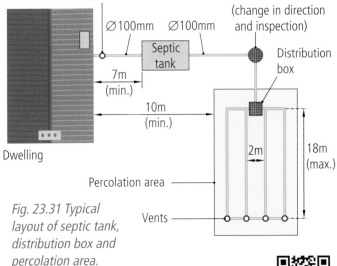

Fig. 23.31 Typical layout of septic tank, distribution box and percolation area.

The trench dug for the percolation pipes must adhere to the following specifications:

- 500mm wide
- 800mm deep
- Backfill 250mm
- Washed gravel aggregate surrounding pipe
- 150mm similar aggregate over pipe
- Geotextile layer – to prevent saturation
- Topsoil to ground surface.

Fig. 23.30 shows a section through the trench indicating all dimensional requirements.

The pipes are laid in gravel to allow the pipes some movement without being damaged, and the ends of the pipes are ventilated to prevent a build-up of gases. Aerobic bacteria break down any remaining impurities in the wastewater as it passes through the gravel. There must be no contaminants present in the liquid when it reaches the ground water. Fig. 23.31 shows a typical layout of the septic tank along with the distribution box and percolation area.

The advantages of using a septic tank and percolation area include:

- Suitable for rural areas
- Simple system
- Cheap to run
- Low maintenance.

Disadvantages of using this system include:

- Not suitable for small sites
- Overpopulation of septic tanks in rural areas
- Foul smells permeating in warm weather
- May not treat waste efficiently, causing pollution.

ALTERNATIVE SYSTEMS

Where a percolation area is not practical or possible in a rural setting, there are a number of alternatives, each of which is used along with the septic tank. These include:

- Intermittent soil filter system
- Intermittent sand filter & polishing filter
- Intermittent peat filter & polishing filter
- Intermittent plastic and other media & polishing filter
- Constructed wetland & polishing filter.

Intermittent systems direct the liquid from the distribution box to a filter made up of special soil or sand, or peat or plastic materials. Each of these systems incorporates a polishing filter, the last layer in the system, which is used to clarify the last remaining contaminants before the liquid enters the ground water. Figs 23.32, 23.33 and 23.34 show different sections through intermittent systems as well as a typical layout for these systems.

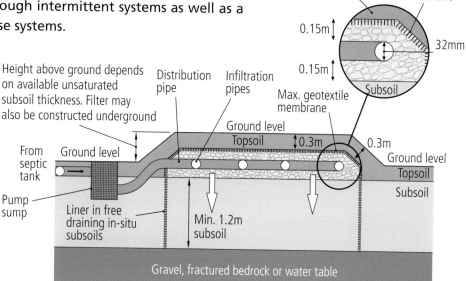

Fig. 23.32
Intermittent soil
filter.

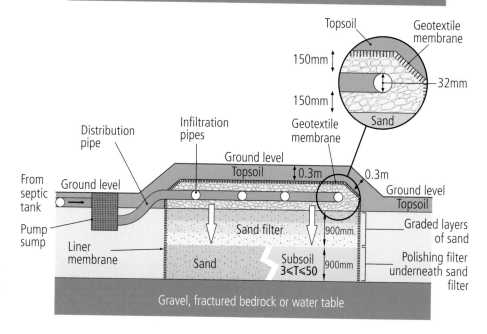

Fig. 23.33
Intermittent sand
filter.

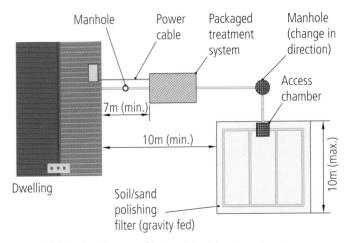

Fig. 23.34 Typical layout of intermittent treatment system.

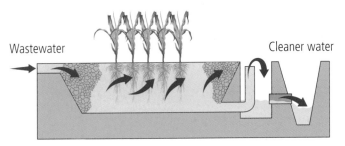

Fig. 23.35 Constructed wetland system.

A constructed wetland uses plants and their natural filtering abilities to purify household wastewater. The wastewater is directed into the wetland, where it passes through the contained plants before being released into a drainage channel as decontaminated water. A constructed wetland is an environmentally sustainable waste treatment system. Fig. 23.35 shows a section through a constructed wetland system.

A mechanical aeration system is used where none of the systems described above can be installed. This is a closed system that completes the entire treatment inside one large tank. Wastewater is fed into the first chamber, which allows a degree of settling. The second chamber is used to introduce aerobic bacteria through a ventilator. The bacteria break down the contaminated water. Liquid flows into the third chamber, where it is further clarified before being pumped out as decontaminated material. The disadvantages of this system are that there are more parts, so it's more expensive, and it needs regular maintenance. Fig. 23.36 shows a section through a mechanical aeration system.

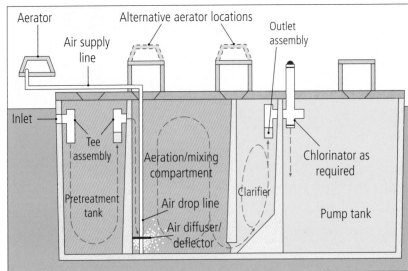

Fig. 23.36 Mechanical aeration system.

PRACTICE QUESTIONS

1. What is surface water?

2. Explain, using notes and neat freehand sketches, how surface water is directed away from a dwelling.

3. What is drainage?

4. Explain the difference between wastewater, soil water and foul water.

5. List the key design features of an underground drainage system.

6. Describe, using notes and neat freehand sketches, both methods of above-ground drainage.

7. Using notes and neat freehand sketches, outline the three types of siphonage that can occur in an above-ground drainage system.

8. Why are access points necessary in below-ground drainage systems?

9. Explain, using notes and neat freehand sketches, the difference between an inspection chamber and a manhole.

10. Outline the testing methods used to ensure that below-ground drainage systems operate effectively.

11. What is a septic tank and why is it necessary?

12. Draw a vertical section through a septic tank to a scale of 1:10. Indicate all main dimensions on your drawing.

13. Draw a line diagram of the layout of a septic tank system to include a distribution box and percolation area. Include all main dimensions on your diagram.

14. Describe, using notes and neat freehand sketches, two alternatives to the septic tank/percolation area system.

SAMPLE EXAMINATION QUESTIONS

2010 Higher Level Question 4

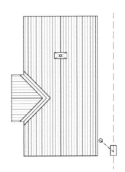

(a) Discuss, using notes and *freehand sketches*, three functional requirements of a below ground drainage system to ensure the safe removal of sewage from a domestic dwelling.

(b) The accompanying sketch shows the location of a manhole at the intersection of a branch drain and a main drain in a below ground drainage system for a domestic dwelling. Using notes and *freehand sketches*, show the typical construction details through the manhole from the foundation to the manhole cover. Indicate on the sketch the typical dimensions.

(c) Using notes and *freehand sketches*, describe in detail one test that may be carried out to ensure that the below ground drainage system is watertight.

2009 Higher Level Question 4

A main bathroom, as shown in the sketch, is located on the first floor of a dwelling house.

(a) Using notes and *freehand sketches* show **two** design considerations that should be taken into account when locating the bathroom on the first floor of a dwelling house.

(b) Using notes and *freehand sketches* show the above-ground pipework necessary for the safe discharge of waste from the following fittings:
   • wash hand basin
   • bath.
Include in your sketch typical sizes of the waste pipe for each fitting.

(c) Using notes and *freehand sketches* show the design detailing necessary to prevent the penetration of sewer gases into the bathroom at the W.C.

2008 Higher Level Question 4

(a) Discuss in detail, using notes and *freehand sketches*, **three** functional requirements of a wastewater treatment system suitable for the on-site treatment of sewage from a single house.

(b) Using notes and *freehand sketches*, show the plan of a typical on-site wastewater treatment system for a single house. Include **three** main dimensions in your sketch.

(c) Using notes and *freehand sketches*, describe **one** test that is carried out to determine if a site is suitable for an on-site treatment system.

SAMPLE EXAMINATION QUESTIONS

2007 Ordinary Level Question 2

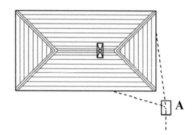

(a) Using notes and *neat freehand sketches*, show **two** considerations that should be taken into account when laying sewer pipes for a domestic dwelling to ensure the safe removal of sewage from the dwelling.

(b) An inspection chamber is located at A in the sketch of the sewerage system for a dwelling house as shown. Using notes and a *neat freehand sketch*, show a vertical section through the inspection chamber.

Your sketch should include the following:
- concrete foundation;
- side walls;
- position of the drain;
- benching to the drain;
- cover of inspection chamber.

(c) Outline **one** reason why the inspection chamber is located at A as shown.

ENVIRONMENTAL SUSTAINABILITY AND PASSIVE DESIGN

LEARNING OUTCOMES:

After studying this chapter students will:

- Understand the need for environmental sustainability.
- Appreciate the need for increased energy efficiency.
- Understand what is meant by the term passive design.
- Understand the criteria that need to be met for passive certification.
- Describe how passive criteria are met.
- Be able to sketch various aspects of a passive design build.

KEYWORDS:

- ENVIRONMENTAL SUSTAINABILITY • ENERGY EFFICIENCY • BIOMASS • SOLAR
- GEOTHERMAL • ZINC • STRAW BALE • PASSIVE • AIRTIGHT • SOLAR ENERGY GAIN
- PASSIVHAUS INSTITUT

INTRODUCTION

Environmental sustainability involves looking at the impact that humans have on nature. Each process we follow, every material we use and every action we take has an impact on our surroundings. Concerns about climate change, depleted resources and CO_2 output mean that it is even more important to take responsibility for our actions. Building sustainably means working positively with our surroundings and using sustainable resources and methods.

The materials and processes used in building can be extremely harmful to the environment, and it is important to think of this when planning a build. Advances in technology as well as greater wealth have contributed to the greenhouse effect (Fig. 24.1). The greenhouse effect is the heating up of the Earth as a result of holes in the ozone layer, which are caused by burning fossil fuels.

Reflected

Absorbed

Escaping radiation

Edge of atmosphere

Absorbed by atmosphere and earth

Radiation absorbed by greenhouse gases

Greenhouse gases and fossil fuels

Deforestation

CFCs

Oil and petrol engines

Fig. 24.1 Causes of the greenhouse effect.

Development, as we saw earlier in this book, is the progression of settlement. The World Commission on Environment and Development describes sustainable development as:

'Development that meets the needs of the present without compromising the ability of future generations to meet their own needs.'

With this idea in mind we must consider the impact of our actions on the generations to come and how they will live their lives. This involves a 'from cradle to grave' approach that looks at how materials are made, transported, used and disposed of over their life cycle. Fig. 24.2 shows the stages in the cycle.

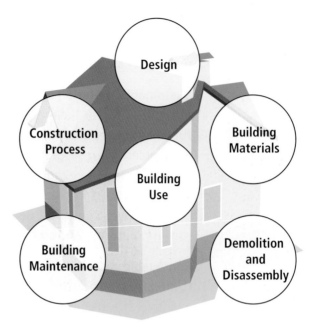

Fig. 24.2 Thought should be given to each of these points when carrying out a sustainable build.

SITE SELECTION AND MATERIALS

The design of a home within a site should be based on how the building is to be used as well as where it is situated. Large housing estates and large commuter towns have in the recent past been built with little concern for the environment or the way people live their lives. Now there is greater emphasis on designing and building more sustainable homes, whose impact on the environment is less damaging, and that are designed to meet the needs of the people who live in them. It is hoped that this pattern will become the norm over time.

Site selection for a sustainable house is slightly different from choosing a site for a conventional house. Earlier in the book we saw how a site can be adapted to suit a building, with planting, access, topography, etc. In sustainable housing the building is designed around the site. This means, for example, that if there is a tree in the middle of the site, rather than replanting or removing it, it can be incorporated into the building.

Plants and grasses can also be incorporated into buildings to offset their carbon footprint, as shown in Fig. 24.3. Carbon footprint means the amount of CO_2 an individual emits in their daily life through energy use, travel and lifestyle. The same principle can also be applied to buildings.

Fig. 24.3 Grass roof on a public services building in Letterkenny, Co. Donegal.

CHAPTER 24

We have seen in this book that many methods and materials can be used in a build, and we have looked at both standard and alternative materials. Some materials can be classified as sustainable; others can be classed as renewable.

Sustainable materials are products that are a waste product of other sectors, are renewable or have a low carbon footprint (i.e. a minimal amount of fossil fuel energy was used to make them). Timber used in sustainable buildings must be sourced from sustainable forests, which helps to reduce deforestation and illegal logging. An example of a sustainable material in Ireland is thatch roofing. When grain was in plentiful supply in Ireland the remaining straw was a waste product. Over centuries, people discovered that the straw could be used as a roofing material, and so the waste product became a valuable resource.

Renewable materials – a sub-category of sustainable materials – are materials that can be produced indefinitely. This means they can be replenished: for example, if a tree is cut down another can be planted to take its place. Other examples are plants and biomass.

STRAW BALE

Straw, grass and reeds were used as building materials for centuries. They were woven together with wood to create panels for use on walls or roofs, or made into bales and stacked on top of each other to create walls. These traditional materials are now being used with modern building methods to make more sustainable homes.

There are many different methods of straw bale housing found across the world. Some methods use the straw bales as a structural element of the building. Others involve making wooden battening for the walls and using the straw as the bulk insulation material in the walls. The advantages of straw bale construction are that it is relatively cheap and the material is renewable. Straw is also a relatively good insulator. Fig. 24.4 shows how straw bales are used in construction.

There are many disadvantages of this system, however: the two most important are that straw is susceptible to rot in damp conditions, and it is extremely bulky.

Fig. 24.4 Straw bales used in construction.

ZINC ROOFING

Because of its useful properties, zinc is becoming popular as a roofing material in environment-conscious builds.

Building-grade zinc sheeting is a mix of zinc, copper and titanium. This maximises pliability and increases strength. In most installations the roof is joined with a seam.

Zinc is durable and lighter than slate. It is also self-healing: over time a layer builds up on the zinc that is both waterproof and prevents chemicals passing through it. If this layer is scratched it will build up again over time. Thus the zinc below is protected. Zinc is also malleable, so it lends itself to designs that are not possible with traditional slate or tiled roofs. Fig. 24.5 shows a zinc roof design.

Advantages of using zinc in roofing include:

Fig. 24.5 A zinc roof.

- Low toxicity
- Nearly 100 per cent recyclable – because it doesn't rust
- Water run-off does not pick up chemicals that could taint soil and/or groundwater
- Low manufacturing cost due to recyclability.

The major disadvantage of using zinc roofing is that it is extremely expensive – twice the price of tiles or slates.

ENERGY EFFICIENCY

Energy efficiency is the effort to reduce the amount of energy used to provide products and/or services. There are a number of areas in the home, including heating, appliances, etc., that can be made more energy efficient.

To improve energy efficiency, wasteful uses of energy must first be identified. For example, heating a room with a window open makes no sense, because the energy that has gone into heating the air is wasted.

Improvements to energy efficiency that we have seen throughout this book include making a building airtight, increasing insulation, controlling the heating system and installing efficient appliances.

CHAPTER 24

Fig. 24.6 Smart home systems can adjust heating, temperature and other factors in the home automatically, or be controlled remotely.

SMART HOMES

Smart technology helps to regulate energy in the home, so that it is used more efficiently. Smart homes use zones to remotely control appliances, services and security systems. These systems can be controlled with built-in panels, computers and/or mobile phones. Smart homes provide a convenient way of controlling systems (heating, lighting, sound etc.) in the house.

Fig. 24.7 Bahrain World Trade Centre incorporated wind turbines into its design to harness natural energy.

RENEWABLE ENERGY

Renewable energy production uses energy sources that occur naturally or materials that can be easily replenished. In recent years developments in both areas have allowed us to harness more of this energy efficiently.

Renewable energy sources include:

- The sun (solar energy) – see Chapters 16 and 19
- Heat below the surface of the earth (geothermal energy) – Chapter 19
- Wind – Chapter 22
- Water – Chapter 22
- Biomass (wood, waste, energy crops).

BIOMASS

Biomass is all plant and animal matter on the earth's surface (i.e. everything that is not man-made). Bioenergy is the energy that is harvested from this matter and used to produce heat or electricity. The most common type of this energy in Ireland is the wood pellets that are commonly burned in stoves to generate heat in homes. Fig. 24.8 shows a wood pellet-burning stove and the section in Fig. 24.9 shows how it works.

Fig. 24.8 A wood pellet-burning stove.

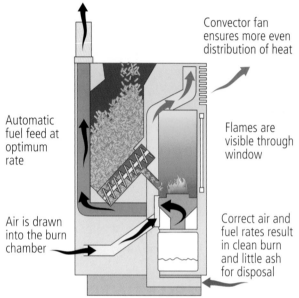

Convector fan ensures more even distribution of heat

Automatic fuel feed at optimum rate

Flames are visible through window

Air is drawn into the burn chamber

Correct air and fuel rates result in clean burn and little ash for disposal

Fig. 24.9 How a wood pellet-burning stove works.

PASSIVE HOUSING

A passive house is a building standard rather than a new construction method. This standard is internationally recognised. Homes built to this standard are comfortable, sustainable and economical. A passive house must not be confused with an energy-efficient dwelling, which is one that uses less energy than the average dwelling. A passive house is one that does not need to use active heating or cooling systems to maintain a comfortable indoor climate. Fig. 24.10 compares the energy consumption of each house type.

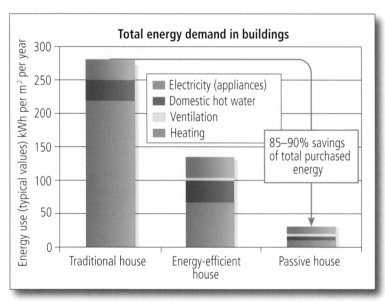

Fig. 24.10 Energy consumption in a traditional house, an energy-efficient house and a passive house.

CHAPTER 24

Fig. 24.11 Passive house design: the new standard in building?

The Passivhaus Institut (PHI) in Germany, which was established in 1996, developed the standard for passive housing. The first passive house, in Darmstadt, Germany, was recorded in 1990. There are a growing number of passive builds in Ireland, including one-off domestic dwellings, schools, healthcare buildings and even a social housing development in Dungannon, Co. Tyrone, the first of its kind on this island. The Passive House Association of Ireland (PHAI) works to educate people and promote the passive house standard in Ireland.

Energy savings of up to 90 per cent can be made in a passive house compared to a normal new build. The interior is kept warm by eliminating thermal bridges and using a highly insulated building envelope. It is likely that in the not too distant future passive regulations will become the standard in Ireland, as is happening across Europe. Fig. 24.11 shows a zero carbon, timber-clad passive house with triple glazed windows and roof covered with solar panels for electricity and hot water.

CRITERIA FOR A PASSIVE HOUSE

The aims of the passive house standard are to increase comfort, lower monthly costs, maintain a high property value and have a low environmental impact.

The principles of passive housing are based on minimising energy loss and maximising solar energy gains.

Criteria that must be satisfied before a house is deemed to be passive include:

- Annual heat requirement = 1.5 litres of heating oil per metre squared per year
- Airtightness
- Super-insulated to an average U-value of less than $0.15kWh/m^2/yr$ (see table)
- No thermal bridges
- Compact building form
- Passive use of solar energy (through orientation)
- Glazing and window frames to a U-value of less than $0.8kWh/m^2/yr$ (triple glazed)
- A1-rated household appliances.

Expressed more generally, a passive house uses no more than $120kWh/m^2/yr$ of energy per year for heating, hot water, ventilation and household electricity.

This is a saving of 75–90 per cent in comparison with non-passive buildings. The air change in the house must be below 0.6 per hour at 50 pascals. This allows for a sufficient supply of fresh air and reduces the risk of mould growth from stale air.

The U-value requirements are different for passive builds and regular builds. Table 24.1 shows a comparison between traditional build U-values and passive build U-values.

TABLE 24.1 U-VALUES IN TRADITIONAL AND PASSIVE BUILDINGS

Building element	Traditional requirement	Passive requirement
Roof	0.16	0.15
Walls	0.21	0.175
Windows	1.6	0.8
Doors	1.6	0.8
Floors	0.21	0.15

AIRTIGHTNESS

Air can pass out of a building through the building fabric. The most common cause of this is imperfections in the building envelope at the construction stage. Reducing the amount of air passage through the building reduces energy consumption because the air does not need to be heated or cooled. Fig. 24.12 shows the common air leakage paths .

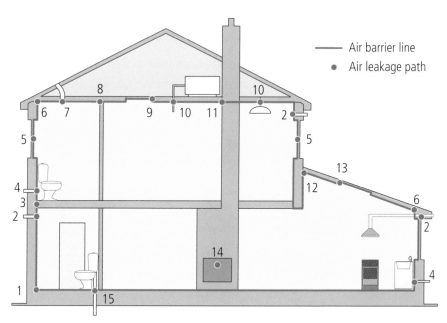

— Air barrier line
• Air leakage path

1. Wall/floor junction
2. Mechanical extract vent or wall vent
3. Wall/intermediate floor junction
4. Service penetrations through walls, e.g. WC, sink, bath or shower, waste pipes (particularly those obscured by vanity units or kitchen units, etc.)
5. Windows and doors
6. Wall/roof junction (eaves)
7. Ceiling penetrations, e.g. mechanical extract vent, soil stack, passive vent stack, etc.
8. Partition junction with external wall or ceiling
9. Attic trap door
10. Ceiling penetrations, e.g. water pipes from attic storage tank, light fittings (particularly recessed fittings)
11. Chimney/ceiling junction
12. Wall/lean-to roof abutment
13. Rooflights
14. Open fireplace
15. Floor penetrations, e.g. waste pipes from WCs, sinks, dishwashers, etc.

Fig. 24.12 Common areas for air leakages.

Fig. 24.13 A blower door fitted for testing the airtightness of a house.

Fig. 24.14 Thermal imaging can be used to show the air leakage from a building.

Air leakage can be combated at three stages of a new build: the design stage; before construction starts; and during construction.

At the design stage an air barrier can be included in the plans. An air barrier is a material used to minimise the passage of air through it. Air barriers take many different forms, including an appropriately sealed radon barrier, plaster finish, plasterboard with sealed joints and vapour control layers.

Air leakage can be detected using smoke detection or thermal imaging. Both methods involve using an infiltrometer (blower door). A blower door has a fan installed in it that depressurises the house by sucking the air out of the house. This in turn draws in air from outside through any air leakage paths. While the fan is on, a technician goes from room to room to check for air leakage. The air leakage rating for a house can be determined using a blower door. Fig. 24.13 shows a blower door in place.

In a smoke test, the technician uses a heatless smoke puffer to direct smoke. This identifies whether there is a leak but does not show the specific path. Using thermal imaging equipment, the technician can not only identify the entry point of the leak, but also the path the air takes: this is because the air outside is colder than the air inside. Fig. 24.14 shows a thermal image of the warm and cold spots in a building, which helps identify any air leakage.

Because a passive building is airtight, it requires a ventilation system to provide fresh air. A mechanical ventilation with heat recovery (MVHR) unit is used to provide warmed fresh air while expelling cold stale air (see Chapter 17).

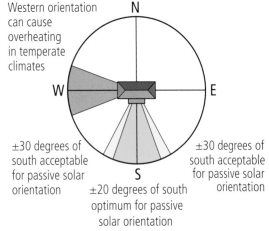

Western orientation can cause overheating in temperate climates

±30 degrees of south acceptable for passive solar orientation

±30 degrees of south acceptable for passive solar orientation

±20 degrees of south optimum for passive solar orientation

Fig. 24.15 The path of the sun during the year; + or − 20 degrees of south is optimum for passive design.

ORIENTATION

While orientation is important in every build, it is essential in a passive build. If the correct angles are not achieved, a significant heat/light source is lost. (Site orientation was discussed in Chapter 3.) For passive building it is essential that the building is designed around the path of the sun at different times of the year. Without this vital solar energy the house will not function. Fig. 24.15 shows the path of the sun during the year.

Orientation alone cannot ensure that the sun's energy will enter the house. Windows must be positioned so that large areas of glazing are south facing; north-facing glazed areas should be small to prevent excessive heat loss. Fig. 24.16 shows the relationship between south-facing glazing and heat requirements. By increasing the number of glazing panels to three and fitting two low-e layers, a south-facing window can be made five times more efficient than a traditional double-glazed window.

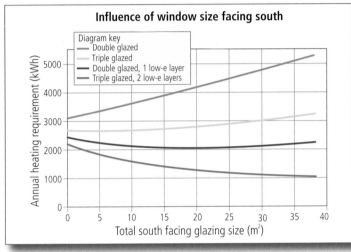

Fig. 24.16 South-facing window size and thermal efficiency.

Fig. 24.17 Correct orientation can help keep a house warm in winter and cool in summer.

Fig. 24.18 Homes can be renovated to incorporate more elements of passive design.

1. More glazing on south face to maximise solar heating
2. Glass sliding door added to the front
3. Garage door replaced with glass sliding door
4. Open plan layout developed to maximise warmth from the south

CHAPTER 24

As well as orientation, the design of the house itself can contribute to the penetration of sunlight and therefore heat.

Finally, orientation works in conjunction with room layout. The rooms used at different times of the day are laid out so that the sun is concentrated on the windows at the time when the rooms are occupied. Fig. 24.18 shows a comparison between good and bad internal layout in relation to sun penetration. The poor internal layout (left) does not make the best possible use of sunlight. Good internal layout (right) means that each room gains the most sunlight possible at an appropriate time of day.

COMPACT BUILDING FORM

Building form refers to the overall shape of the building. More heat is lost through large surface areas than small ones, so for passive design a compact building form is required. A compact building form relates to a simple design with a minimum of extensions and/or additions.

Compactness of the building form is a ratio between the surface area of the building and its volume. The building should have the largest possible volume for the smallest possible surface area. For passive certification this ratio needs to be 0.7 or less. Fig. 24.19 shows the footprint of two buildings with identical volumes but different surface areas. The house on the right has a greater surface area and hence a greater compactness ratio.

Footprint of two houses with identical volumes (assuming equal heights) – the house on the right has a greater surface area and hence a higher compactness ratio.

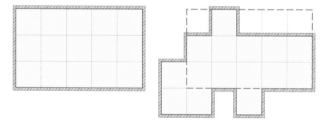

Fig. 24.19 Two buildings with the same volume but different surface areas.

The trend in recent years has been to build bigger and bigger houses, but passive design does not always allow for this. At the same time, while a passive house is designed for use rather than grandeur, this is not to say that large passive homes cannot be built.

PASSIVE FOUNDATIONS

In traditional foundations the concrete is in contact with the subsoil, whose temperature can affect the foundation and the rising walls. Foundations for a passive build are highly insulated to prevent cold bridging, something that is not done for traditional builds. This creates a break between the concrete, the surrounding soil and the internal floor, and it prevents heat loss through the foundations. Fig. 24.20 shows the difference between a normal concrete foundation and a passive foundation, and Figs 24.21 and 24.22 shows the technical specifications associated with this foundation type for block-built and timber frame passive homes.

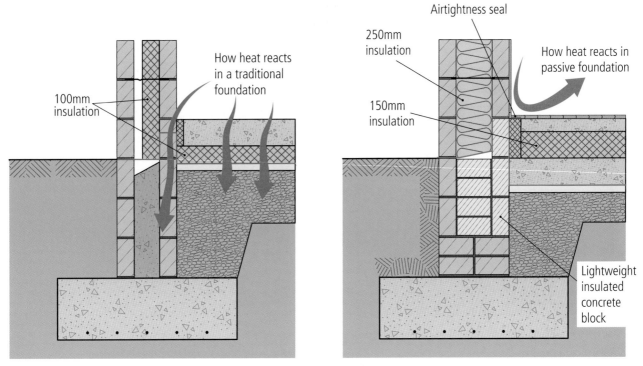

Fig. 24.20 A normal foundation (left) and a passive foundation (right).

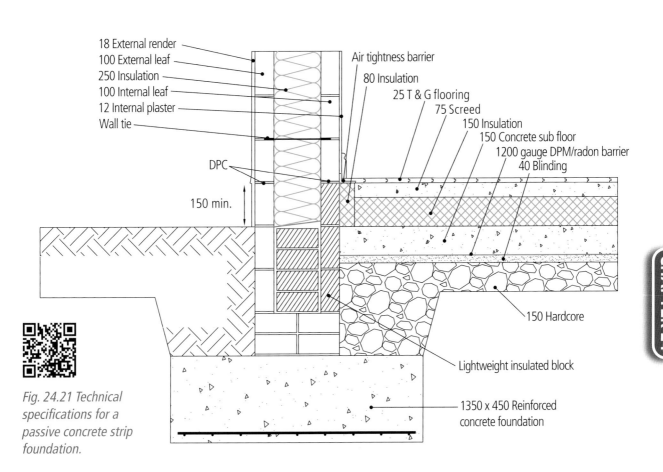

Fig. 24.21 Technical specifications for a passive concrete strip foundation.

CHAPTER 24

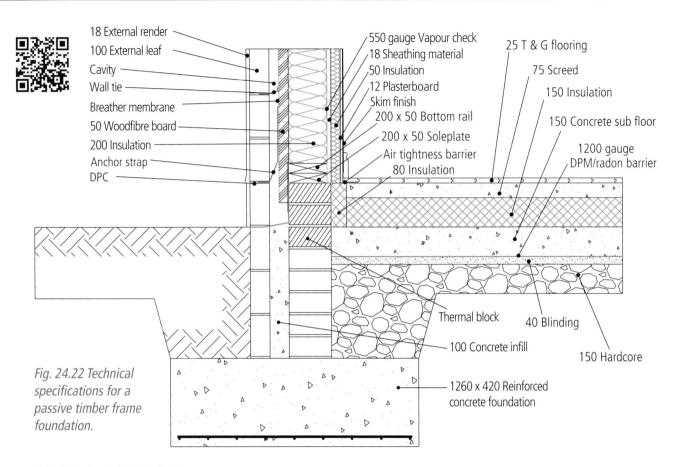

18 External render
100 External leaf
Cavity
Wall tie
Breather membrane
50 Woodfibre board
200 Insulation
Anchor strap
DPC

550 gauge Vapour check
18 Sheathing material
50 Insulation
12 Plasterboard
Skim finish
200 x 50 Bottom rail
200 x 50 Soleplate
Air tightness barrier
80 Insulation

25 T & G flooring
75 Screed
150 Insulation
150 Concrete sub floor
1200 gauge
DPM/radon barrier

Thermal block
100 Concrete infill
40 Blinding
150 Hardcore

1260 x 420 Reinforced
concrete foundation

Fig. 24.22 Technical specifications for a passive timber frame foundation.

PASSIVE WALLS

In order for walls to reach the passive standard, they must be airtight with high levels of insulation. To ensure that the wall is airtight, it should have a plaster finish with no breaks or cracks (plaster itself is airtight). Junctions must be taped to prevent air leakage (i.e. between walls and window boards). Creating this airtightness and increasing levels of insulation eliminates thermal bridges and air passage routes. Figs 24.23 and 24.24 show the technical specifications necessary to ensure a wall (block and timber frame) is suitable as a passive build.

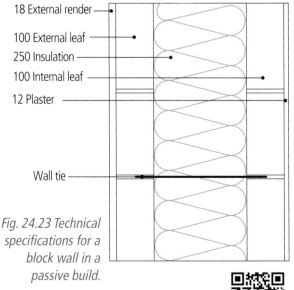

18 External render
100 External leaf
250 Insulation
100 Internal leaf
12 Plaster

Wall tie

Fig. 24.23 Technical specifications for a block wall in a passive build.

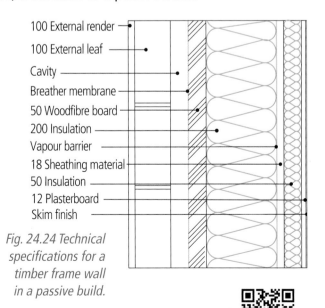

100 External render
100 External leaf
Cavity
Breather membrane
50 Woodfibre board
200 Insulation
Vapour barrier
18 Sheathing material
50 Insulation
12 Plasterboard
Skim finish

Fig. 24.24 Technical specifications for a timber frame wall in a passive build.

PASSIVE WINDOWS AND DOORS

Because 15 per cent of the heat in a building is lost through doors and 10 per cent through windows it is important to deal with these areas of heat loss when building a passive house.

Doors and windows must be airtight (as discussed earlier) to prevent air and therefore heat escaping. Window and door frames are in contact with both the outside and the inside. To prevent frames acting as a cold bridge they must be highly insulated. If heat is allowed to bridge the gap between outside and inside, the house cannot be deemed passive. Fig. 24.26 shows an illustration of a passive door.

It is important to keep the frame of the window as small as possible in a passive build as more heat escapes through the frame than through the glass. Fig. 24.25 shows a triple-glazed window with dual materials. Note that this window cannot be deemed passive unless the hollow section is filled with insulation. Figs 24.27 and 24.28 show the technical specifications for passive windows in block-built and timber frame dwellings.

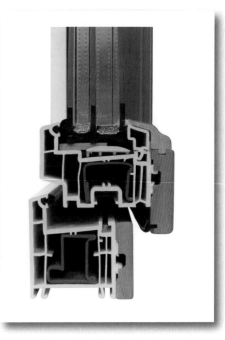

Fig. 24.25 A triple-glazed window with uPVC and timber.

① **Insulation core**
High-strength, damp-resistant, provides improved noise insulation and optimum heat insulation

② **Extra-strong door leaf**
Approx. 92mm thick, optimum heat insulation

③ **Top sealing function**
Double silicon seal. No signs of fatigue, high levels of heat insulation, a full-bodied sound, no door banging

④ **Thermal threshold substructure (optional)**
Optimum thermal separation, no underfloor cold or damp bridges, no door sagging

Fig. 24.26 A passive door.

CHAPTER 24

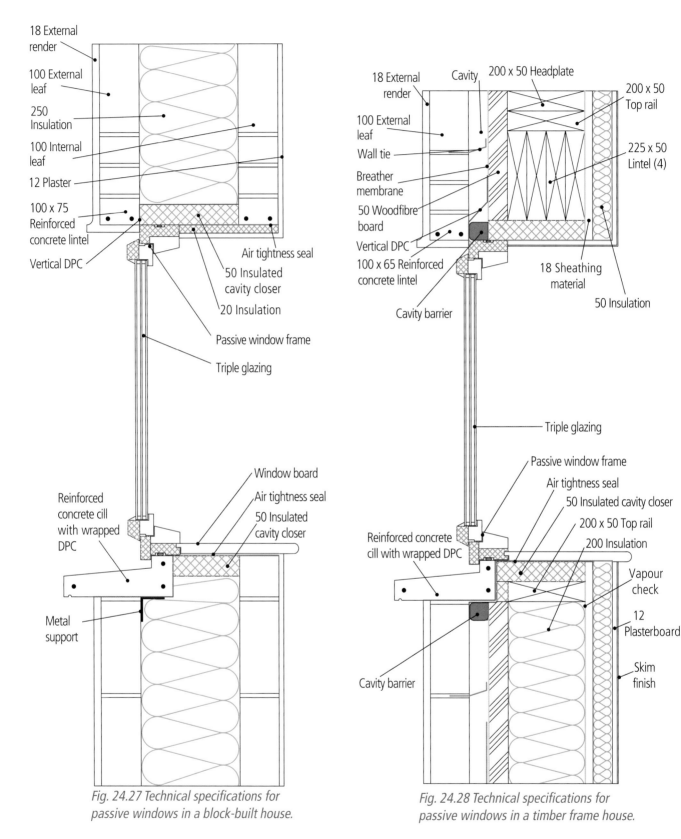

18 External render

100 External leaf

250 Insulation

100 Internal leaf

12 Plaster

100 x 75 Reinforced concrete lintel

Vertical DPC

Air tightness seal

50 Insulated cavity closer

20 Insulation

Passive window frame

Triple glazing

Window board

Air tightness seal

50 Insulated cavity closer

Reinforced concrete cill with wrapped DPC

Metal support

Fig. 24.27 Technical specifications for passive windows in a block-built house.

18 External render

Cavity

200 x 50 Headplate

200 x 50 Top rail

100 External leaf

225 x 50 Lintel (4)

Wall tie

Breather membrane

50 Woodfibre board

Vertical DPC

100 x 65 Reinforced concrete lintel

18 Sheathing material

50 Insulation

Cavity barrier

Triple glazing

Passive window frame

Air tightness seal

50 Insulated cavity closer

200 x 50 Top rail

200 Insulation

Reinforced concrete cill with wrapped DPC

Vapour check

12 Plasterboard

Skim finish

Cavity barrier

Fig. 24.28 Technical specifications for passive windows in a timber frame house.

PASSIVE ROOFS

A traditional roof on a block cavity wall is quite efficient, but it needs to be more efficient in order to satisfy passive house standards. The main area where the traditional roof fails to meet passive house standards is in the level of insulation. By increasing the amount of insulation, combined with an airtight membrane, passive house standards can be met. Figs 24.29 and 24.30 show the technical specifications associated with passive roofing.

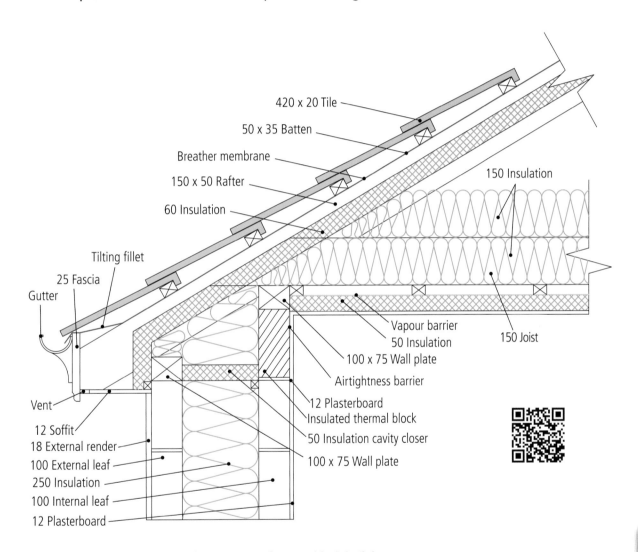

Fig. 24.29 Technical specifications for passive roofing in a block-built house.

CHAPTER 24

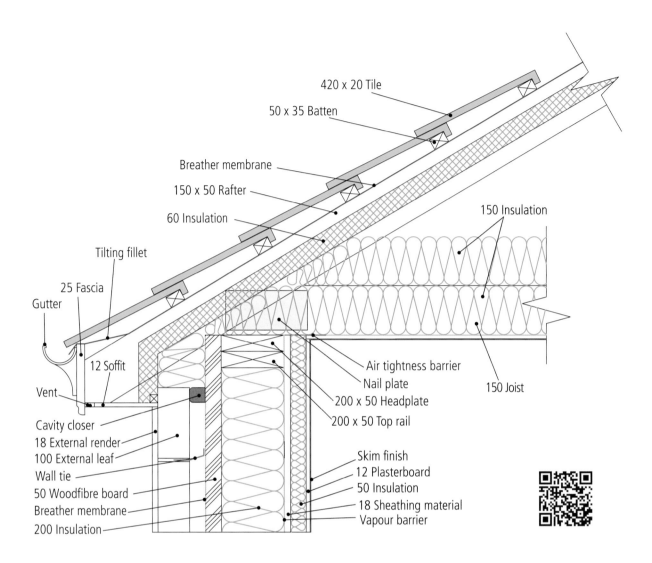

Fig. 24.30 Technical specifications for passive roofing in a timber frame house.

ADVANTAGES OF PASSIVE DESIGN

There are a number of advantages in choosing passive building over traditional block or timber frame building. These include:

- Low energy consumption – 75 per cent less than traditional houses
- Consistent level of comfort – 18–21°C all year round
- Reduced environmental impact – lower CO_2 emissions (because less fuel is used for heating).

DISADVANTAGES OF PASSIVE DESIGN

The disadvantages of building a passive dwelling rather than a typical block or timber frame dwelling include:

- High level of workmanship required
- Precise detailing (for airtightness, insulation, etc.), which is very time consuming
- MHRV is arguably unnecessary in the Irish climate
- Heavy maintenance – constant change of filters needed to provide clean air in MRHV system
- Lack of available expertise
- Cost.

PRACTICE QUESTIONS

1. What is environmental sustainability?

2. What does 'from cradle to grave' mean in relation to environmental sustainability?

3. Name and describe two renewable products that can be used in building.

4. How can energy efficiency be improved in a domestic setting?

5. List and explain four renewable energies.

6. What is a passive house?

7. List the criteria necessary to ensure a house is passive.

8. Explain, using notes and neat freehand sketches, how airtightness of a dwelling is achieved.

9. Explain fully, using notes and neat freehand sketches, how orientation affects a passive building.

10. To a scale of 1:10, draw a vertical section through a passive foundation. Include all typical dimensions in your drawing.

11. To a scale of 1:5, draw a vertical section through either a block-built passive wall or a timber frame passive wall. Include all typical dimensions in your drawing.

12. To a scale of 1:10, draw a vertical section through both a block-built wall with passive window and a timber frame wall with passive window. Include all typical dimensions in your drawings.

13. To a scale of 1:10 draw a vertical section through either a passive roof atop a timber frame wall or a passive roof atop a block-built cavity wall.

14. Explain in detail the advantages and disadvantages of passive building.

SAMPLE EXAMINATION QUESTIONS

2012 Higher Level Question 9

Designing for airtightness presents one of the most challenging aspects of contemporary house design.

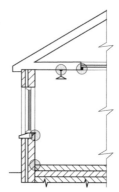

(a) Discuss in detail the importance of careful design detailing in improving the airtightness performance of a dwelling house.

(b) The drawing shows an outline section through a portion of a single storey house of timber frame construction. The outer leaf is of rendered concrete block and the ground floor is an insulated solid concrete floor. Select any three locations from those circled on the sketch and show, using notes and freehand sketches, the typical design detailing which will prevent air leakage at each of the locations selected.

(c) Discuss the advantages of including a service cavity in an external wall of timber frame construction, as shown in the accompanying sketch.

2012 Higher Level Question 10

(a) Using notes and freehand sketches as appropriate, discuss in detail the importance of any two of the following in the design of a Passive House:

- building form
- indoor environment
- energy performance.

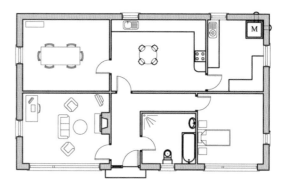

(b) It is proposed to install a Mechanical Heat Recovery with Ventilation (MHRV) system for a Passive House, as shown in the drawing. The location of the MHRV unit - M - in the utility room is shown. Draw a single line diagram of the given plan and show a typical design layout for the ducting to such a unit. Indicate clearly the direction of airflow in all the ducts and describe how a Mechanical Heat Recovery with Ventilation (MHRV) system works.

Note: While a plan of the room layout is required, it is not necessary to show the furniture.

(c) Discuss in detail two advantages and two disadvantages of Passive House construction.

SAMPLE EXAMINATION QUESTIONS

2011 Higher Level Question 10

(a) Using notes and *freehand sketches*, discuss in detail the importance of any two of the following in the design of a Passive House:

- foundations suitable for a Passive House
- airtight building envelope
- windows and glazing.

(b) A Mechanical Heat Recovery with Ventilation (MHRV) system for a Passive House is shown in the accompanying sketch. Using notes and *freehand sketches*, describe how such a system operates.

(c) Discuss in detail **two** advantages and two disadvantages of using a Mechanical Heat Recovery with Ventilation system in a domestic dwelling.

2009 Higher Level Question 10

(a) Using notes and *freehand sketches* discuss in detail the importance of any **two** of the following in the design of a passive solar house:

- insulated building envelope
- controlled air changes
- optimum benefit from passive solar gain.

(b) The accompanying sketch shows a terrace of houses with fully glazed façades. Using notes and *freehand sketches* show the preferred orientation of the houses to maximise passive solar gain. Justify your choice of orientation.

(c) Overheating may occur in summer as a result of glazing the full façade as shown. Using notes and *freehand sketches* show, for one of the houses, two design details that would help prevent such overheating.

2008 Higher Level Question 10

The following considerations are important in passive solar design:

- insulation;
- orientation and shade;
- energy efficient glazing and frames.

(a) Using notes and *freehand sketches*, discuss in detail the importance of **each** of the above in the design of a passive solar house.

(b) The accompanying sketch shows a dwelling house with an attached sunspace. Using notes and *freehand sketches*, propose a design layout for the rooms adjoining the sunspace that would maximise the passive solar heat gain from the sunspace.

(c) Give **two** reasons for the proposed room layout adjoining the sunspace.

CHAPTER 24

TECHNICAL DRAWINGS
AND
3D MODELS

STRIP FOUNDATION

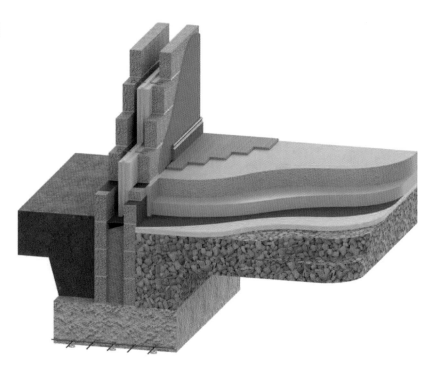

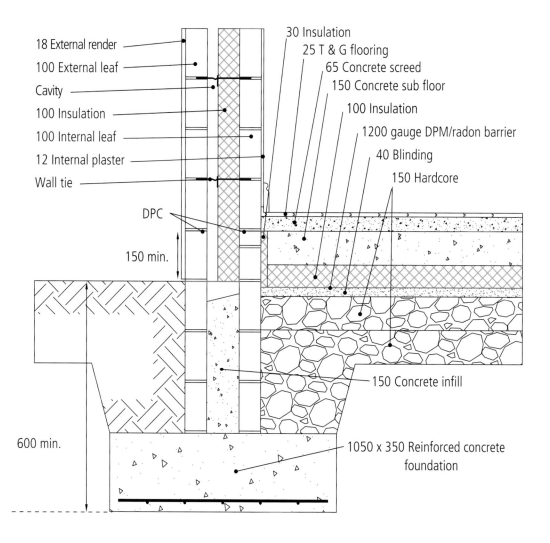

18 External render

100 External leaf

Cavity

100 Insulation

100 Internal leaf

12 Internal plaster

Wall tie

DPC

150 min.

600 min.

30 Insulation

25 T & G flooring

65 Concrete screed

150 Concrete sub floor

100 Insulation

1200 gauge DPM/radon barrier

40 Blinding

150 Hardcore

150 Concrete infill

1050 x 350 Reinforced concrete foundation

TIMBER FRAME FOUNDATION

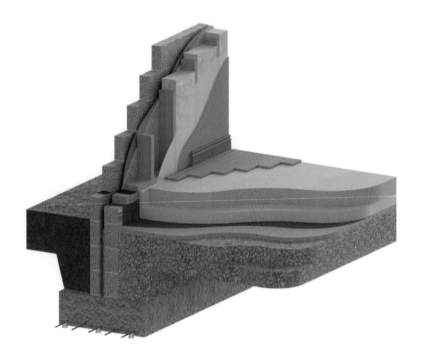

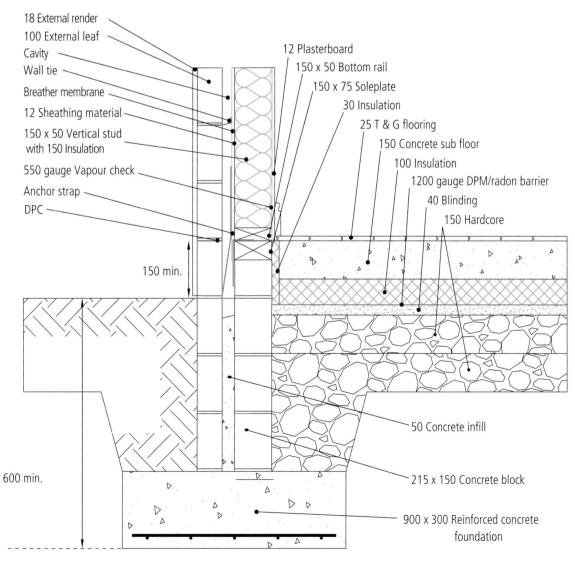

18 External render

100 External leaf

Cavity

Wall tie

Breather membrane

12 Sheathing material

150 x 50 Vertical stud with 150 Insulation

550 gauge Vapour check

Anchor strap

DPC

12 Plasterboard

150 x 50 Bottom rail

150 x 75 Soleplate

30 Insulation

25 T & G flooring

150 Concrete sub floor

100 Insulation

1200 gauge DPM/radon barrier

40 Blinding

150 Hardcore

150 min.

600 min.

50 Concrete infill

215 x 150 Concrete block

900 x 300 Reinforced concrete foundation

RAFT FOUNDATION

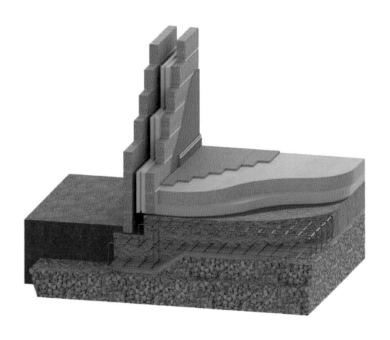

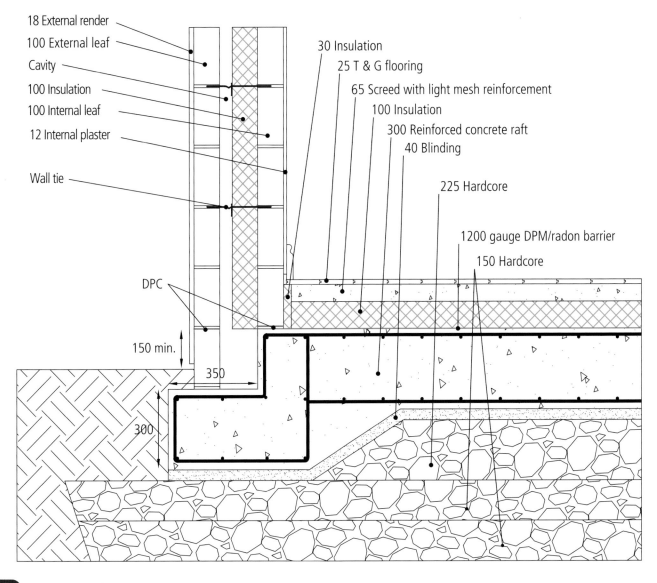

18 External render
100 External leaf
Cavity
100 Insulation
100 Internal leaf
12 Internal plaster

Wall tie

30 Insulation
25 T & G flooring
65 Screed with light mesh reinforcement
100 Insulation
300 Reinforced concrete raft
40 Blinding
225 Hardcore
1200 gauge DPM/radon barrier
150 Hardcore

DPC

150 min.

350

300

PILE FOUNDATION

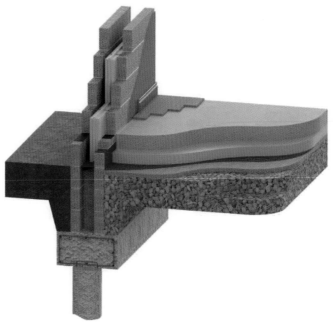

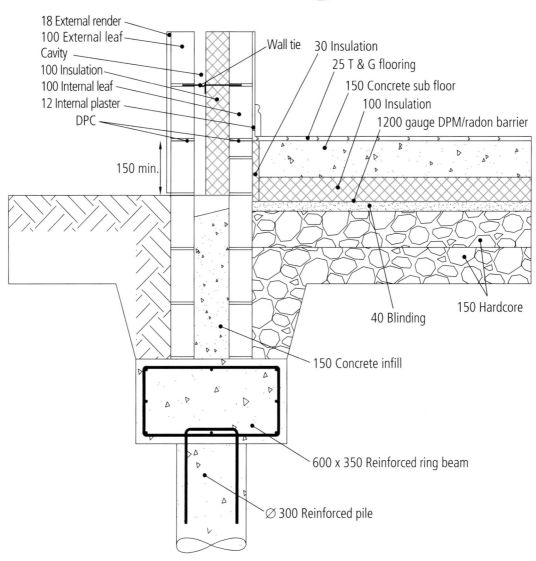

18 External render
100 External leaf
Cavity
100 Insulation
100 Internal leaf
12 Internal plaster
DPC

Wall tie
30 Insulation
25 T & G flooring
150 Concrete sub floor
100 Insulation
1200 gauge DPM/radon barrier

150 min.

150 Hardcore

40 Blinding

150 Concrete infill

600 x 350 Reinforced ring beam

Ø 300 Reinforced pile

PASSIVE CONCRETE STRIP FOUNDATION

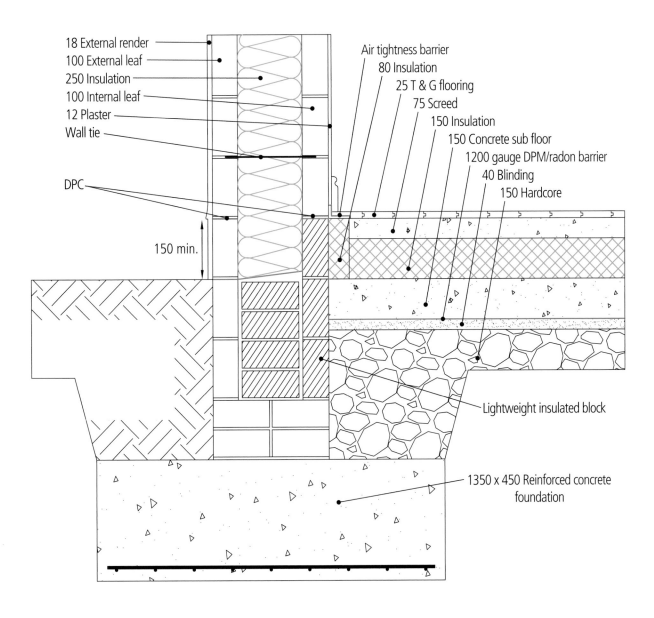

18 External render
100 External leaf
250 Insulation
100 Internal leaf
12 Plaster
Wall tie

DPC

150 min.

Air tightness barrier
80 Insulation
25 T & G flooring
75 Screed
150 Insulation
150 Concrete sub floor
1200 gauge DPM/radon barrier
40 Blinding
150 Hardcore

Lightweight insulated block

1350 x 450 Reinforced concrete foundation

PASSIVE TIMBER
FRAME FOUNDATION

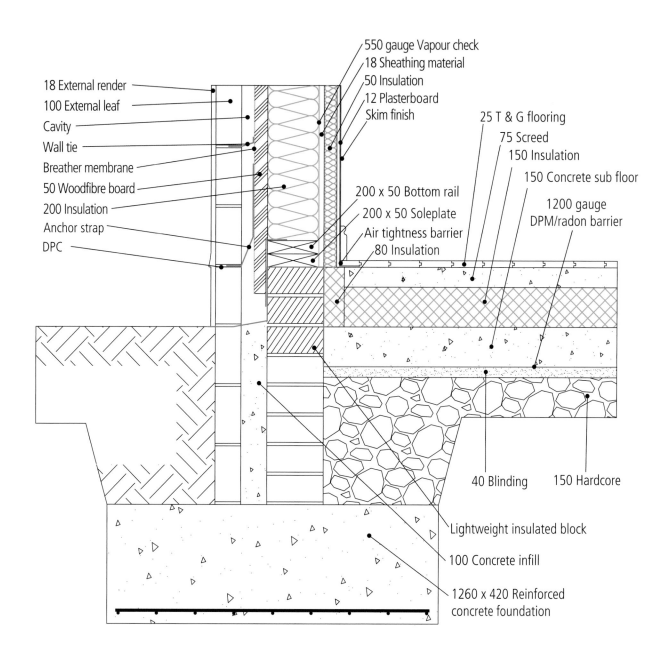

18 External render
100 External leaf
Cavity
Wall tie
Breather membrane
50 Woodfibre board
200 Insulation
Anchor strap
DPC

550 gauge Vapour check
18 Sheathing material
50 Insulation
12 Plasterboard
Skim finish

200 x 50 Bottom rail
200 x 50 Soleplate
Air tightness barrier
80 Insulation

25 T & G flooring
75 Screed
150 Insulation
150 Concrete sub floor
1200 gauge
DPM/radon barrier

40 Blinding   150 Hardcore

Lightweight insulated block

100 Concrete infill

1260 x 420 Reinforced
concrete foundation

SUSPENDED TIMBER FLOOR

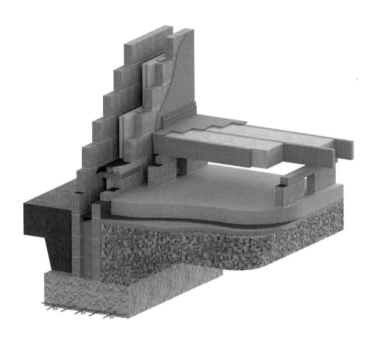

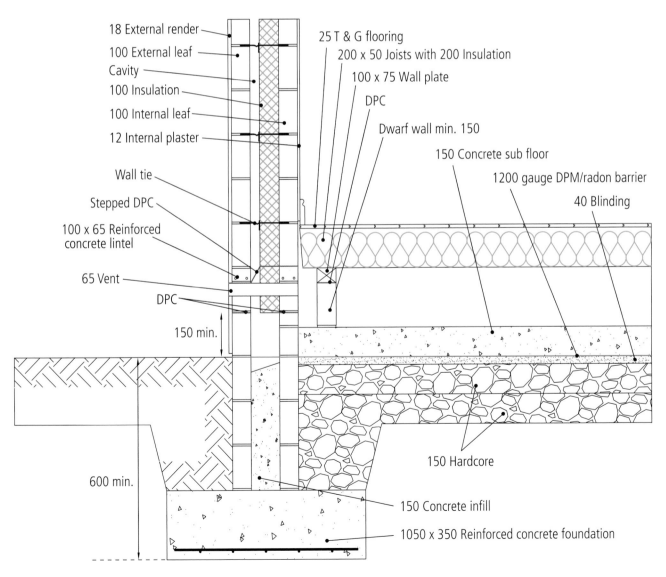

18 External render

100 External leaf

Cavity

100 Insulation

100 Internal leaf

12 Internal plaster

Wall tie

Stepped DPC

100 x 65 Reinforced concrete lintel

65 Vent

DPC

150 min.

600 min.

25 T & G flooring

200 x 50 Joists with 200 Insulation

100 x 75 Wall plate

DPC

Dwarf wall min. 150

150 Concrete sub floor

1200 gauge DPM/radon barrier

40 Blinding

150 Hardcore

150 Concrete infill

1050 x 350 Reinforced concrete foundation

SUSPENDED CONCRETE FLOOR

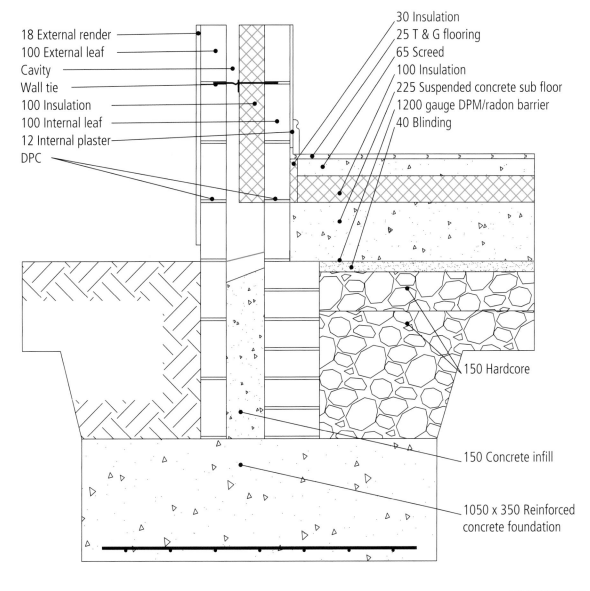

18 External render
100 External leaf
Cavity
Wall tie
100 Insulation
100 Internal leaf
12 Internal plaster
DPC

30 Insulation
25 T & G flooring
65 Screed
100 Insulation
225 Suspended concrete sub floor
1200 gauge DPM/radon barrier
40 Blinding

150 Hardcore

150 Concrete infill

1050 x 350 Reinforced concrete foundation

LINKED FLOOR

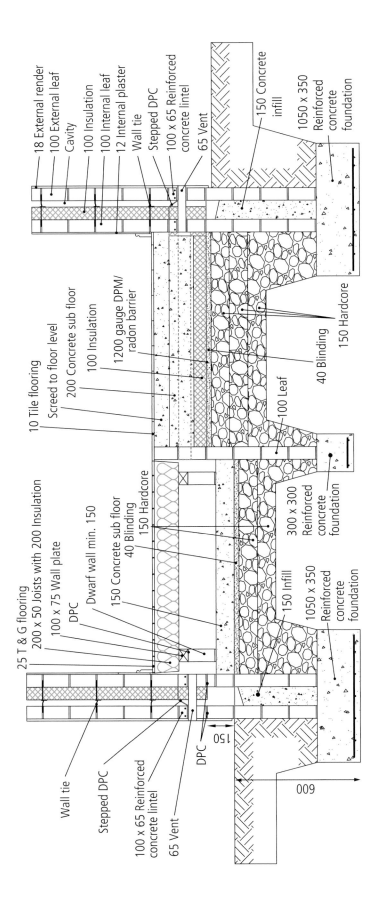

18 External render
100 External leaf
Cavity
100 Insulation
100 Internal leaf
12 Internal plaster
Wall tie
Stepped DPC
100 x 65 Reinforced concrete lintel
65 Vent
150 Concrete infill
1050 x 350 Reinforced concrete foundation

10 Tile flooring
Screed to floor level
200 Concrete sub floor
100 Insulation
1200 gauge DPM/radon barrier
40 Blinding
150 Hardcore
100 Leaf

25 T & G flooring
200 x 50 Joists with 200 Insulation
100 x 75 Wall plate
DPC
Dwarf wall min. 150
150 Concrete sub floor
40 Blinding
150 Hardcore
300 x 300 Reinforced concrete foundation
150 Infill
1050 x 350 Reinforced concrete foundation

Wall tie
Stepped DPC
100 x 65 Reinforced concrete lintel
65 Vent
DPC
150
600

UPPER FLOOR
TIMBER FRAME

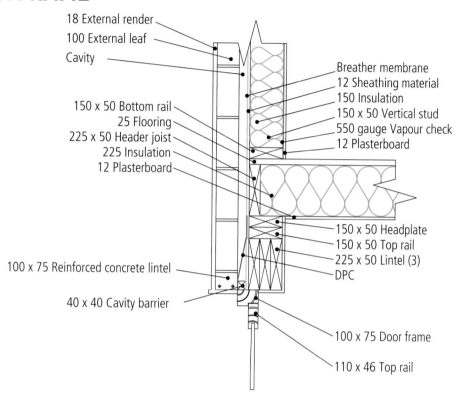

18 External render
100 External leaf
Cavity

Breather membrane
12 Sheathing material
150 Insulation
150 x 50 Vertical stud
550 gauge Vapour check
12 Plasterboard

150 x 50 Bottom rail
25 Flooring
225 x 50 Header joist
225 Insulation
12 Plasterboard

150 x 50 Headplate
150 x 50 Top rail
225 x 50 Lintel (3)
DPC

100 x 75 Reinforced concrete lintel

40 x 40 Cavity barrier

100 x 75 Door frame

110 x 46 Top rail

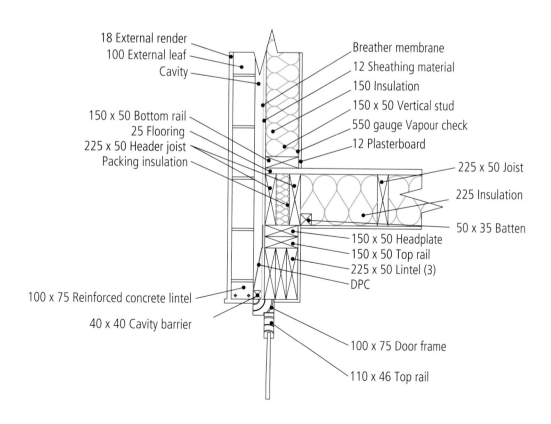

18 External render
100 External leaf
Cavity

Breather membrane
12 Sheathing material
150 Insulation
150 x 50 Vertical stud
550 gauge Vapour check
12 Plasterboard

150 x 50 Bottom rail
25 Flooring
225 x 50 Header joist
Packing insulation

225 x 50 Joist
225 Insulation
50 x 35 Batten

150 x 50 Headplate
150 x 50 Top rail
225 x 50 Lintel (3)
DPC

100 x 75 Reinforced concrete lintel

40 x 40 Cavity barrier

100 x 75 Door frame

110 x 46 Top rail

ROOFLIGHT

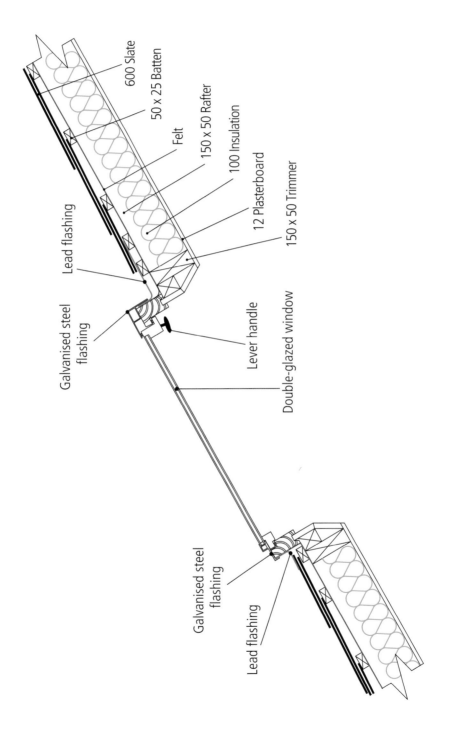

600 Slate

50 x 25 Batten

Felt

150 x 50 Rafter

100 Insulation

12 Plasterboard

150 x 50 Trimmer

Lead flashing

Galvanised steel flashing

Lever handle

Double-glazed window

Galvanised steel flashing

Lead flashing

CONCRETE WINDOW

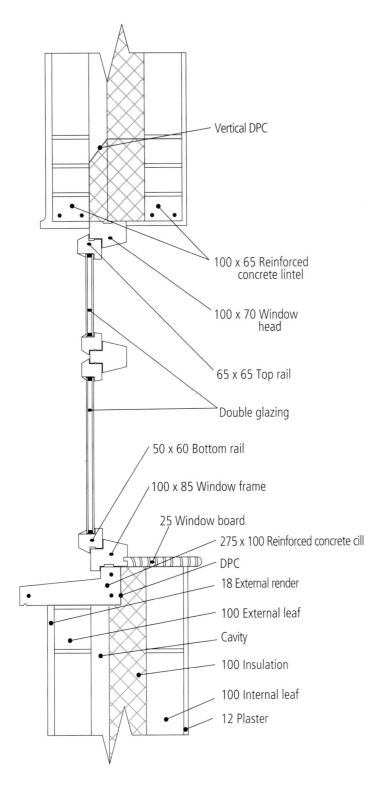

Vertical DPC

100 x 65 Reinforced concrete lintel

100 x 70 Window head

65 x 65 Top rail

Double glazing

50 x 60 Bottom rail

100 x 85 Window frame

25 Window board

275 x 100 Reinforced concrete cill

DPC

18 External render

100 External leaf

Cavity

100 Insulation

100 Internal leaf

12 Plaster

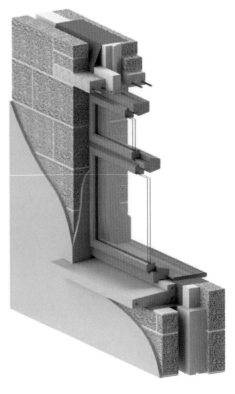

TIMBER FRAME WINDOW

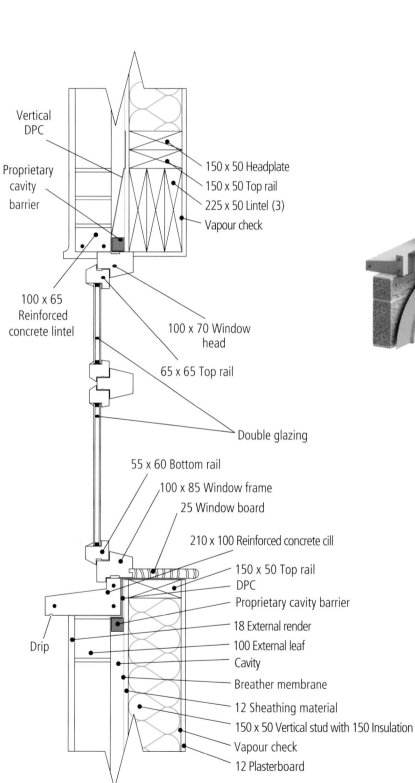
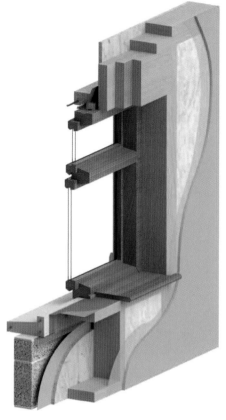

Vertical DPC

Proprietary cavity barrier

150 x 50 Headplate

150 x 50 Top rail

225 x 50 Lintel (3)

Vapour check

100 x 65 Reinforced concrete lintel

100 x 70 Window head

65 x 65 Top rail

Double glazing

55 x 60 Bottom rail

100 x 85 Window frame

25 Window board

210 x 100 Reinforced concrete cill

150 x 50 Top rail

DPC

Proprietary cavity barrier

18 External render

100 External leaf

Cavity

Breather membrane

12 Sheathing material

150 x 50 Vertical stud with 150 Insulation

Vapour check

12 Plasterboard

Drip

STORM-PROOF TRIPLE-GLAZED TIMBER CASEMENT WINDOW

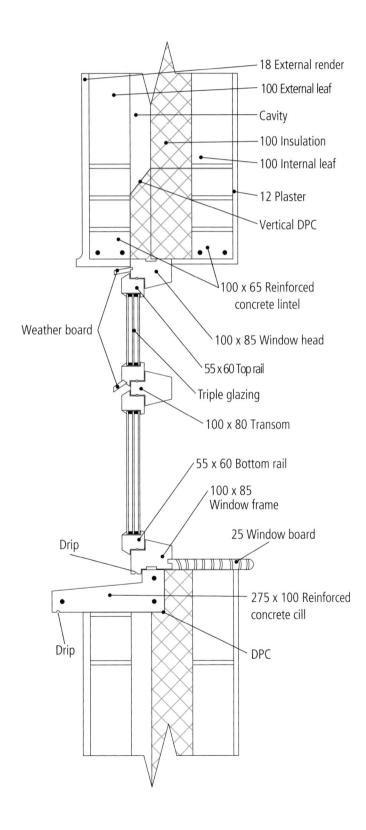

18 External render

100 External leaf

Cavity

100 Insulation

100 Internal leaf

12 Plaster

Vertical DPC

100 x 65 Reinforced concrete lintel

100 x 85 Window head

55 x 60 Top rail

Weather board

Triple glazing

100 x 80 Transom

55 x 60 Bottom rail

100 x 85 Window frame

25 Window board

Drip

275 x 100 Reinforced concrete cill

Drip

DPC

PASSIVE CONCRETE BLOCK WINDOW

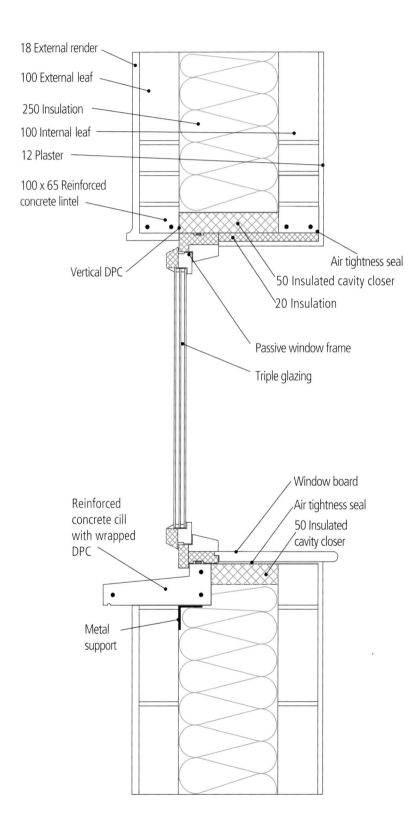

18 External render

100 External leaf

250 Insulation

100 Internal leaf

12 Plaster

100 x 65 Reinforced
concrete lintel

Vertical DPC

Air tightness seal

50 Insulated cavity closer

20 Insulation

Passive window frame

Triple glazing

Reinforced
concrete cill
with wrapped
DPC

Window board

Air tightness seal

50 Insulated
cavity closer

Metal
support

PASSIVE TIMBER FRAME WINDOW

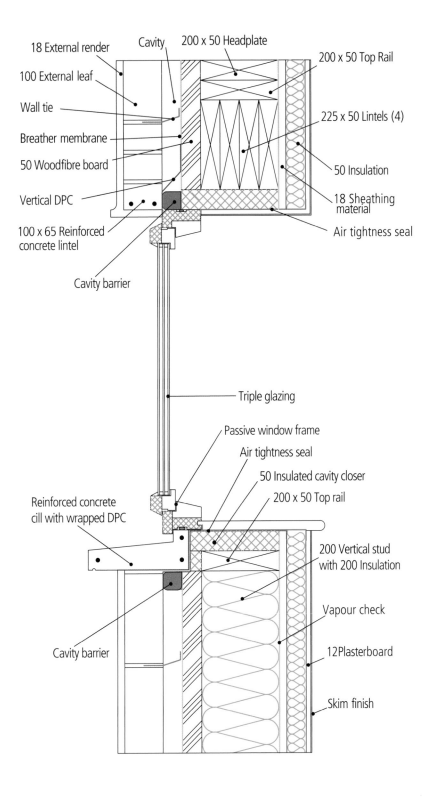

18 External render

Cavity

200 x 50 Headplate

200 x 50 Top Rail

100 External leaf

Wall tie

225 x 50 Lintels (4)

Breather membrane

50 Woodfibre board

50 Insulation

Vertical DPC

18 Sheathing material

100 x 65 Reinforced concrete lintel

Air tightness seal

Cavity barrier

Triple glazing

Passive window frame

Air tightness seal

50 Insulated cavity closer

200 x 50 Top rail

Reinforced concrete cill with wrapped DPC

200 Vertical stud with 200 Insulation

Vapour check

12 Plasterboard

Cavity barrier

Skim finish

THRESHOLD DETAIL OF A DOOR

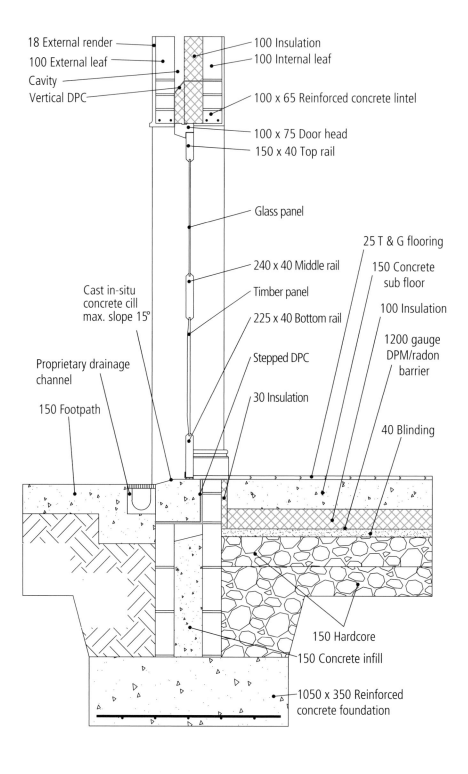

18 External render

100 External leaf

Cavity

Vertical DPC

100 Insulation

100 Internal leaf

100 x 65 Reinforced concrete lintel

100 x 75 Door head

150 x 40 Top rail

Glass panel

25 T & G flooring

150 Concrete sub floor

240 x 40 Middle rail

100 Insulation

Cast in-situ concrete cill max. slope 15°

Timber panel

225 x 40 Bottom rail

1200 gauge DPM/radon barrier

Proprietary drainage channel

Stepped DPC

150 Footpath

30 Insulation

40 Blinding

150 Hardcore

150 Concrete infill

1050 x 350 Reinforced concrete foundation

RIDGE DETAIL

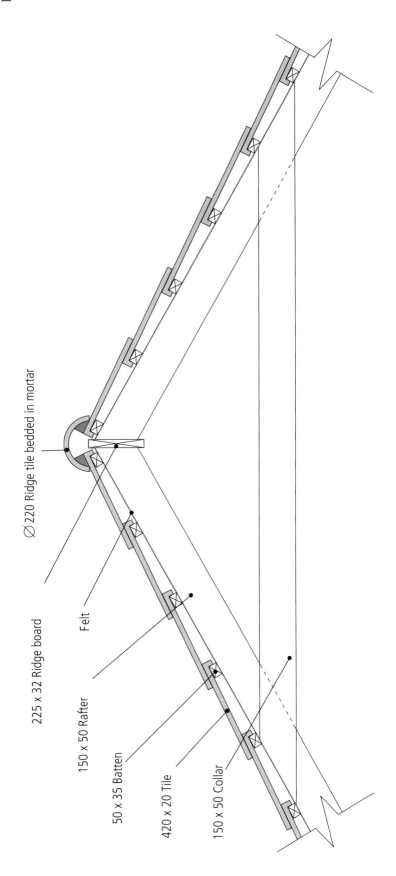

⌀ 220 Ridge tile bedded in mortar

225 x 32 Ridge board

Felt

150 x 50 Rafter

50 x 35 Batten

420 x 20 Tile

150 x 50 Collar

CONCRETE BLOCK
EAVES DETAIL

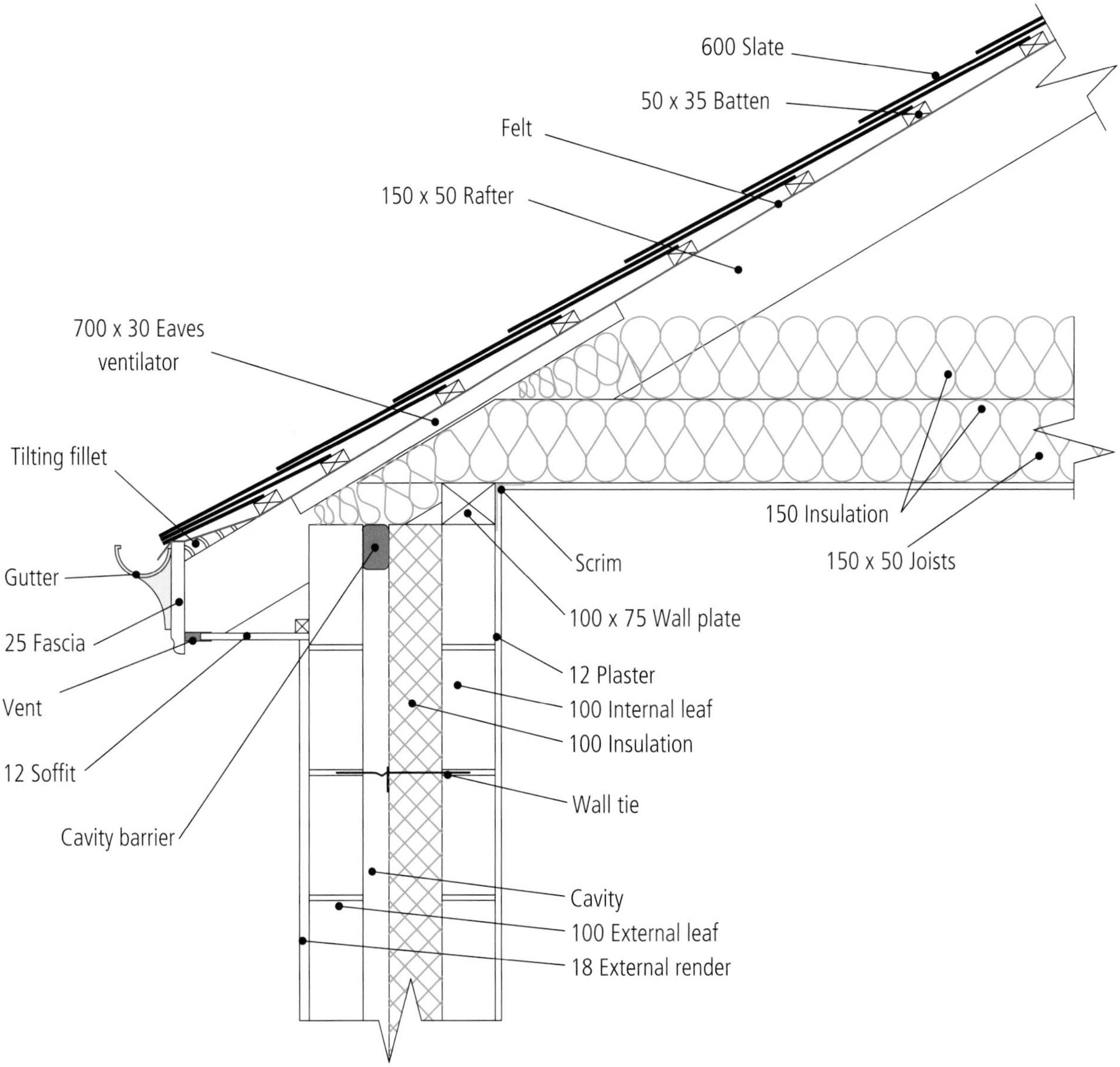

- 600 Slate
- 50 x 35 Batten
- Felt
- 150 x 50 Rafter
- 700 x 30 Eaves ventilator
- Tilting fillet
- Gutter
- 25 Fascia
- Vent
- 12 Soffit
- Cavity barrier
- Scrim
- 100 x 75 Wall plate
- 12 Plaster
- 100 Internal leaf
- 100 Insulation
- Wall tie
- Cavity
- 100 External leaf
- 18 External render
- 150 Insulation
- 150 x 50 Joists

TIMBER FRAME EAVES DETAIL

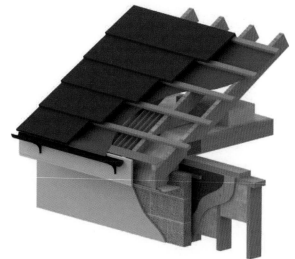

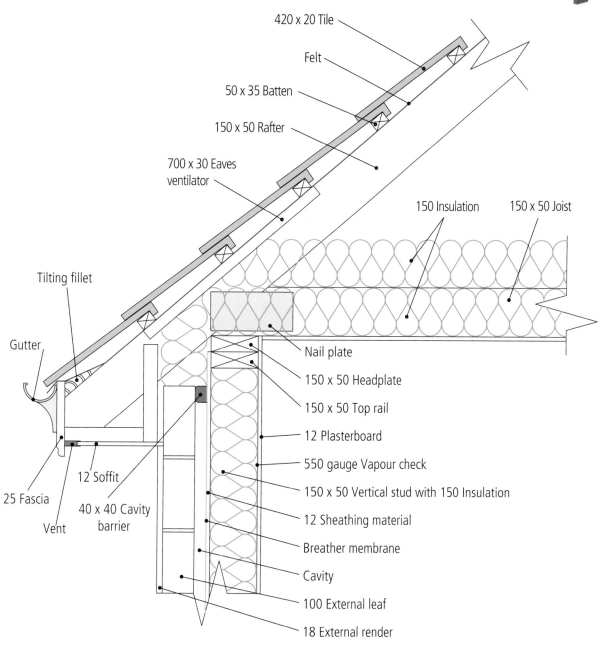

420 x 20 Tile

Felt

50 x 35 Batten

150 x 50 Rafter

700 x 30 Eaves
ventilator

150 Insulation

150 x 50 Joist

Tilting fillet

Gutter

Nail plate

150 x 50 Headplate

150 x 50 Top rail

12 Plasterboard

550 gauge Vapour check

150 x 50 Vertical stud with 150 Insulation

12 Sheathing material

12 Soffit

Breather membrane

25 Fascia

40 x 40 Cavity
barrier

Cavity

Vent

100 External leaf

18 External render

LEAN-TO ROOF WITH CONCRETE EAVES

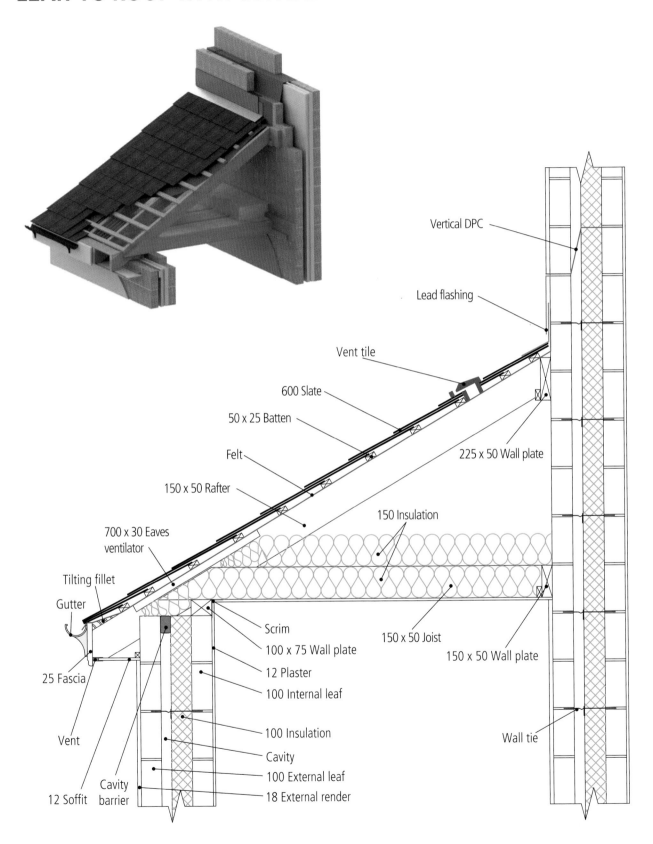

Vertical DPC

Lead flashing

Vent tile

600 Slate

50 x 25 Batten

225 x 50 Wall plate

Felt

150 x 50 Rafter

150 Insulation

700 x 30 Eaves ventilator

Tilting fillet

Gutter

Scrim

100 x 75 Wall plate

150 x 50 Joist

25 Fascia

12 Plaster

100 Internal leaf

150 x 50 Wall plate

Vent

100 Insulation

Cavity

Wall tie

Cavity barrier

100 External leaf

12 Soffit

18 External render

CONCRETE EAVES DETAIL ALTERNATIVE WITH CAVITY CLOSER BLOCK

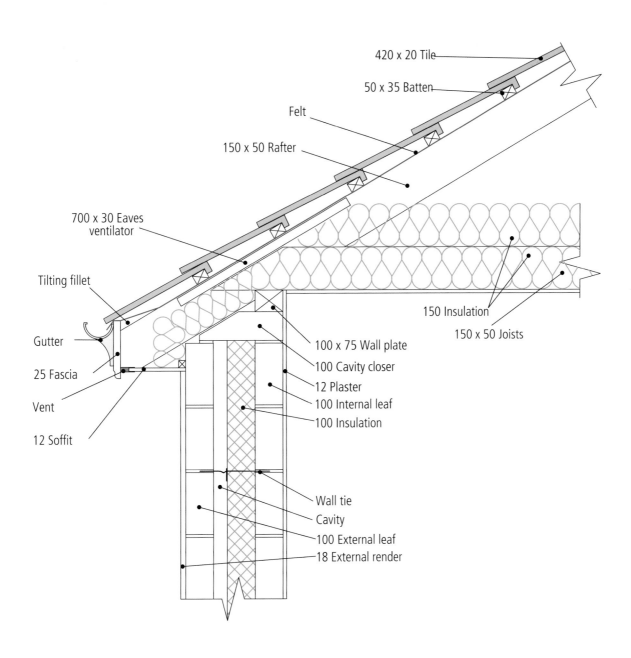

420 x 20 Tile

50 x 35 Batten

Felt

150 x 50 Rafter

700 x 30 Eaves ventilator

Tilting fillet

Gutter

25 Fascia

Vent

12 Soffit

150 Insulation

150 x 50 Joists

100 x 75 Wall plate

100 Cavity closer

12 Plaster

100 Internal leaf

100 Insulation

Wall tie

Cavity

100 External leaf

18 External render

PASSIVE CONCRETE
BLOCK EAVES DETAIL

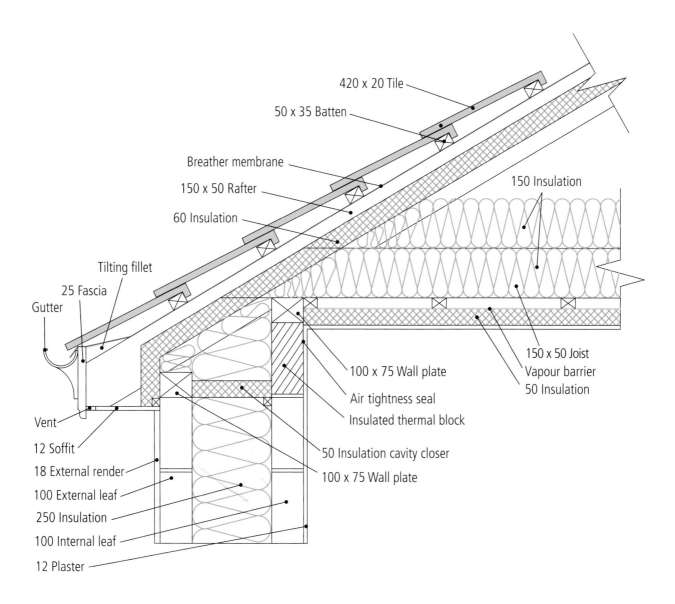

420 x 20 Tile

50 x 35 Batten

Breather membrane

150 x 50 Rafter

60 Insulation

150 Insulation

Tilting fillet

25 Fascia

Gutter

100 x 75 Wall plate

Air tightness seal

Insulated thermal block

150 x 50 Joist

Vapour barrier

50 Insulation

Vent

12 Soffit

18 External render

100 External leaf

250 Insulation

100 Internal leaf

12 Plaster

50 Insulation cavity closer

100 x 75 Wall plate

PASSIVE TIMBER FRAME
EAVES DETAIL

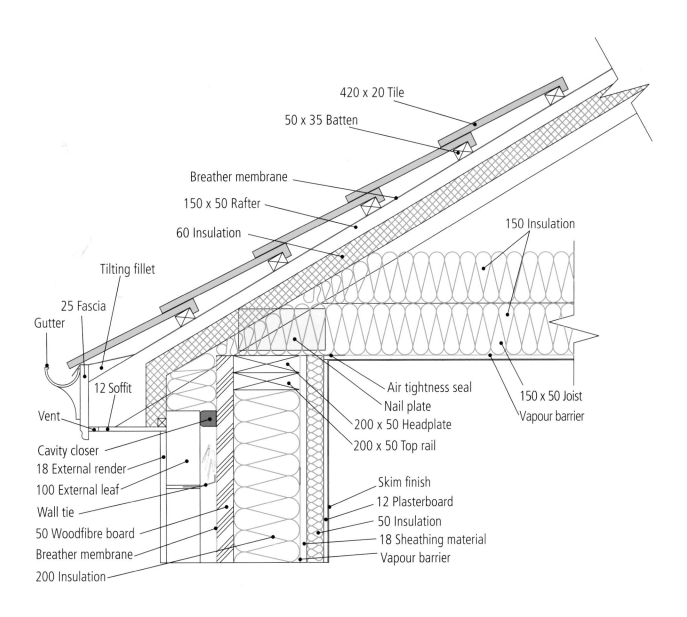

420 x 20 Tile

50 x 35 Batten

Breather membrane

150 x 50 Rafter

60 Insulation

Tilting fillet

25 Fascia

Gutter

12 Soffit

Vent

Cavity closer

18 External render

100 External leaf

Wall tie

50 Woodfibre board

Breather membrane

200 Insulation

150 Insulation

Air tightness seal

Nail plate

200 x 50 Headplate

200 x 50 Top rail

150 x 50 Joist

Vapour barrier

Skim finish

12 Plasterboard

50 Insulation

18 Sheathing material

Vapour barrier

FLAT ROOFS

COLD DECK

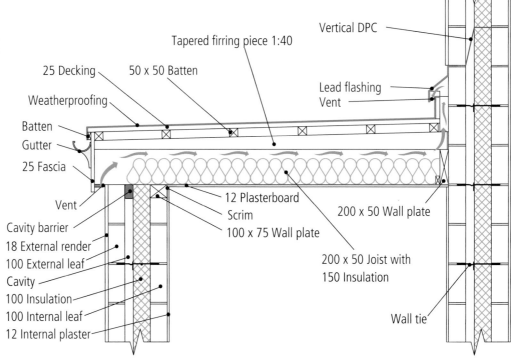

Tapered firring piece 1:40
Vertical DPC
25 Decking
50 x 50 Batten
Weatherproofing
Lead flashing
Vent
Batten
Gutter
25 Fascia
Vent
12 Plasterboard
Scrim
200 x 50 Wall plate
100 x 75 Wall plate
Cavity barrier
18 External render
100 External leaf
Cavity
200 x 50 Joist with
100 Insulation
150 Insulation
100 Internal leaf
12 Internal plaster
Wall tie

WARM DECK

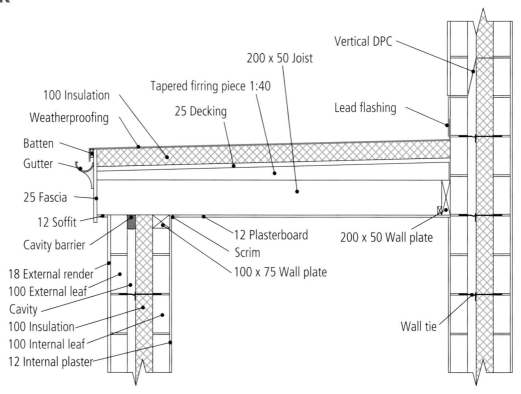

200 x 50 Joist
Vertical DPC
100 Insulation
Tapered firring piece 1:40
Weatherproofing
25 Decking
Lead flashing
Batten
Gutter
25 Fascia
12 Soffit
12 Plasterboard
Scrim
200 x 50 Wall plate
Cavity barrier
100 x 75 Wall plate
18 External render
100 External leaf
Cavity
100 Insulation
100 Internal leaf
12 Internal plaster
Wall tie

FULL VERTICAL SECTION
CONCRETE BLOCK

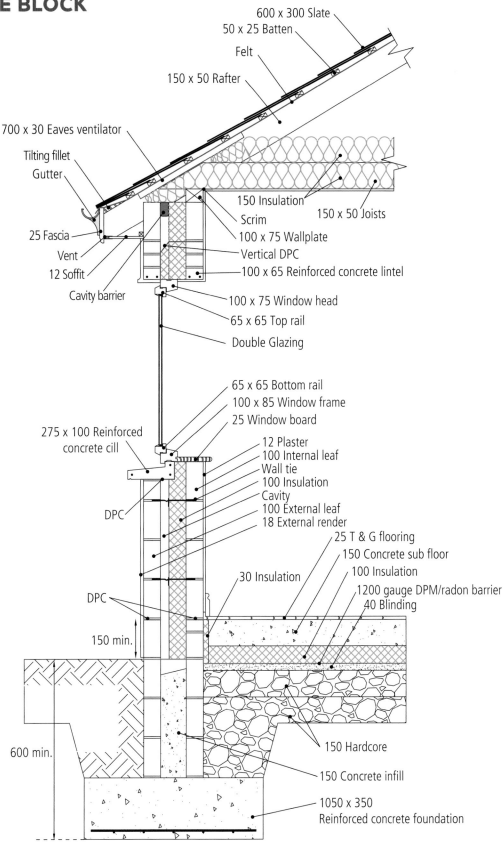

600 x 300 Slate
50 x 25 Batten
Felt
150 x 50 Rafter

700 x 30 Eaves ventilator

Tilting fillet
Gutter

150 Insulation
Scrim
150 x 50 Joists
100 x 75 Wallplate
Vertical DPC

25 Fascia
Vent
12 Soffit
Cavity barrier

100 x 65 Reinforced concrete lintel
100 x 75 Window head
65 x 65 Top rail
Double Glazing

65 x 65 Bottom rail
100 x 85 Window frame
25 Window board

275 x 100 Reinforced
concrete cill

12 Plaster
100 Internal leaf
Wall tie
100 Insulation
Cavity
100 External leaf
18 External render

DPC

25 T & G flooring
150 Concrete sub floor
100 Insulation
1200 gauge DPM/radon barrier
40 Blinding

30 Insulation

DPC

150 min.

150 Hardcore

600 min.

150 Concrete infill

1050 x 350
Reinforced concrete foundation

FULL VERTICAL SECTION
TIMBER FRAME

420 x 20 Tile

50 x 35 Batten

Felt

150 x 50 Rafter

700 x 30 Eaves ventilator

150 Insulation

Tilting fillet

Nail plate

150 x 50 Joists

150 x 50 Head plate

Gutter

150 x 50 Top rail

25 Fascia

150 x 50 Headplate

Vent

Vertical DPC

12 Soffit

225 x 50 Lintel (3)

Cavity barrier

100 x 70 Window head

65 x 65 Top rail

Double glazing

65 x 65 Bottom rail

210 x 100 Reinforced concrete cill

100 x 80 Window frame

25 Window board

150 x 50 Top rail

12 Plasterboard

550 gauge Vapour check

150 x 50 Vertical stud with 150 Insulation

12 Sheathing material

Breather membrane

Cavity barrier

Cavity

Wall tie

100 External leaf

18 External render

150 x 50 Bottom rail

150 x 75 Soleplate

30 Insulation

25 T & G flooring

150 Concrete sub floor

100 Insulation

40 Blinding

Anchor strap

DPC

150 min.

1200 gauge DPM/radon barrier

150 Hardcore

600 min.

50 Concrete infill

900 x 300 Reinforced concrete foundation

FULL VERTICAL SECTION PASSIVE CONCRETE BLOCK

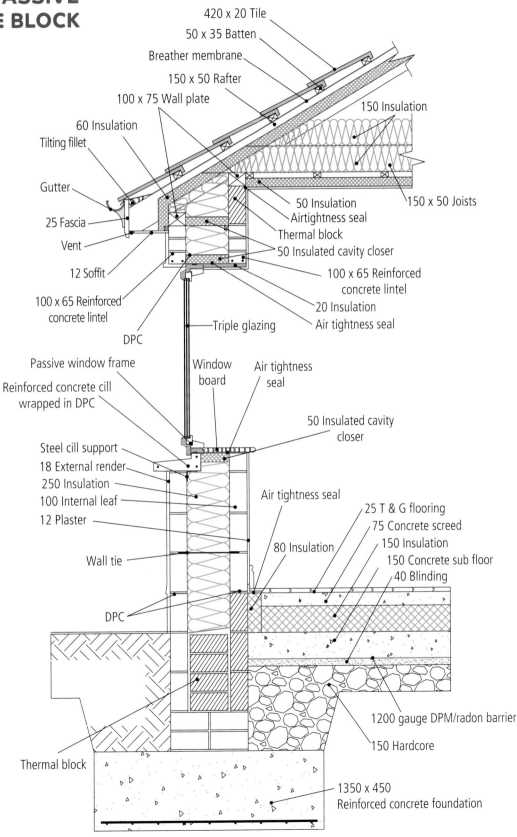

420 x 20 Tile

50 x 35 Batten

Breather membrane

150 x 50 Rafter

100 x 75 Wall plate

150 Insulation

60 Insulation

Tilting fillet

150 x 50 Joists

50 Insulation

Airtightness seal

Thermal block

50 Insulated cavity closer

100 x 65 Reinforced concrete lintel

20 Insulation

Air tightness seal

Gutter

25 Fascia

Vent

12 Soffit

100 x 65 Reinforced concrete lintel

DPC

Triple glazing

Passive window frame

Reinforced concrete cill wrapped in DPC

Window board

Air tightness seal

50 Insulated cavity closer

Steel cill support

18 External render

250 Insulation

100 Internal leaf

12 Plaster

Air tightness seal

25 T & G flooring

75 Concrete screed

150 Insulation

150 Concrete sub floor

40 Blinding

80 Insulation

Wall tie

DPC

1200 gauge DPM/radon barrier

150 Hardcore

Thermal block

1350 x 450 Reinforced concrete foundation

FULL VERTICAL SECTION PASSIVE TIMBER FRAME

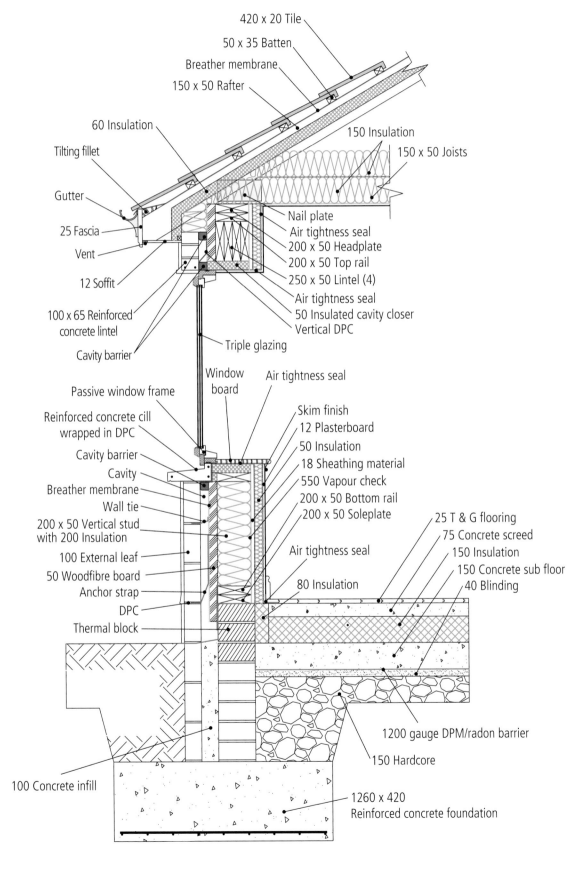

420 x 20 Tile

50 x 35 Batten

Breather membrane

150 x 50 Rafter

60 Insulation

Tilting fillet

Gutter

25 Fascia

Vent

12 Soffit

100 x 65 Reinforced concrete lintel

Cavity barrier

Passive window frame

Reinforced concrete cill wrapped in DPC

Cavity barrier

Cavity

Breather membrane

Wall tie

200 x 50 Vertical stud with 200 Insulation

100 External leaf

50 Woodfibre board

Anchor strap

DPC

Thermal block

100 Concrete infill

150 Insulation

150 x 50 Joists

Nail plate

Air tightness seal

200 x 50 Headplate

200 x 50 Top rail

250 x 50 Lintel (4)

Air tightness seal

50 Insulated cavity closer

Vertical DPC

Triple glazing

Window board

Air tightness seal

Skim finish

12 Plasterboard

50 Insulation

18 Sheathing material

550 Vapour check

200 x 50 Bottom rail

200 x 50 Soleplate

Air tightness seal

80 Insulation

25 T & G flooring

75 Concrete screed

150 Insulation

150 Concrete sub floor

40 Blinding

1200 gauge DPM/radon barrier

150 Hardcore

1260 x 420 Reinforced concrete foundation

STAIRS

TOP OF CLOSED STRING STAIRS WITH LANDING

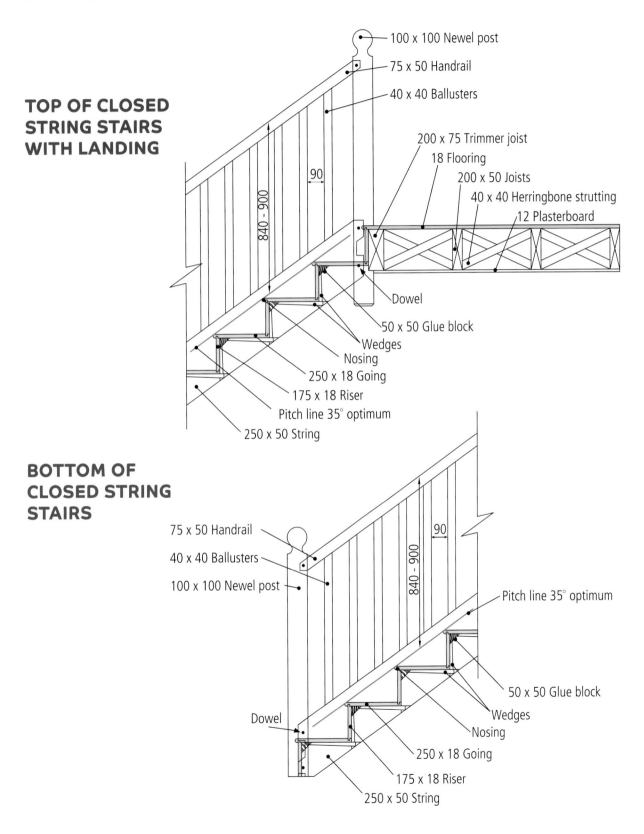

100 x 100 Newel post

75 x 50 Handrail

40 x 40 Ballusters

200 x 75 Trimmer joist

18 Flooring

200 x 50 Joists

40 x 40 Herringbone strutting

12 Plasterboard

90

840 - 900

Dowel

50 x 50 Glue block

Wedges

Nosing

250 x 18 Going

175 x 18 Riser

Pitch line 35° optimum

250 x 50 String

BOTTOM OF CLOSED STRING STAIRS

75 x 50 Handrail

40 x 40 Ballusters

100 x 100 Newel post

90

840 - 900

Pitch line 35° optimum

50 x 50 Glue block

Wedges

Nosing

Dowel

250 x 18 Going

175 x 18 Riser

250 x 50 String

CHIMNEY

SECTIONAL VIEW OF CHIMNEY STACK THROUGH A ROOF

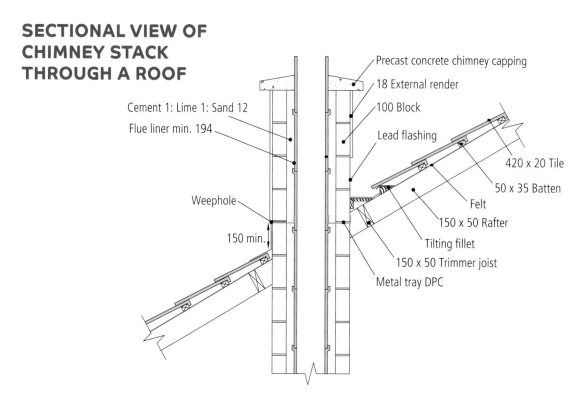

Cement 1: Lime 1: Sand 12
Flue liner min. 194
Weephole
150 min.

Precast concrete chimney capping
18 External render
100 Block
Lead flashing
420 x 20 Tile
50 x 35 Batten
Felt
150 x 50 Rafter
Tilting fillet
150 x 50 Trimmer joist
Metal tray DPC

FIREPLACE SPECIFICATION

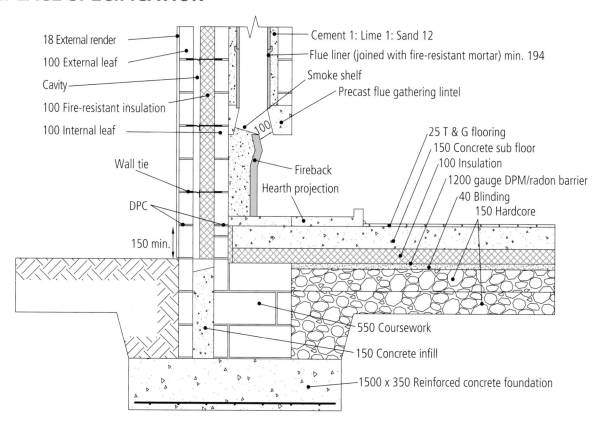

18 External render
100 External leaf
Cavity
100 Fire-resistant insulation
100 Internal leaf
Wall tie
DPC
150 min.

Cement 1: Lime 1: Sand 12
Flue liner (joined with fire-resistant mortar) min. 194
Smoke shelf
Precast flue gathering lintel
Fireback
Hearth projection
25 T & G flooring
150 Concrete sub floor
100 Insulation
1200 gauge DPM/radon barrier
40 Blinding
150 Hardcore
550 Coursework
150 Concrete infill
1500 x 350 Reinforced concrete foundation

WATER SUPPLY

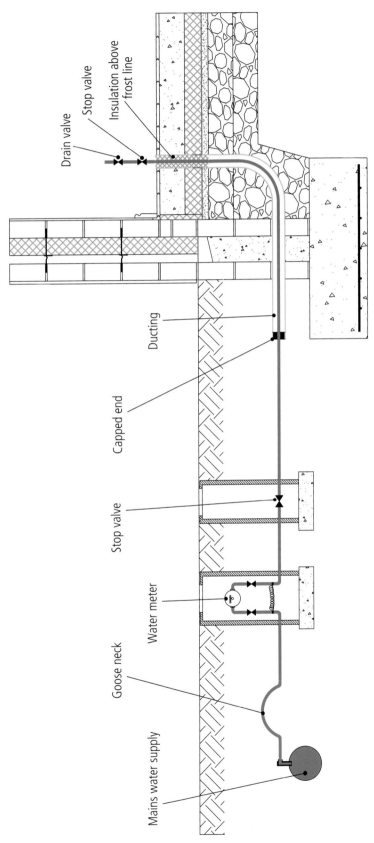

DIRECT COLD WATER

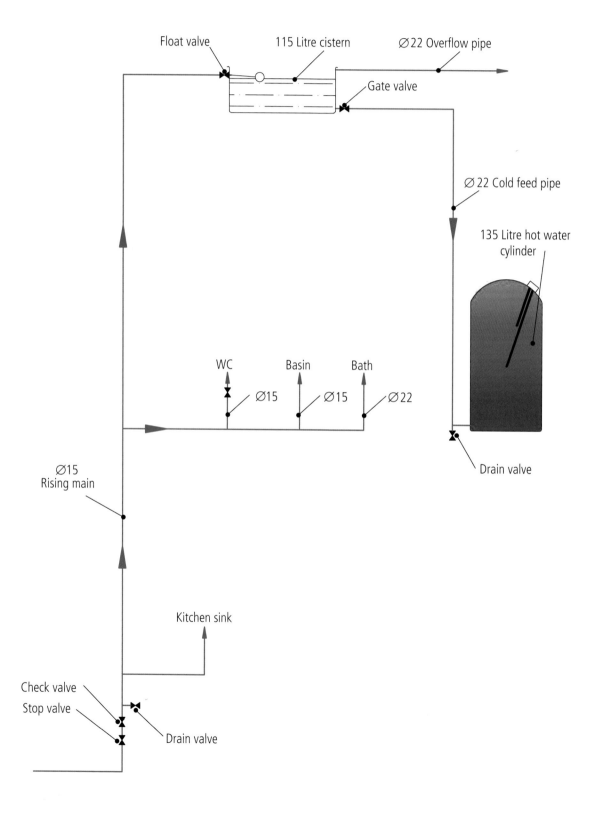

INDIRECT COLD WATER

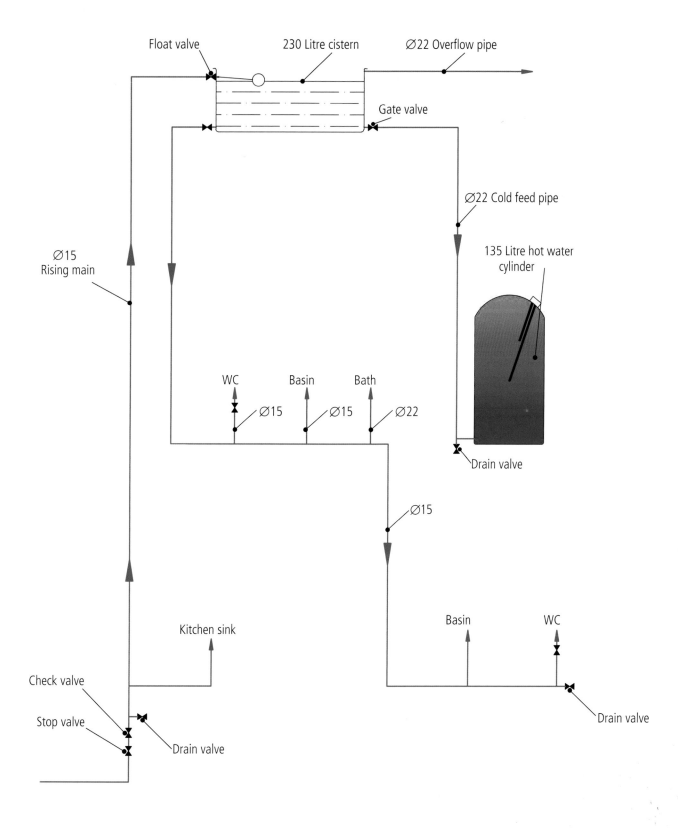

Float valve
230 Litre cistern
Ø22 Overflow pipe
Gate valve
Ø22 Cold feed pipe
135 Litre hot water cylinder
Ø15 Rising main
WC
Basin
Bath
Ø15
Ø15
Ø22
Drain valve
Ø15
Kitchen sink
Basin
WC
Check valve
Drain valve
Stop valve
Drain valve

DIRECT HOT WATER

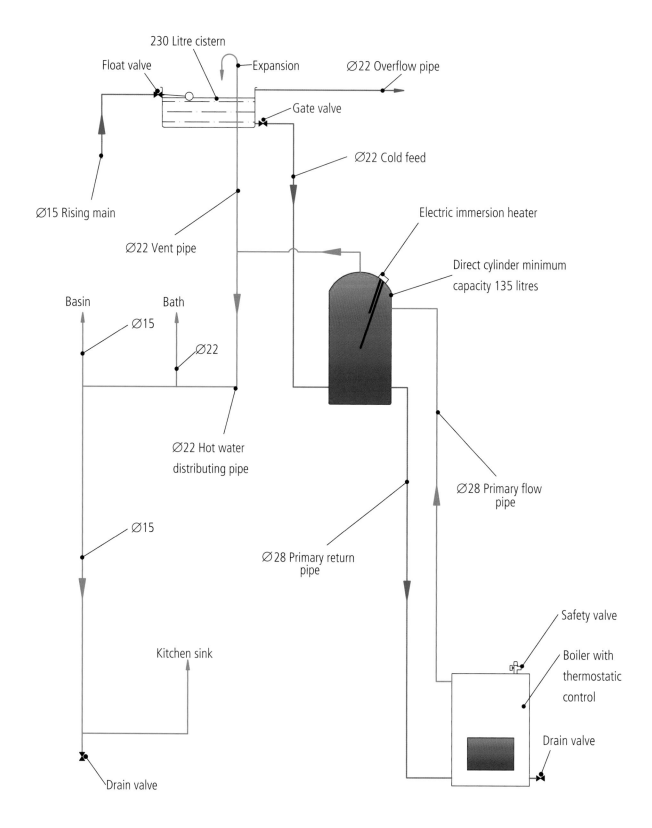

230 Litre cistern

Float valve

Expansion

Ø22 Overflow pipe

Gate valve

Ø22 Cold feed

Electric immersion heater

Direct cylinder minimum capacity 135 litres

Ø15 Rising main

Ø22 Vent pipe

Basin

Bath

Ø15

Ø22

Ø22 Hot water distributing pipe

Ø28 Primary flow pipe

Ø15

Ø28 Primary return pipe

Safety valve

Boiler with thermostatic control

Kitchen sink

Drain valve

Drain valve

INDIRECT HOT WATER

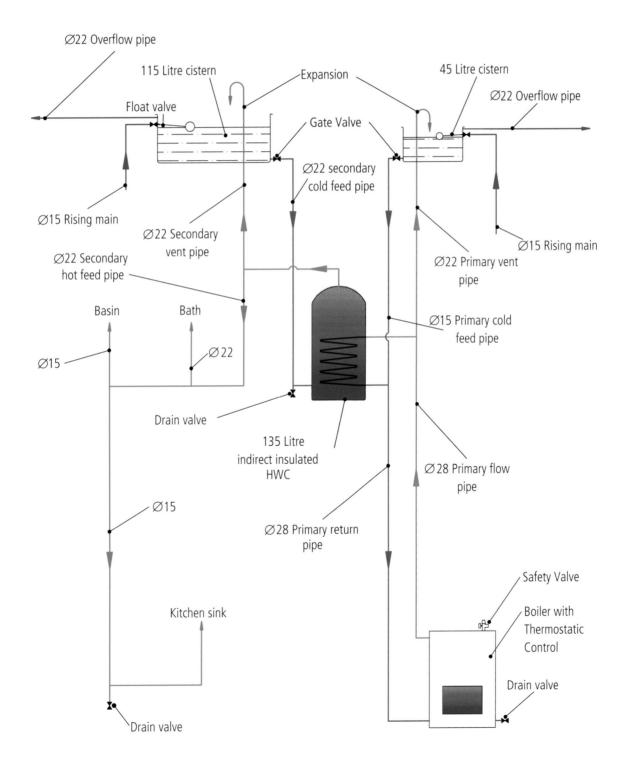

Ø22 Overflow pipe

115 Litre cistern

Expansion

45 Litre cistern

Ø22 Overflow pipe

Float valve

Gate Valve

Ø22 secondary
cold feed pipe

Ø15 Rising main

Ø22 Secondary
vent pipe

Ø15 Rising main

Ø22 Secondary
hot feed pipe

Ø22 Primary vent
pipe

Basin

Bath

Ø15 Primary cold
feed pipe

Ø15

Ø22

Drain valve

135 Litre
indirect insulated
HWC

Ø28 Primary flow
pipe

Ø15

Ø28 Primary return
pipe

Kitchen sink

Safety Valve

Boiler with
Thermostatic
Control

Drain valve

Drain valve

ONE & TWO PIPE RADIATORS

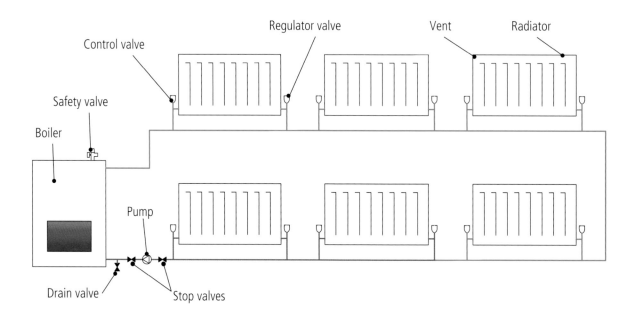

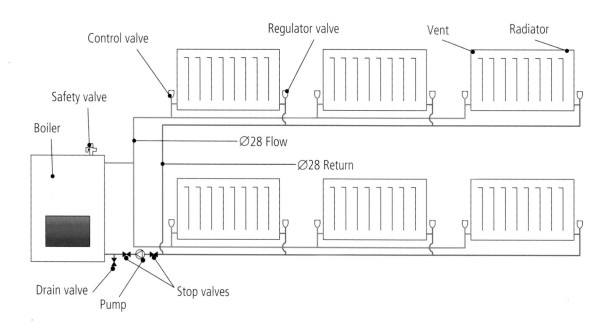

NDIRECT HOT WATER & HEATING

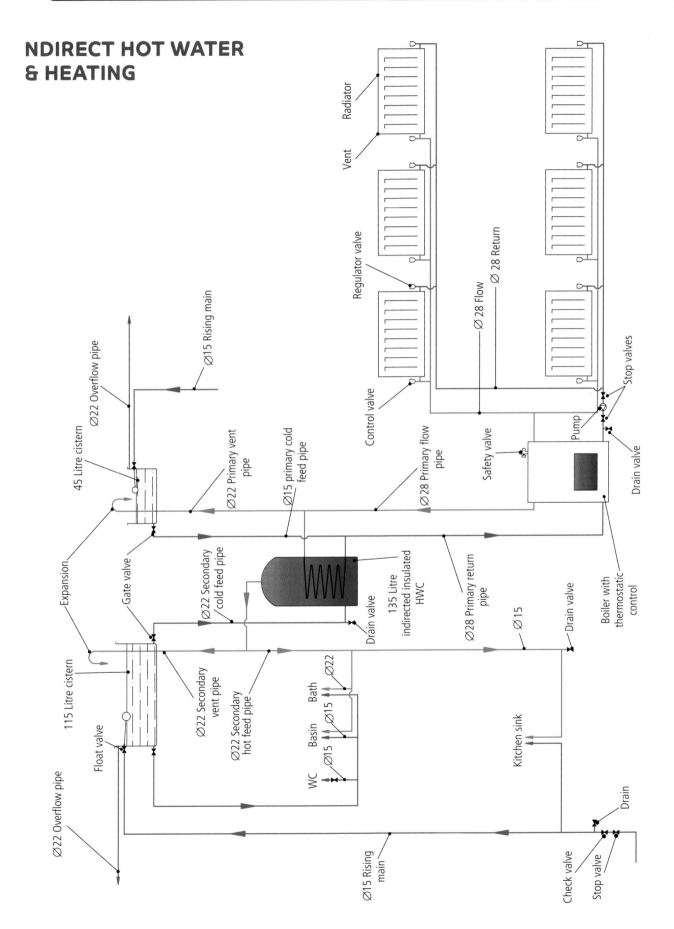

UNDERFLOOR HEATING

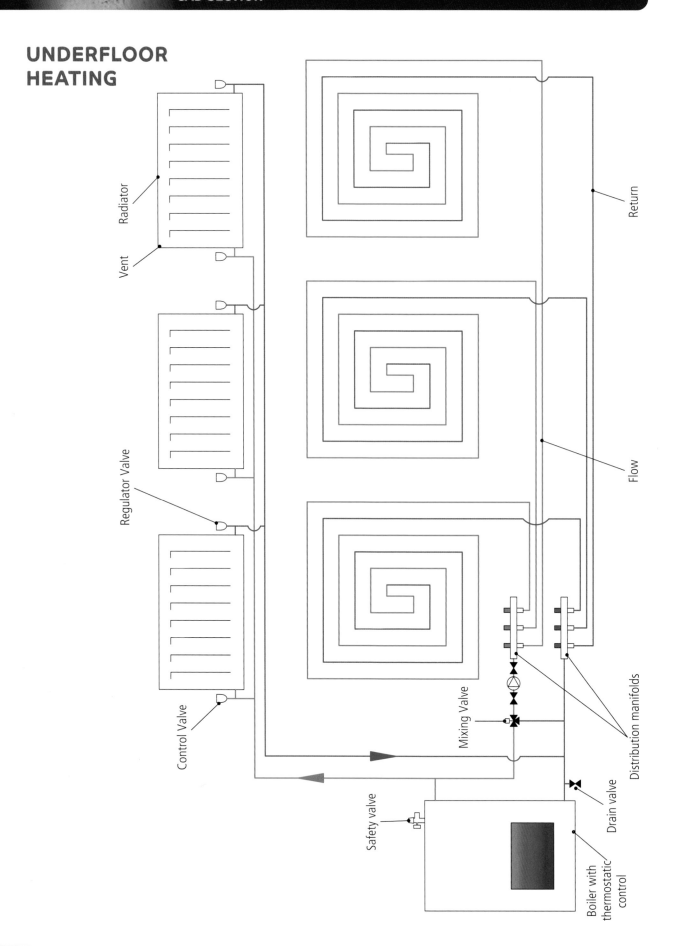

Radiator

Vent

Regulator Valve

Control Valve

Safety valve

Mixing Valve

Drain valve

Boiler with thermostatic control

Distribution manifolds

Flow

Return

UNDERFLOOR HEATING UNVENTED

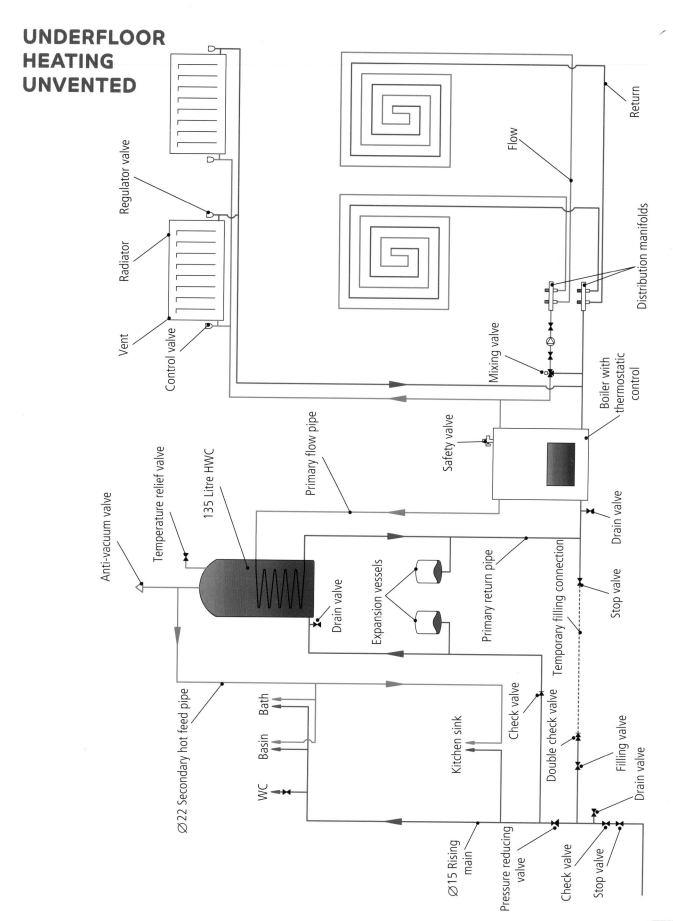

Regulator valve

Radiator

Vent

Control valve

Return

Flow

Distribution manifolds

Mixing valve

Boiler with thermostatic control

Safety valve

Primary flow pipe

Anti-vacuum valve

Temperature relief valve

135 Litre HWC

Drain valve

Expansion vessels

Primary return pipe

Temporary filling connection

Drain valve

Stop valve

Ø22 Secondary hot feed pipe

Bath

Basin

WC

Kitchen sink

Check valve

Double check valve

Filling valve

Drain valve

Ø15 Rising main

Pressure reducing valve

Check valve

Stop valve

SOLAR HOT WATER

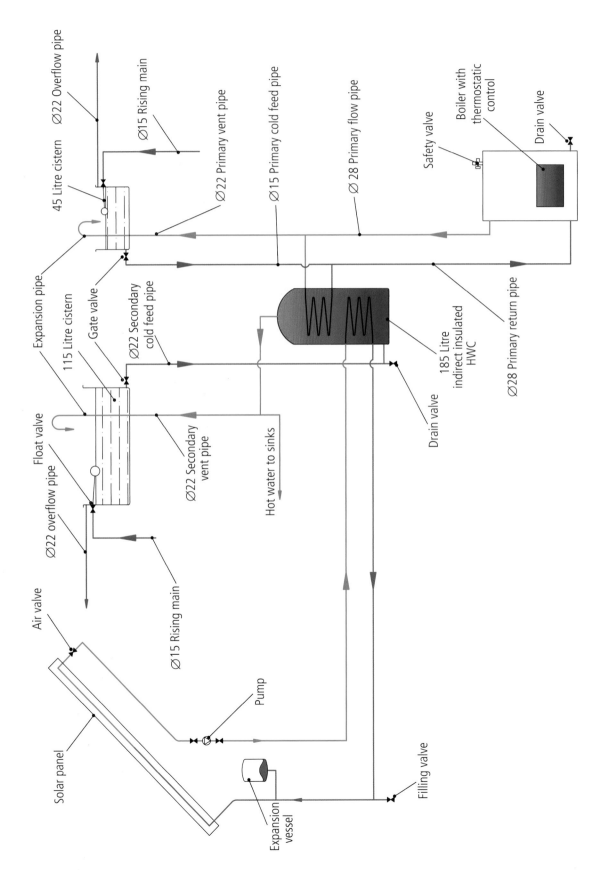

45 Litre cistern

Ø22 Overflow pipe

Ø15 Rising main

Ø22 Primary vent pipe

Ø15 Primary cold feed pipe

Ø28 Primary flow pipe

Safety valve

Boiler with thermostatic control

Drain valve

Expansion pipe

115 Litre cistern

Gate valve

Ø22 Secondary cold feed pipe

185 Litre indirect insulated HWC

Ø28 Primary return pipe

Drain valve

Float valve

Ø22 overflow pipe

Ø22 Secondary vent pipe

Hot water to sinks

Ø15 Rising main

Air valve

Solar panel

Pump

Expansion vessel

Filling valve

GEOTHERMAL HEATING

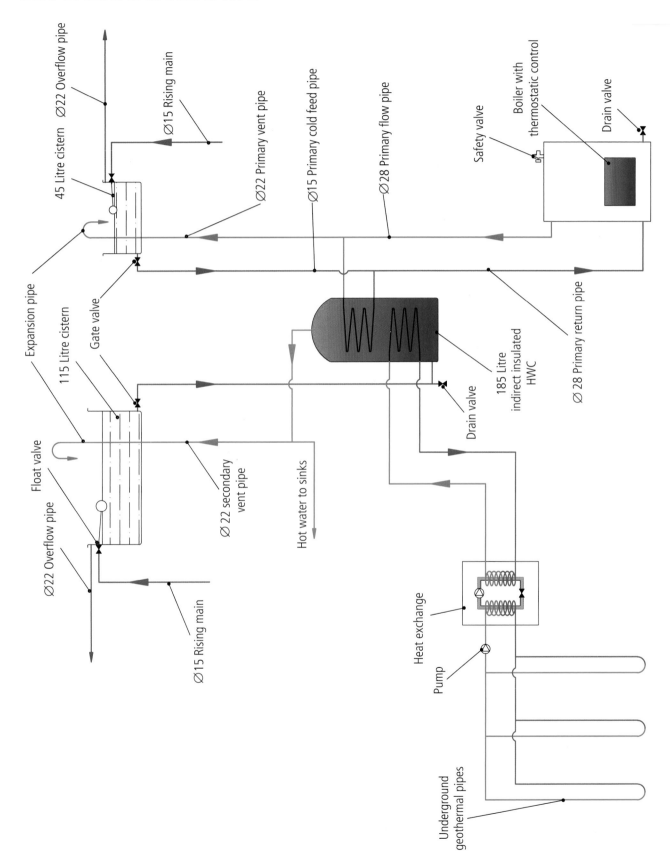

DRAINAGE SYSTEMS

The separate system

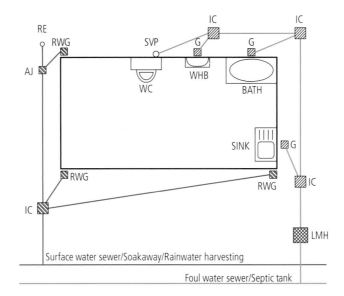

The combined system

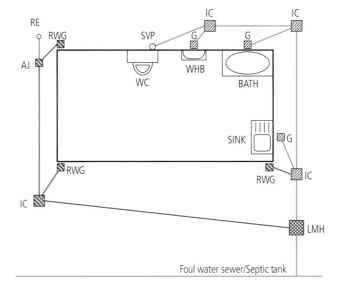

The partially separate system

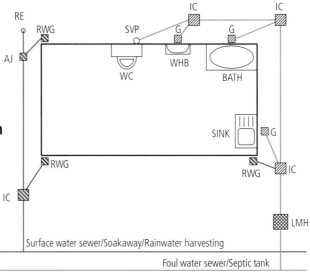

Key:
IC = Inspection chamber
G = Gully
RE = Rodding eye
RWG = Rainwater gully
SVP = Soil vent pipe
LMH = Last manhole
AJ = Access junction

SINGLE STACK SYSTEM

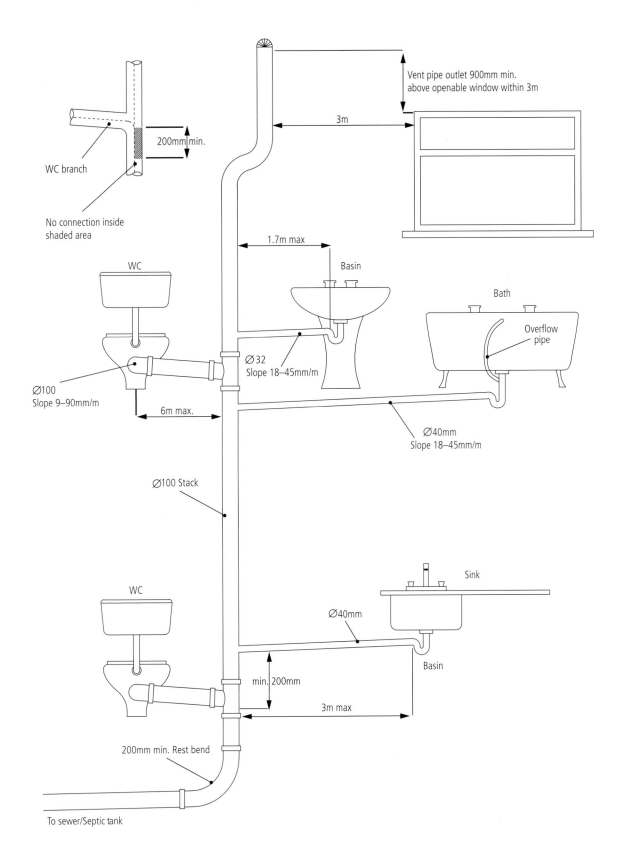

Vent pipe outlet 900mm min.
above openable window within 3m

3m

200mm min.

WC branch

No connection inside
shaded area

1.7m max

WC

Basin

Bath

Overflow
pipe

Ø 32
Slope 18–45mm/m

Ø100
Slope 9–90mm/m

6m max.

Ø40mm
Slope 18–45mm/m

Ø100 Stack

Sink

Ø40mm

WC

Ø40mm

min. 200mm

Basin

3m max

200mm min. Rest bend

To sewer/Septic tank

SEPTIC TANK

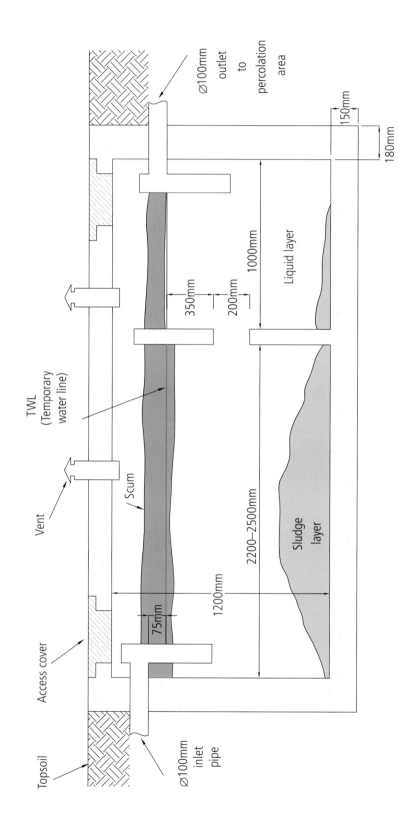

EXPERIMENTS

It is important to note that, as part of their coursework, students are expected to carry out individual experiments with their own unique results. These experiments are worth 30 marks out of 150. It is recommended that the experiments undertaken are related to the topic of the students' project, but this is not essential.

It is recommended that there is photographic evidence of the student undertaking their experiments and/or other proof that the experiment was carried out.

The following is a list of suggested experiments, with some ideas for varying the experiments. Please note that this is not an exhaustive list and all other syllabus-related experiments are equally relevant.

Deflection of timber How much a piece of timber bends when weight is applied.
Variations:
- Different timber types
- Different support methods, i.e. held at both ends, held at one end
- Placing the wood supports in different places
- Orientation of the timber.

Finish of timber To determine the suitability of wood finishes for use in contact with heat and water.
Variations:
- Choice of finishes
- Varying heat exposure time
- Varying heat temperature
- Varying time in contact with water
- Varying length of time over which the experiment is carried out (e.g. 1 day, 1 week, 1 month).

Hydroscopic properties of timber How water is drawn into timber (staining the water with food colouring will make results easier to see).
Variations:
- Different timbers

- Comparison between softwoods and hardwoods
- Effect of finishes (wax, stain, varnish) on absorption of water
- Comparison of moisture content using moisture meter.

Effect of knots on timber strength Testing strength with weights.
Variations:
- Samples with no knots
- Samples with some knots
- Samples with excessive knots
- How the timber is clamped (resting on supports, cantilever).

Glue strength Glue a butt joint and add weight until it fails.
Variations:
- Size of timber used (surface area that is glued)
- Type of timber
- Type of glue
- Comparison between different glue types.

Joint strength Testing joint strength by clamping in a vice and adding weights until it fails.
Variations:
- Testing different types of joint
- Varying the size of the timber (are smaller joints stronger?)
- Varying the type of wood used
- Orientation of joints
- Comparison of joint strength under different stresses (compression, tension, etc.).

Water absorption test on glue on different timbers Testing to see whether water affects glued joints.
Variations:
- Using different adhesives
- Varying the amount of time the joint is exposed to water.

Slump test Testing the workability of concrete.

Effects of cement amount on concrete sample What happens if too much/too little cement is used?

Capillary action in concrete blocks How does capillary action affect different block types?
Variations:

- Testing a variety of different block types
- Adding a DPC and recording results.

Water absorption test on insulation Testing how much water different types of insulation absorb.

Heat test on insulation How long does material attached to insulation retain heat when heat source is removed?
Variations:

- Different insulation products
- Distance of material from heat source
- Exposure time of heat to material
- Different materials attached to insulation
- How does wet insulation affect the results?

Silt test Testing the amount of silt present in a soil sample. If each student brings in own soil sample this experiment can be undertaken as a whole class.

Load-bearing capacity of soil This is a visual experiment to determine the reaction of soil to weight.
Variations:

- Size of soil sample
- Compaction of soil sample
- Weights used
- Shape of weights.

Filtration of water How filtration can remove visual impurities in a water sample.
Variations:

- Using water samples with more or fewer impurities
- Increasing the amount of layers in the filter
- Varying the types of layers in the filter.

Effects of materials in relation to sound insulation Testing different materials for their sound insulation properties.
Variations:

- Varying the materials
- Varying the amount of material
- Changing the level of sound
- Changing distance from sound to material
- Changing reverberation time.

TECHNICAL GUIDANCE DOCUMENTS

Below is a brief outline of the current Technical Guidance Documents, which are essentially Ireland's building regulations. These regulations set out the minimum code or standard to which all buildings must adhere. They are regularly reviewed and changed when necessary to reflect international best practice and methods of construction.

Part A: Structure

This section stipulates that buildings must be structurally sound. It covers a range of building types and various materials that are used in construction. It sets out minimum standards for structure loadings and proportions for support.

Part B: Fire Safety

Dealing with all aspects of fire safety, protection and access in the event of fire, this document lays out minimum fire safety standards in new buildings and renovated buildings. It also deals with fire detection, warning systems, and fire resistance required of building materials.

Part C: Site Preparation and Resistance to Moisture

Part C covers the preparation of a building site, including drainage of the site; precautions taken to combat dangerous substances found on or in the ground; and preventing the passage of moisture to the inside of the building.

Part D: Materials and Workmanship

Quality control of workmanship and material properties are dealt with in this document. It stipulates the specific standards required of materials, including CE marks, European technical approval and compliance with Irish Standards, and specifies that all work must be carried out in a workmanlike manner by qualified persons. Material dimensions and tolerances listed in this section are minimum requirements.

Part E: Sound

Part E outlines the maximum permissible levels of various types of sound and measures to prevent them. It covers the transmission of airborne sound through walls and floors and impact sound through flooring.

Part F: Ventilation

This section deals with standards of ventilation in buildings; the moisture content of the air; and the level of harmful pollutants in a building.

Part G: Hygiene

Part G specifies minimum hygiene provisions for a dwelling, including fitted fixtures for bathrooms and kitchens, and the provision of hot and cold water. It also covers hygiene requirements for other types of building. Among other requirements, it specifies that all fittings must be installed to facilitate effective cleaning.

Part H: Drainage and Waste

This paper deals with drainage systems and wastewater treatment systems. These systems must be hygienic, safe and appropriate for the situation they are used in. The capacity and location of these systems are covered, and the regulations stipulate that the two water systems must be separate.

Part J: Heat Producing Appliances

As burning materials to create heat can be dangerous, it is important that these appliances are fully regulated. Part J shows the details required for heat-producing appliances, including ventilation (where relevant).

Part K: Stairways, Ladders, Ramps and Guards

Stairs must be built so that they are safe to use, and this section sets out the maximum and minimum measurements for key aspects of stairs, including head room, width, handrail measurements, etc.

Part L: Conservation of Fuel & Energy

The aim of this document is to limit the amount of fossil fuel energy used in homes and to reduce carbon dioxide emissions, while ensuring that homes have adequate levels of lighting and thermal comfort.

Part M: Access for People with Disabilities

Part M aims to ensure that people with disabilities can safely and independently access and use buildings. The residential section of the document covers the definition of disabilities, access and application of the regulations.

EUROCODES

Eurocodes are a set of guidance documents that aim to harmonise structural design codes across the European Union (EU). The codes also allow for the free movement of building materials and services across the EU. However, each member state retains control of and responsibility for building safety. The Irish Eurocodes are published by the National Standards Authority (NSAI). Every material used on a building site in Ireland should have NSAI certification. For further information see www.nsai.ie.

INDEX

Everyone hates u.

:-(

//:DON'T REPLY/
KEEP THE MESSAGE/
BLOCK THE SENDER/
TELL SOMEONE YOU TRUST://

WWW.WATCHYOURSPACE.IE

Don't Accept Bullying

This Anti-Bullying campaign is supported by the Department of Education and Skills with the co-operation of the Irish Educational Publishers Association.